THE TWO STROKE DIRT BIKE ENGINE BUILDING HANDBOOK

Precision Engine Building Knowledge For Beginners And Experts

WRITTEN BY PAUL OLESEN

First Edition: November 2017
ISBN-13: 978-0-9964915-1-8
LCCN: 2017914813

NOTICE: Tampering with, altering, modifying, or removing any emissions-control device is a violation of federal law. Author and DIY Moto Fix, LLC., disclaim all liability incurred in connection with the use of this information.

The information in this book is true and complete to the best of our knowledge. However, all information is presented without any guarantee on the part of the Author or DIY Moto Fix, LLC., who disclaim any liability incurred with the use of the information and any implied warranties of merchantability or fitness for a particular purpose. Readers are responsible for taking suitable and appropriate safety measures when performing any of the operations or activities described in this book.

Cover Design by Kimberly Zamora-Pearson
Edited by Sheldon Olesen and Kelsey Jorissen
Photography and layout by Kelsey Jorissen Photography, LLC.

Printed in the United States Of America

TABLE OF CONTENTS

ACKNOWLEDGEMENTS

I want to start off by thanking you, my fans and supporters, who have embraced DIY Moto Fix over the past few years. DIY Moto Fix started off as a simple idea and with your support it has slowly grown into a place where people come to increase their dirt bike knowledge. Without you, the opportunity to write a second book would not have presented itself.

Acquiring two-stroke knowledge is challenging for numerous reasons and I'm grateful to the folks who have directly and indirectly expanded my understanding of the subject. I want to say thanks to Jan Thiel and Frits Overmars who have selflessly shared much of the information they learned as they designed and developed the Aprilia RSA 125 Moto GP engine. Thanks to Wayne Wright for his contributions to tuning and simulating two-strokes. Thanks to Gordon Blair who pioneered two-stroke simulation. Thanks to Neels Van Niekerk for his amazing two-stroke simulation software and the time he has taken to help me understand the finer details of simulating two-strokes. Thanks to Steve Bethel of Leadfoot engineering who has shared his expertise with me on piston design. Thanks to Ian Harrison of Viper Racing UK who has shared much of his two-stroke knowledge. Thanks to my friend Tim Hickox for his engineering and two-stroke mentorship. Thanks to Malcolm McDonald, a professor of mine, who made learning about the internal combustion engine fun and easy.

A special thanks to my best friend and business partner, Kelsey Jorissen, for her patience as the two-stroke book project carried on much longer than intended. I want to also recognize the great work she put into the book which includes all the photos, formatting, and editing.

Once again, I want to thank my parents for their continued support. They have helped me in more ways than I can list and I am eternally thankful.

Lastly a big thank you, to the countless influencers not specifically mentioned, but who no doubt have helped me get where I am today. I appreciate you all more than you know.

INTRODUCTION

The two-stroke engine has been on my mind for close to a decade now. To an outsider, the simplicity of the engine can be taken for granted. For those who know two-strokes best, they know there are countless intricate details that go into executing a successful engine design.

For me, my fascination with two-strokes started after high school and progressed into college. I was not able to get into any sort of powersports when I was young, so in many ways I was a late bloomer. I had a bit of exposure to snowmobiles and dirt bikes so I had some awareness of the power density of the two-stroke, but full comprehension had not yet occurred. The light bulb went on and things started to click in my mind as to how great the two-stroke was when I was reading about vintage motorcycles. Unbeknownst to me, the 1970s were littered with great examples of two-stroke motorcycles! All of which appeared significantly lighter and more powerful than any of their four-stroke counterparts. From that point on, the simplicity of the engine and its intricacies fascinated me.

Once I connected the dots, I decided I needed a two-stroke motorcycle of my own so I set my sights on the 750cc Kawasaki H2. For those of you that don't know, the H2 is a three cylinder air cooled two-stroke road bike which was produced in the early 1970s. I patiently awaited a Craigslist sale I could afford and then pounced on it. By pounced, I mean I skipped a college exam and drove from Minneapolis to Dallas in the middle of the week to go collect two rusty basketcases that needed more work than any sane person would ever want to undertake.

As my fascination for engines and motorcycles quickly took hold, my life quickly unraveled due to my disinterest in the academic path I was on at the time. In short, I ended up dropping out of college, taking approximately a year off, and then moving overseas where I attended the University of Wales. I spent a fantastic three years in the United Kingdom and earned a bachelor's degree in Motorcycle Engineering.

Many important events happened during this period of my life. I took on a large extracurricular project of my own, which entailed designing and building a single cylinder road racing bike. This taught me a ton of skills, was incredibly fun and challenging, and helped me get numerous job offers after college.

I got into the motorcycle industry early on by securing a summer position with S & S Cycle. I met great people, learned a lot about manufacturing, and engineering due to this experience. My design work and final year projects were good enough to attract the interest of a few companies, some of which, I worked part time as a consultant for. All of these experiences ultimately helped me confirm that I wanted to be an engine designer and that my enthusiasm for engines wasn't going anywhere.

Since college I've worked at Erik Buell Racing, continued consulting, and started DIY Moto Fix. Erik Buell Racing (EBR) was definitely not an experience I would classify as positive from a career standpoint; however, I learned many valuable skills, made some good friends, got more firmly rooted in dirt bikes, and it forced me to look critically at what I wanted out of a career. By the time I was ready to leave EBR I had acquired another dirt bike, was ice racing, and was dabbling in hare scrambles. My enthusiasm for the sport was high and I decided that if I could try to create a business around my interests and provide value to the riding community, that would be worth doing. That, in a nutshell, is how DIY Moto Fix was started.

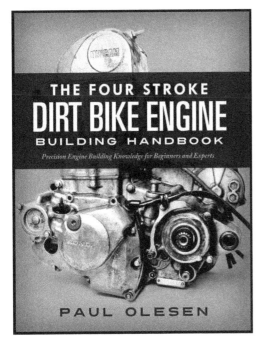

DIY Moto Fix is my platform for sharing information about dirt bike maintenance with special emphasis on engine building. My goal is to provide hard earned, not easily attainable, knowledge and skills to the average rider so that they can learn to build their own engines and fix their own bikes. The ultimate goal is to ensure that the sport remains affordable and accessible to everyone. My first book, The Four Stroke Dirt Bike Engine Building Handbook, was published in 2015 and the response to it and all the work that has gone into DIY Moto Fix is the reason this book is here. In some ways you can thank your fellow four-stroke riders for making this book possible!

My original plan was to publish this book much sooner; however, opportunity struck and derailed those ambitions. Aviation is another area of high interest to me and in many ways it has been in my blood since a very early age. I'm a third generation private pilot who got their first plane ride from my dad at the age of 11 months. I've been attending EAA Airventure in Oshkosh, Wisconsin almost religiously throughout my life and in 2015 ran into an intriguing company, Deltahawk. They were working on developing a two-stroke diesel aircraft engine, so naturally I was interested.

I joined the Deltahawk team in the fall of 2015 as an engineer and have been working there ever since. I currently oversee Deltahawk's engineering program and am enjoying my numerous roles as we work on engine and aircraft projects.

My hope is that this book is the knowledge toolbox you need to feel confident performing your own engine builds, gives you insight into how different features affect performance, and helps you get your project done with a high level of quality. Let's get started.

CH 1 | HOW TO USE THIS BOOK

I wrote this book with the intention of creating a tool that enthusiasts at any level could read and utilize. If you are someone who has never rebuilt a two-stroke dirt bike engine before, this book provides you with all the wisdom, techniques, and how-to knowledge required to do the job at a professional level. While there is no substitute for experience and practice, this book provides the fundamental groundwork required to progress at the fastest rate possible. Whether you are a total beginner or an experienced builder, this book will bring you valuable knowledge and insight into the world of engine building.

This book is designed to compliment a service manual. Service manuals are great at providing torque specifications, service specifications, etc. Where a service manual falls short though is that it does not explain the how or why behind the processes of engine building, nor does it teach you the proper techniques. Throughout this book the how and why behind every fundamental task associated with building an engine is covered. In addition, the proper way to perform all the various techniques associated with a build are explained and taught in full detail, allowing you to step away to work on your bike with the highest quality information.

The primary focus of this book is to detail a complete engine build from disassembly to reassembly. You can also use this book for reference to perform top end builds and other service tasks. The degree to which you want to complete your rebuild will be entirely up to you. If you simply want to get your engine running again, you're covered. If you want to prepare your engine for racing, you're also covered.

Throughout this book you'll notice that I use pictures and talk about examples from three different engines, a Yamaha YZ250, a KTM 380EXC, and a Kawasaki KX500 engine as I detail the build process. The reason I used three engines as examples was not to confuse you, but to provide you with all the variations in design and assembly techniques you are likely to encounter on any make and model of engine. Believe it or not, design differences between all the major manufacturers is limited. Once you learn all the necessary techniques, the reasons parts interact the way they do, and understand what you are dealing with you will be in a good position to tackle any engine project.

This book is laid out in chronological order, unlike a service manual where jumping around is the norm. While major disassembly, inspection, and assembly orders are right for the engines I've used as examples, you may find small sequential differences on other engines. The Table of Contents has been designed to be your navigational beacon so that you can easily find the information that you are looking for. Simply browse through the table of contents to find the topic you are seeking information on and jump to that page as necessary.

Throughout the chapters dedicated to the actual build process you will find highlighted sections called **Technical Takeaways**. Just like the build process, these takeaways are presented in chronological order as they become relevant. Technical Takeaways are how-to instruction for repeated tasks, technical concepts, and advanced building techniques that are discussed in full detail only once, and then summarized thereafter as you read through the book. While only discussed once, these Technical Takeaways should be kept in the back of your mind as you progress through the build. For example, one technical takeaway covers how to correctly install seals, this is a task that must be performed numerous times and once covered it will be expected that you use the knowledge found in the Technical Takeaway to perform the remaining seal installation tasks.

Additional highlighted sections of text that will be found throughout the book are called **Hot Tips**. Hot Tips are to be regarded as my own personal experiences and preferences when working through a build. Use them as you see fit!

Finally, highlighted sections called **Race Engine Techniques** illustrate all additional tasks that are required when building a performance engine. If you are just repairing a stock engine, these tasks won't be necessary to perform. However, you may enjoy reading about them and learning about why builders must do them.

The level of involvement you want to have in the build process is entirely up to you. While precision measuring is not for everyone, it is covered in complete detail in this book. If you aren't equipped or don't feel comfortable with some of the tasks outlined, simply farm the work out to a professional. *The Two Stroke Dirt Bike Engine Building Handbook* will give you an extremely thorough overview on a full engine build. What you decide to do will be up to you and the suggestions found throughout this book are here to help you in your decision making process.

CH 2 | WHEN TO REBUILD

When should you rebuild your two-stroke dirt bike engine? The answer to this question is not a simple one nor is there a definite right answer. Truly, the only way to know for sure is if the engine has already catastrophically failed - then it definitely is time! This is the costly way of doing things and I am going to teach you the proper steps to help you avoid the engine failure scenario entirely.

Engine wear is directly related to RPM and mechanical stress. Riders engaging in riding where the engine is near redline frequently, the engine is operating at a high RPM without any load on it, the gearbox is loaded or unloaded abruptly, or gears are selected hastily require the rider or mechanic to service the engine frequently. Most of you will relate this scenario to motocross racing. At the top levels of racing, mechanics are constantly checking or rebuilding the engines to make sure they are operating at maximum power.

Fortunately most of us are not riding or racing at the top level, so our bikes and engines last much longer. Unfortunately, everyone's scenario is different depending on the type of riding you do, the environment you ride in, how often the air filter is changed, etc. These factors make it difficult to standardize or pinpoint specific service intervals for your bike without knowing more about the way you ride and care for your bike.

As an engineer, mechanic, and rider, my philosophy has always been to replace components preventatively before they fail. My reasoning here is that the costs incurred with a failed component are much higher than a replaced component. Let us consider a scenario where a piston fails. This could have been avoided had the piston been replaced at a cost of around $140. Instead the entire engine will need to be opened up and serviced, making the price of the repair skyrocket to anywhere from $250 to a whopping $1200 depending on the damage done.

Now let's look at rebuilding from an opportunity cost mindset. If any part fails on the bike while I'm out riding or racing, I've lost out on a significant amount of time, a significant amount of points if I'm racing, and a wad of cash when it comes to paying for travel to and from the venue. So apart from saving a small amount of money by not replacing a serviceable part, there is no upside to trying to prolong the life of a component. The ramifications of engine neglect are costly.

The best way to determine when components need to be serviced is to keep a detailed log of the health of your engine. This means from the time of purchase to the day you sell. By keeping track of all the engine hours, maintenance, and repairs you do to the bike, you'll start to develop patterns and be able to establish your own service intervals. Maintenance logging is a great way to keep track of the health of your engine and will be covered in more detail at the end of the book.

Paying attention to your engine as you ride is the next vital thing you should be doing. In most cases your engine will give you signs that it is time to service one component or another. Some common signs that may indicate your engine is due for servicing soon are:

• THE ENGINE IS HARD TO START
Hard starting can be an indicator of a clogged pilot jet circuit within the carburetor, a worn spark plug, or in more severe cases low compression and worn out piston rings.

• THE ENGINE DOESN'T HOLD A TUNE
If an engine frequently requires jetting changes to keep it running right, despite relatively stable atmospheric conditions, it may have a sealing issue and ultimately an air leak. Faulty seals or gaskets which reside anywhere in the engine and between it and the carburetor can make the engine run erratically. The specifics of this will be covered in further detail later. Another sign of an air leak occurs when the state of tune must be changed when the engine transitions from cold to warmed up. For example the engine may idle and run fine when it is cold, but once it is warmed up and ridden it fails to idle or seems to run lean.

• THE TRANSMISSION OIL IS CREAMY
Whenever the transmission oil is creamy in color, moisture is getting into the oil. While some moisture getting into the oil is normal, excessive amounts are a cause for alarm and may indicate that a water pump seal is leaking into the gearbox.

• THE TRANSMISSION OIL HAS LARGE PIECES OF METAL IN IT
Metallic particles are common in transmission oil, but if larger metal pieces are found in the oil this is a cause for concern and should be associated with damaged components. An example of this could be finding fragments of chipped gear teeth in the oil.

• THE ENGINE VIBRATES EXCESSIVELY
Excessive engine vibration may be caused by an out of true crankshaft, worn crank bearings, a loose clutch, or loose engine mount bolts.

• ENGINE POWER HAS DIMINISHED
This could be due to restricted fuel flow in the carburetor or throttle body, a clogged air cleaner, the clutch slipping, worn rings, leaking gaskets, or ignition issues.

• THE TOP END IS NOISY
A noisy top end could be caused by a piston that is worn and loose to the bore (think piston slap), damaged rings, or a worn wrist pin bearing.

• THE BOTTOM END IS NOISY
A worn clutch basket which has started to rattle, damaged or stuck bearings, a worn bushing and needle bearing between the clutch basket and primary shaft, or gears which are improperly lubricated may all contribute to bottom end noise.

• EXCESSIVE BLUE SMOKE/THE ENGINE CONSUMES TRANSMISSION OIL

Smoke coming from the exhaust on a two-stroke is normal and most noticeable at startup when the engine is cold. The smoke is simply a byproduct of combustion due to the oil that was mixed in with the fuel to lubricate the engine. Excessive smoke that is emitted after the engine has been warmed up; however, can be an indicator that transmission oil is leaking into the combustion chamber. This usually occurs when a crankshaft seal fails.

• WHITE SMOKE

White smoke is emitted when the engine is burning coolant. This typically occurs when a head gasket or o-ring starts leaking.

I wish I could state quantifiable numbers so that you know precisely when the right time is to rebuild your engine; however, I feel that by doing this I would be doing a disservice to you. I would either be giving you information that tells you to rebuild your engine too early or too late in its life, which wouldn't be fair or honest. There are so many variables ranging from riding style, engine displacement, manufacturer, riding environment, and maintenance intervals that I am unable to quantify all these factors into one number or even several numbers for specific groups.

There are a few guidelines pertaining to engine health which do hold true across brands which are:

• High performance purpose built race engines will always have shorter service intervals than stock engines.

• Anyone engaging in racing (even with stock engines) will put more stress on their engine than the casual trail rider. This will result in the maintenance interval of racers' engines being more frequent.

• Large displacement engines, like 250/300cc engines, almost always last longer than 125cc engines because the number of riders that can utilize all the power of a 250/300cc engine are fewer. Thus the service intervals of 125cc and smaller engines are more frequent than their larger displacement counterparts.

• Poor engine maintenance practices will always reduce the life of an engine and require the engine to be serviced more frequently.

Your best bet is to pay close attention to your engine, keep track of the hours on your engine, take care of it, and learn as much as you can about your particular make and model so that you can begin to formulate a service interval schedule tailored to you.

In the next chapter we'll take a look at three diagnostic tests that can further aid in determining whether to service the engine or not.

CH 3 | DIAGNOSING TROUBLE

Along with observations of how the engine is running, performing, and sounds - a handful of simple tests can be carried out to help determine the overall health of the engine. The three diagnostic tests I'm going to share with you are the compression, cylinder leak down, and crankcase leak down tests.

A compression test is the first of these tests I'd like to discuss. A compression test measures the peak pressure in the engine's cylinder as the engine is turned over. The measured pressure can be compared to a specified pressure in the service manual or a previously recorded test pressure to determine if there are problems with the engine.

Compression tests are great because they don't require much in the way of tools to execute and they can be done quickly. They are especially powerful for two-stroke engines since there are only a couple of variables involved in the diagnosis, the piston rings and the head gasket/o-rings. Bear in mind on the odd occasion the spark plug could also be a leak path. Since compression tests provide a great deal of information about the engine, they should be performed routinely throughout the engine's life. For the serious racer, a compression test after every race weekend is a good regimen while the casual trail rider can get by with less frequent testing.

The second test I will cover is a cylinder leak down test. With the piston at TDC, a leak down test pressurizes the combustion chamber to a specified pressure. A comparison is made between how much air is supplied to the combustion chamber and how much leaks out. The amount of air leaking out of the combustion chamber is used to determine the health of the engine. For example if 50% of the air is leaking out the combustion chamber there are serious problems! By carefully listening for the air leak(s) it is possible to determine the source of the problem on the engine and address it.

Cylinder leak down tests are more advantageous in determining problems on four-stroke engines; however, I believe there is a place for them in the two-stroke world as well. A cylinder leak down test is another good way to quantify the condition of the piston rings and pinpoint any problems with either the rings or head gasket/o-rings. While testing, any head gasket problems will be more apparent than they would be during a compression test and the health of the piston rings can be more accurately assessed. This is because a steady air supply is used to pressurize the combustion chamber, and since the engine is not rotated during the test, the rotational speed of the engine is not a factor, as it is with a compression test.

The final test I'm going to cover is called a crankcase leak down test. A crankcase leak down test confirms the integrity of the seals and gaskets throughout an engine. In summary, a crankcase leak down test is performed by blocking off all openings leading to the atmosphere (think intake entry and exhaust port exit) and then slightly pressurizing the crankcases. The crankcase pressure is then monitored and leaks can be observed.

Performing a crankcase leak down test is a good idea anytime the engine is partly or fully disassembled/rebuilt or anytime the engine is running inconsistently. If alterations to the engine's tuning do not address inconsistencies in the way the engine runs, there could be an air leak somewhere within the engine. Any air leaks present in the engine will have an adverse affect on the air/fuel mixture, potentially creating a lean or rich condition, depending on where the leak is within the engine. A crankcase leak down test can be used to pinpoint any leaks within the engine allowing the problem to quickly be addressed.

Compression Testing Methods

While a compression test seems straightforward it can actually be a bit more complicated than you would expect. There are two different ways the engine can be tested, warm or cold.

The hypothesis behind performing the compression test with a warm engine is that the engine is closer to its operating temperature, thus the compression test is more accurate. The piston, cylinder, and rings have all increased in temperature and thermally expanded so the clearances between these parts is more representative of what would be found in a running engine.

While this is a good thought, it can be difficult to perform repeatedly in real life. The seat and tank first have to be removed to get at the spark plug, then the plug has to come out and the gauge has to be installed. The amount of time that the engine is warmed plus the amount of time it takes to prepare for the test will have an effect on how warm the engine will ultimately be when the test is finally performed. Performing the compression test cold is much easier on the mechanic. The resulting compression values of cold tests are lower than those of warm, this due to the extra clearances found within the engine. The lower number of variables affecting the test may also make testing compression more repeatable.

Some OEMs, mechanics, and tuners believe adamantly that the tests should be carried out warm, while others suggest cold testing is the way to go. There is no definitive answer to which is the best way. My personal experiences lead me to believe that cold testing is easier, introduces less variables, and is easily repeatable. Repeatability is what you are looking for as a mechanic. As long as you can obtain repeatable results, you can choose the method that is best for you.

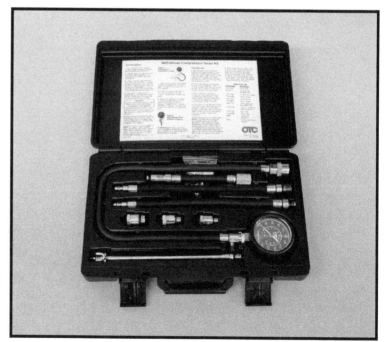

Compression Testing Best Practices

Compression testers' measurements can vary slightly from model to model, because of this it is never a good idea to test an engine with brand A one day and brand B the next. Assuming this is done, brand A could read high while brand B could read low, giving a false indication that there is a problem with the engine. All that has actually occurred is a difference in the calibrations of the testers' pressure gauges.

While many acceptable compression numbers are thrown around on the internet, in shops, and when bench racing for various models of bikes - these numbers are less important than you might be led to believe. Compression testing is definitely a great tool to assess the health of an engine; however, it is an even more powerful tool when used for comparative testing. To illustrate this, consider a scenario where an engine has been freshly rebuilt from top to bottom. The engine has just been broken in and the total time on the engine is around three hours. A compression test is performed at this point and a reading of 170 psi is taken. After some time the bike has been ridden a lot and seems to be a little down on power. A compression test is done again, but this time it reads 136 psi. This is a 20% loss in compression compared to the first reading and now the mechanic knows there is something going on with the engine. The great thing about testing in this way is that it would not have mattered if the first reading was 160, 180, or any other number. The only thing that matters is the difference in compression between the first and second tests.

Another note on compression tester values is that the readings will vary depending on altitude. If your buddy in Florida checks his compression at sea level and gets a reading of 180 psi and you live in Colorado at an elevation of 6,000ft, it would be unreasonable to expect to have your engine read 180 psi too. Just because the engine tested at higher elevation does not read as high does not mean there is anything wrong with it. At higher elevations the air density is much less dense, resulting in less air to compress which effectively lowers the maximum value recorded by the compression tester.

The best way to get meaningful information from your compression tests is by comparative testing. One of the first things you should do when you finish rebuilding an engine or pick up a used bike is perform a compression test. This way you can monitor the health of the engine from the beginning and have a number to relate back to when the engine starts to wear.

Comparative testing may not always be practical though if the owner or mechanic didn't plan ahead, and in this case, the numbers do matter. In this scenario, the best use of the compression tester is to determine if something major has happened to the engine. For example, if an engine is tested and the reading is 120psi or less, there are definitely problems. If the reading ends up being in the ballpark of what is deemed acceptable for that particular engine, then it would be best to perform a leak down test on the engine to confirm if there is a problem or not.

Repeatability is the most important aspect for any type of test being performed. Compression testing is no different. It is best to have a set method for performing the test each and every time. Examples of variables to keep track of include how many times you kick the bike over, whether the test is performed hot or cold, and who is doing the kicking. The rate at which the engine is kicked can have an influence on the compression recorded. This means you may get different results when you kick the bike over compared to when your buddy with thunder thighs kicks the bike over. However you decide to perform your tests, be sure you keep track of your methods so the next time you do them you can be as accurate as possible when repeating the procedure.

How to Perform a Compression Test

First, I would recommend confirming if a compression value is provided by the manufacturer in the service or owner's manuals. If a value is provided, further details should also be provided on how the value was obtained. For example, some manufacturers may specify a certain number of kicks or a kicking RPM used to obtain results. Once you know this information you can attempt to recreate their test conditions as best as you can. This usually means kicking as hard and as fast as you can for a certain number of kicks!

Steps for Performing a Compression Test (Cold)

1. Remove the seat from the bike.

2. Remove the fuel tank and radiator shrouds from the bike. Make sure the petcock is turned off before removing the fuel line. Use a rag to catch any fuel draining from the line.

3. Remove the spark plug cap and wipe the cylinder head of dirt. Then partially loosen the spark plug. Prior to removing the plug, blow compressed air around the base of the plug to rid it of dust and debris so that it can't get into the engine. Then remove the spark plug.

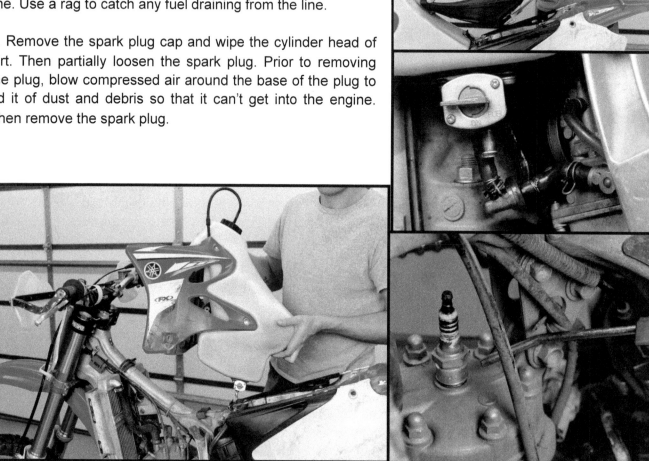

4. Install the compression tester in the spark plug hole. Make sure any adapters used to fit the compression tester to the spark plug hole are tight so there is no chance of getting false readings and they aren't separated from the tester upon removal. It is also a good idea to apply anti-seize to the adapter threads.

5. Hold the throttle wide open.

6. Kick the bike over 5 times as hard and as fast as you can.

7. Check the value recorded by the compression tester.

8. Reset the gauge and repeat the test at least three times to make sure your results are accurate and repeatable. Write your results down in your maintenance log or somewhere safe so you can refer back to them at a later date.

HOT TIP: If you have performed a compression test and the compression is low it may be possible to further diagnose the problem. Use a piece of fuel tubing to suck up approximately a teaspoon of oil. With your finger over the end of the fuel tubing lower the oil down into the cylinder bore then try to distribute the oil evenly throughout the bore by rotating the tubing and releasing your finger. Rotate the engine over a few times to help distribute the oil. Perform the compression test again. If the compression increased a noticeable amount the problem is within the cylinder bore and the rings are not sealing well. If compression doesn't increase then the problem is with the cylinder head gasket/o-rings.

If you want to perform the test on a warm engine, warm the engine up for a set period of time. Keep track of how long you warmed the engine then quickly proceed to step two in the outline above. Use a thermometer or infrared temp gauge to keep track of how warm the coolant or cylinder head is so that the test is more easily repeated the next time you perform it.

Leak Down Testing Methods

Leak down testing can be a more definitive way to assess the health of an engine compared to compression testing because a leak down test allows the mechanic to pinpoint the problematic area within the engine. In the case of the two-stroke, a leak down test will either identify a problematic head gasket/o-rings or worn piston rings. Along with identifying problems I like to rely on leak down testing to help monitor piston ring wear.

A leak down test works as follows. With the piston just shy of TDC, air pressurizes the cylinder to a defined pressure which is recorded by a pressure gauge. A second pressure gauge is used to monitor the amount of air escaping the combustion chamber. A comparison is made between the air going into the cylinder and the air escaping. The percentage of air escaping is used to determine the overall health of the engine.

The amount of air escaping can roughly be quantified to assess the overall health of the engine. When race engines are built, the accuracy and precision that goes into the build results in the lowest leakage values. Most race engines will have a pressure loss of between 0% and 5%. Standard builds resulting in good running engines typically lose up to 15%. Any engine that is close to or past being ready for service will leak from 16% to 30%. These engines will most likely be running poorly, if at all. Engines beyond 30% leakage are usually broken and will not run. The more the engine leaks, the worse the engine's health. Keep in mind these values are provided as a reference point; however, each engine can be a little different.

It is possible to pinpoint where leaks are coming from once the cylinder is pressurized. When performing the test, the throttle should be fully opened and the radiator cap should be removed. Air can only exit the combustion chamber at two points making the diagnoses easy: past the piston rings or past the head gasket. Both of these points will exhibit a unique tell-tale sign if air is leaking.

Excessive leakage past the piston rings will result in air escaping out the exhaust and intake. A leaking head gasket will result in air bubbles showing up at the radiator fill cap neck.

I want to address one concern you may have at this point. You have probably heard before that the piston should be at TDC when performing a leak down test. In reality there are a couple problems with this that I want to go over. First, with the relatively short strokes two-stroke dirt bike engines use, keeping the piston precisely at TDC with 100 psi of pressure pushing down on it is next to impossible. The piston and crank will want to rock to either side of TDC. Controlling which side of TDC the piston rests is important. Depending on which side of the engine is used to lock the crankshaft in place and the direction of rotation of the engine, the nut or bolt used to lock the crank in place may either try to tighten or loosen itself from the air pressure pushing against the piston. Even though these are highly torqued fasteners, the air pressure can still occasionally loosen the nut or bolt. This creates a serious problem because now you've got to figure out how to lock out the crankshaft and retorque the fastener.

The second issue is not so much a problem as it is a minor detail. To best simulate ring sealing conditions, the rings should sit in the bottom of the ring grooves. This is how they would sit on a running engine and how the test should be performed. By ensuring the rings always sit in the bottom of their grooves, another level of repeatability is added to the test. Simply make sure when setting piston position that the piston is always traveling up just before you hold it in position. If you are working from the left side on a forward rotating engine, it will be necessary to rotate the piston past TDC, then reverse direction so the rings sit in the bottom of their grooves and the flywheel nut will not try to loosen itself from the air pressure.

How to Perform a Leak Down Test

To perform a leak down test you will need an air source capable of at least 115psi output pressure. Most leak down tests are performed at a regulated pressure of 100psi. This makes testing simple and the correlation of leakage a breeze since you're working on a scale from 0-100. Lower test pressures such as 90psi can be used in the event that the air system isn't capable of anything over 100psi or the specific leak down tester you have doesn't work on a 100psi scale. Just remember if you test at a value other than 100psi, you will need to mathematically determine the leakage percentage since it is no longer a direct correlation.

> HOT TIP: For top level racers, perform a leak down test after every race weekend or every five hours.

Leakage testing can be tricky when working by yourself so if you're able to round up a friend to help you out it makes things a lot easier. With 100psi of pressure being applied to the piston, it is a full-time job making sure the piston and crankshaft don't move. Even with a long breaker bar, holding the crank in place can be quite a task, couple that with having to operate the pressure regulator and obtain a good reading. I highly recommend having two sets of hands on deck for this procedure.

How To Calibrate Your Leak Down Tester

A leak down tester consists of an air inlet, a pressure regulator, two pressure gauges, and an air outlet which pressurizes the cylinder. It is important to check to see if both pressure gauges read the same prior to any testing. If they do, this is great; however, occasionally the gauges won't read exactly the same so a baseline will need to be established.

1. Start by setting your air source so that its output pressure is 115 psi. Setting the air source higher than the test pressure will ensure it does not interfere with the pressure regulation during the test.

2. Slowly increase the leak down tester pressure by adjusting the regulator. Set the incoming air pressure to 100psi.

3. Once the incoming air pressure is set at 100psi, read the outlet pressure gauge. If the outlet gauge reads 100psi, you are good to go. If the outlet gauge is adjustable, set the gauge so it also reads 100psi. If the outlet gauge is non-adjustable (most common), write down the outlet gauge pressure reading.

Here you can see the outlet gauge reads 97psi. Since no pressure is being lost between gauges, the only explanation for the difference in reading is gauge deviation. The 97psi value will be equivalent to 100psi.

4. After you have recorded the outlet gauge pressure that corresponds to the inlet gauge pressure, you are ready to start leakage testing. Set the initial regulated pressure back to 0psi so that the tester doesn't rapidly and unexpectedly pressurize the cylinder when you reconnect the air line for the test.

Leak Down Test Steps

1. Make sure the petcock is turned off and remove the fuel line from the carburetor. Use a rag to catch any fuel draining from the line.

2. Remove the seat and fuel tank from the bike.

3 . Remove the radiator cap.

4. Remove the spark plug cap and wipe the cylinder head of dirt. Then partially loosen the spark plug. Prior to removing the plug, blow compressed air around the base of the plug to rid it of dust and debris so that it can't get into the engine. Then remove the spark plug.

5. Remove the left side cover so that you can gain access to the crankshaft.

6. Assuming you are working from the flywheel side of the engine, rotate the engine over so that the piston passes TDC by around a ¼ of a rotation of the crankshaft. Reverse direction and set the crank so that it is just past TDC. TDC can usually be easily referenced by aligning the raised timing boss on the flywheel with the ignition pickup. On the Yamaha pictured, you can see the timing boss is just shy of the ignition pickup.

7. Install the leak down tester in the spark plug hole with the regulated pressure set at 0psi initially. Make sure any adapters used to connect the tester to the engine are tight so air cannot leak past them and so that they don't separate from the tester upon removal. It is also a good idea to apply anti-seize to the adapter threads.

8. It usually takes a breaker bar and two hands to lock the crankshaft from moving once the cylinder is pressurized. This is where having an extra set of hands helps immensely. One person should focus on keeping the crankshaft in position while the other operates the leak down tester. Remember to set the piston just shy of TDC and to lock the crankshaft in place while the piston is still traveling upwards so the rings sit in the bottom of the ring grooves.

9. Once the crankshaft is locked in place pressurize the cylinder. Slowly turn the pressure regulator up to 100psi.

10. Note the reading of the outlet pressure gauge. This corresponds to the amount of air the combustion chamber is retaining. If both pressure gauges read 100psi when they were calibrated the difference in pressure on the outlet gauge is the cylinder leakage. For example if the outlet gauge reads 95psi the cylinder leakage would be 5%.

If however during calibration both gauges did not read 100psi then the leakage will need to be calculated. For example, if the outlet pressure gauge read 97psi during calibration and 92psi when the combustion chamber was pressurized then the leakage could be found by dividing 92 by 97.

92 ÷ 97 = 0.948

0.948 x 100 = 94.8%

100 - 94.8 = 5.2% leakage

11. Open the throttle and listen for an audible hissing sound coming from the intake or exhaust. Also look in the radiator for air bubbles.

Here are the two problems that can result:

> **1. Air passing through the intake or exhaust indicates worn rings.**
> **2. Air bubbles forming in the radiator indicates a leaking head gasket.**

12. Depressurize the combustion chamber by turning the regulator back so it is at 0psi and no air is entering the combustion chamber. Unhook the air source and disconnect the leak down tester.

13. Reinstall the spark plug and plug cap.

14. Reinstall the radiator cap and crankshaft hole cap.

15. Reinstall the fuel tank and seat.

To help quantify results, here is a helpful table:

Racing Engines	0 - 5 Percent Leakage
Standard Builds	6 - 15 Percent Leakage
Close to or Past Due for Service	16 - 30 Percent Leakage
Broken or Barely Running Engines	30 + Percent Leakage

HOT TIP: Occasionally you'll find yourself in a situation where you just don't have an extra set of hands to help with performing the leak down test. I want to share with you my method for locking out the crankshaft and operating the leak down tester by myself. On certain engines, by carefully positioning your breaker bar or socket wrench so that it rests against the foot peg, you can partly eliminate the task of locking the crankshaft in place. The piston will still need to be positioned just shy of TDC and the socket or allen head socket which engages with the crankshaft will need to be positioned so the breaker bar lays flat against the foot peg. Once pressurized, the crank will try to turn the breaker bar down into the foot peg. You can then use one hand to make sure the breaker bar stays engaged with the crankshaft and the other hand to operate the pressure regulator. This is a fairly safe one-man method because if the breaker bar does happen to slip off the foot peg it will simply rotate away from you.

Crankcase Leak Down Testing Methods

A crankcase leak down test is performed by sealing off the crankcase cavity from all openings to the atmosphere and then pressurizing the crankcases. Normally the exhaust port is plugged and a special plug with a Schrader or other type of valve is used to plug the intake manifold. Additional plugs may be necessary to plug things such as power valve breathers.

Once the engine is plugged, it is pressurized to 5 psi so that the integrity of the seals and gaskets can be checked. Keeping test pressures low and within the bounds of around 6 - 7 psi is important because anything higher can risk seal blowout and compromise their integrity.

There are two primary goals we are trying to achieve by performing the crankcase leak down test. The first is to ensure there are no air leaks. To put some definition to this, the goal is to maintain 5 psi of pressure for five minutes. If the crankcase pressure has not dropped over a five minute period, the seals within the engine are sound. In reality this can be difficult to achieve and I will normally consider an engine good to go even if it loses up to 1/2 psi of pressure within five minutes.

The second goal is to pinpoint leaks if the crankcase pressure is continually dropping. There are numerous locations around the engine that air can escape from so this can be quite a task. To the right you will find a table of common leak locations that can be checked.

Large leaks will usually emit an audible hissing sound while small leaks will be difficult to locate by sound alone. The best way to determine where a leak is originating is to spray each suspect location with soapy water and to look for air bubbles. Once an air leak is found, appropriate actions can be taken to remedy the problem.

Now that the process of crankcase leak down testing is understood we'll take a look at the tools and supplies necessary to perform the test. Most of the equipment needed can be purchased as a kit from a specialty tool company, but they usually carry a fairly hefty price tag. The more economical approach is to build the necessary testing equipment from readily available hardware.

DIY Leak Down Tester

To successfully perform a crankcase leak down test the following items will be needed:

1. Exhaust port plug - I have found plugs used for pipe testing can be used effectively for sealing off exhaust ports. These plugs can be found in the plumbing section of most hardware stores. Depending on the port geometry, some shaping of the plug may be required.

2. Intake plug - There are a couple of ways to block off the intake. First, a plug which fits inside the intake manifold can be fabricated. Alternatively, a plate can be made which blocks off the intake once the intake manifold and reed valve are removed. My preference is for the plug so that I can test the seals between the engine, reed valve, and intake manifold.

HOT TIP: A well designed plug can be used on multiple engines even if the intake manifold diameters are all different sizes. Electrical tape or duct tape are great ways to increase the diameter of the base plug to accommodate larger manifolds. Simply size your plug to accommodate the smallest manifold diameter you intend to work with.

I machined my manifold from aluminum; however, a bit of ingenuity and a trip to the hardware store can be just as effective. All the plug has to do is fit inside the intake manifold, incorporate a fitting for a pressure gauge, and accommodate a valve or fitting so that the crankcase can be pressurized. Metal pipe fittings or PVC pipe could both be used effectively to create manifold plugs.

3. Schrader valve - A Schrader valve from just about anything can be used to pressurize the crankcase. I prefer valves from street motorcycle tires because most of them have a nice seal on them, making it easy to integrate them into the manifold plug. When installing the Schrader valve into the manifold, make sure there are no air leaks between the valve and plug.

4. Pressure gauge - A pressure gauge with fine graduations from 0 - 10 psi should be used. If the gauge can also read vacuum, that is an added bonus. This is handy incase you ever want to see how the crankcases respond to vacuum pressure.

5. Hand pump - A bicycle pump works great for pressurizing the crankcases. The main consideration when selecting a pump is to ensure that the delivery of air is at low pressure and is accurately metered. Bulb pumps work great too in combination with the correct manifold plug fitting for their utilization.

6. Small plugs for power valve breathers - Just about anything small and cylindrical can be used as a plug in conjunction with a hose clamp. To plug small tubes I've used bolts, drill bits, nails, and pens to name a few.

7. Spray bottle with soapy water - I'm not going to elaborate on the spray bottle part, but a nice soapy water mixture is essential to being able to see where air bubbles are originating.

Crankcase Leak Down Steps

1. Make sure the petcock is turned off and remove the fuel line from the carburetor. Use a rag to catch any fuel draining from the line.

2. Remove the seat and fuel tank from the bike.

3. Remove the rear side cover to gain access to the muffler, then remove the muffler.

4. Remove any necessary hardware securing the exhaust pipe to the frame, then remove the exhaust pipe.

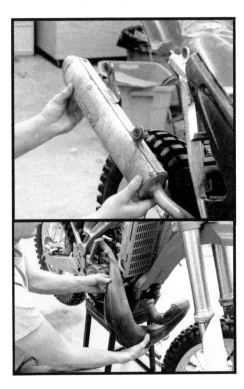

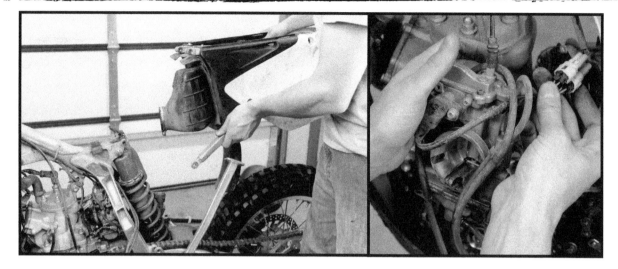

5. Remove the airbox and rear subframe.

6. Loosen the hose clamp securing the carburetor to the intake manifold, then remove the carburetor.

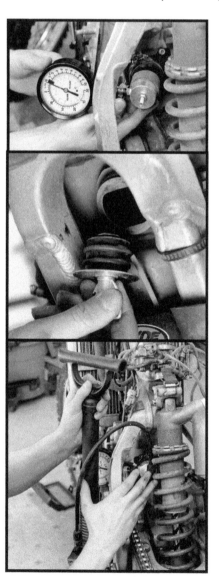

7. Install the leak down tester in the intake manifold. Be sure to tighten down the hose clamp so that an air tight seal is created between the tester and manifold.

8. Look through the exhaust port and position the piston at approximately BDC (bottom dead center). The positioning doesn't have to be perfect, it simply ensures air pressure will easily reach the top end of the engine as well as the bottom end.

9. Use a suitably sized plug to plug the exhaust port.

10. Depending on the engine, there may be additional orifices that need to be plugged to keep pressure in the crankcases. In the case of the Yamaha shown, there is a breather tube connected to the power valve assembly that must be plugged. You may have to attempt to pressurize the cases a couple times to determine if there are other breathers or areas that need attention.

11. Once all the necessary passages have been plugged, proceed to pressurize the crankcases to 5psi. Depending on the condition of the engine, pressure may be lost quickly or pressure may be maintained.

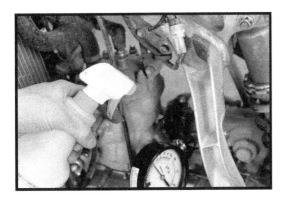

If pressure is lost quickly, there is a serious air leak somewhere within the engine. To determine where the leak is first carefully listen for any audible hissing. Audible leaks are generally large and easy to find. If the leak cannot be heard, use soapy water to spray down all potential leak points. Start with all the artificial leak points created when the tester and plugs were installed. Due to the irregular shapes of many exhaust ports, leaks can often originate between the port and plug.

If the leak was not traced back to the testing equipment the leak must reside somewhere within the engine. As a reminder, common leak points include the crank seals, cylinder base gasket, o-rings/head gasket, power valve seals, crankcase gaskets, spark plug, intake manifold, and reed valve. Continue pressurizing and spraying down the engine until the leak is found.

Once the leak is found the severity of the problem can be determined and either corrective actions taken or the decision made to strip the engine down further. If the faulty component can be remedied and the crankcase pressurized at 5 psi for five minutes, the engine can be reassembled and you can get back to riding.

HOT TIP: Depending on the design of the power valve system, some engines will seal easier or yield fewer leak points than others. If you're unfamiliar with how the power valve system should seal and the service manual lacks clarity, take a look at a microfiche of the system. Often times reviewing the microfiche will make it possible to understand where air leaks can occur.

CH 4

LEADING CAUSES OF ENGINE WEAR & FAILURE

Why do engines break? This is a complicated question and while every single scenario can't possibly be covered in this book, I can tell you with certainty six factors that you should pay attention to in order to decrease your chances of premature wear and/or catastrophic engine failure.

#1 Lean Mixture/Incorrect Jetting

Maintaining the correct air/fuel mixture in a two-stroke engine is critical to its longevity. Incorrectly tuned carburetors or fuel injection systems which result in lean mixtures, where there is not enough fuel for the incoming air charge, can cause engines to fail quickly. The reason for this is due to the fact that lean mixtures lead to very high combustion temperatures. When combustion temperatures are excessive, more heat is dissipated into the piston. As a result, the piston becomes hotter, expands, and weakens.

Commonly, three things can happen. First, the clearances between the piston and cylinder can be reduced to nothing, causing the piston to seize in its bore. Second, the piston crown can deteriorate to the point where a hole has melted all the way through it. Finally, since aluminum weakens at elevated temperatures, the piston can break because it can no longer cope with the forces being exerted on it.

Ensuring the jetting or fuel injection parameters are set correctly is incredibly important. A number of resources are available to help with engine tuning. Starting with the service manual, jetting tables are often prescribed for stock engines and feature comprehensive charts detailing the correct carburetor configuration for specific elevations and temperatures. For modified engines, many aftermarket companies detail solid baseline jetting to use in combination with their products.

Engine builders and tuners often solicit their tuning expertise as well, which in many cases can be a valuable service; however, I will suggest that learning to tune a carburetor is not out of reach for most people. There is a plethora of tuning information available online nowadays and the process can be safe and enjoyable if executed correctly. Opinions may differ, but my general advice is to tune the carburetor starting with the idle circuit and working up one circuit at a time until it is time to tune the main jet. Always work conservatively starting too rich and working towards the ideal mixture, versus starting too lean and richening.

Lean mixtures (and occasionally rich mixtures) can also occur as a result of seal and gasket failures. Faulty crank seals or gaskets anywhere between the engine and carburetor can be potentially problematic. Due to the varying pressures (above and below atmospheric conditions) occurring within the cylinder and crankcase throughout the engine's cycle, additional air can be drawn in through a defective seal or gasket. This additional air has not been accounted for in the tuning of the carburetor, which leads to a lean air/fuel mixture in most cases. A rich mixture can result if the right crank seal fails because oil will be drawn in from the gearbox cavity and it will dilute the air/fuel mixture.

Periodically checking the integrity of the crankcase using the aforementioned crankcase leak down testing procedure is the solution to tracking and eliminating the worry of malfunctioning seals and gaskets.

#2 Lean Oil Mixture

Since the only way a two-stroke engine is lubricated is through the oil mixed in with the fuel or a metered oil pump, the amount of oil becomes very important to the engine's durability. Depending on the manufacturer, oil ratios are commonly specified anywhere from 20:1 - 50:1.

Truthfully, pre-mixed oil is a very inefficient way to lubricate a two-stroke engine. Due to the oil being diluted into the fuel, its ability to lubricate is reduced. Furthermore, the oil is being thrown everywhere inside the engine instead of at specific points. This results in needing to use more oil than necessary to lubricate critical points within the engine.

Problems arise for many riders when they decide to veer away from the manufacturer's recommended oil ratio. Whatever the reason may be, the results are always the same. Engines that are run with severely lean oil ratios will wear much more quickly than engines run at the recommended oil ratios. There simply is not enough oil to adequately lubricate the rotating and reciprocating components.

Lastly, as an aside, incase you are wondering about how power is affected by lean or rich oil ratios, I have not seen any studies performed which indicate two-stroke engines tested with lean oil ratios produce more power than two-strokes with relatively rich oil ratios (20:1, 30:1); however, the contrary is quite true.

Following the recommended premix ratio suggested by the manufacturer is an easy way to ensure your engine is not starved of oil and does not prematurely wear out.

#3 Keeping A Clean Air Filter

The air filter is the entrance into your engine and because of this its job is extremely important. The air filter must make sure incoming air entering the engine is clean. If air entering the engine is dirty, the rings, crank bearings, piston, power valves, and cylinder bore will all wear. Correct air filter maintenance is critical to maintaining a healthy engine.

After building your engine, start things off on the right foot by installing a new air filter. Always make sure your air filter has a healthy coating of oil on it and be sure to use a suitable filter oil. Filter oils are formulated so that once the oil is exposed to air, certain chemicals will evaporate out of the oil leaving the filter oil tacky allowing the trapping of dust and dirt.

When preparing a new filter, use a pair of rubber gloves, then apply oil to the inner and outer surfaces. Rub the oil in by hand so that both the inside and outside of the filter is saturated with oil. The goal is to achieve complete saturation of the filter without over oiling. If you apply too much oil you can squeeze the excess out by hand. Make sure the airbox flange is free of dirt before installing, then carefully secure the filter in place.

#4 Eliminating Over Revving

One of the leading causes of rod failure is from mechanically over revving the engine. This happens when the engine RPM exceeds the maximum RPM the engine components were designed to withstand. Usually the rod will fail when a rider is operating the bike near the rev limit of the engine and then downshifts into a lower gear. The drop to a lower gear forces the engine RPM even higher. The rod cannot cope with the excessive inertia forces created by the extremely high engine RPM and will break. Usually the break occurs just below the small end bore of the rod.

One final scenario that can lead to rod failures occurs when an inexperienced engine builder increases the RPM and/or the weight of the piston assembly without taking into consideration the additional stress that will be put on the rod. As RPM and piston mass increase, the resulting inertia force exerted on the rod also increases. If the strength of the rod is not accurately assessed or a stronger rod is not fitted, the performance engine won't last long.

For non-builder related over revving scenarios, making alterations to the way you ride the bike is the best way to cure this problem. Asking engineers to economically design the rod to withstand such forces would result in heavier, lower revving, less powerful engines. One common mistake made among riders occurs when they lose track of what gear they are in. Any time a rider misses a shift, accidentally shifts into an unknown gear, or double downshifts, instead of letting the clutch out in that gear, the rider should shift up a gear instead. In most cases the upshift will prevent the engine from mechanically over revving. If racing, some time may be lost, but at least the rider will have a better chance of finishing the race instead of bringing back a bike with an engine that has a hole in the crankcase.

#5 Improper Rebuilding Of The Engine

Occasionally an engine will be destined to fail even before it fires up. Most commonly this occurs when an inexperienced builder puts an engine together and either installs parts incorrectly or doesn't do a thorough job identifying worn or damaged parts. With the complexities of today's modern high performance two-strokes, the combination of ways mistakes can accrue throughout a build are almost endless. Once together, the engine is run again and either fails completely or wears out at an accelerated rate shortly thereafter. Luckily, the correct assembly techniques, necessary measurements, and inspection points will be covered in later chapters so you can avoid this scenario altogether!

#6 Running Parts Too Long

As the saying goes, "nothing good lasts forever". Engines are the epitome of good things and they do wear out as they are used. Some engines will fail because their internal parts have been run well beyond their useful life. Pistons, rings, cylinders, and bearings are all examples of wear items that must be replaced at regular intervals. The good news is that most of these parts will all give good indicators that they are in need of replacement long before the engine is reduced to a pile of broken bits.

In conclusion, the most probable causes of engine problems can be broken down into four categories: tuning, maintenance, exceeding the mechanical limits of the engine, and incorrectly building the engine.

Tuning problems can be reduced by carefully following the manufacturer's recommendations on carburetor settings and oil ratios, seeking the advice of experienced tuners, or learning the craft yourself.

If you keep up on your maintenance by regularly changing the transmission oil, keeping the air filter clean, and replacing worn parts routinely, maintenance related problems will become non-existent.

Keeping the engine operating within its mechanical limits at all times will be a big help in avoiding catastrophic failures. I know that this can be tough, especially when racing, but incorporating riding techniques to keep from inadvertently sending engine RPM skyrocketing to the moon will go a long way in prolonging engine life and avoiding major blow ups.

Lastly, the modern two-stroke dirt bike engine is a high performance piece of machinery that is designed to exacting tolerances. Builders need to have a good understanding of how these engines work, know what to look for throughout the build, and exercise care and patience as they put them together.

CH 5 | WHAT TO REPLACE

Once you have decided that you will be rebuilding the engine from top to bottom, knowing what to replace becomes important. This subject deserves some attention for a few reasons. First and foremost, if the necessary parts are not replaced, you may find yourself doing things twice or experiencing engine problems which could have otherwise been avoided. Second, if you depend on the internet or forums for researching and gathering information, you are likely to find that opinions vary and you may be left wondering what is right. Finally, with the way aftermarket companies present their "rebuild kits," one can be lead to believe that an all encompassing kit is being sold and nothing else is needed. This is often not the case.

When possible, it is advisable to plan a full rebuild so that all major wear components are replaced at once. Since parts wear at different rates this can be difficult to orchestrate. The advantage to this methodology is that once the engine is built you are starting with a clean slate and everything within the engine is new. There are no old parts left within the engine which are half worn, which can cause other parts to wear more quickly, nor are there any weak links that may fail and take out all the other new parts.

The majority of the parts that will be getting replaced can be sourced before even opening up the engine. Along with these parts there are parts I like to assess on a case by case basis, namely the expensive components which may require machining services or other outside services. Of course, in addition to these parts, I almost always find one or two parts that catch me off guard when inspecting the condition of the engine. Naturally, these outliers are the main reasons builds get stopped in their tracks and are what frustrate me and other builders the most.

All the likely part candidates for outright and inspection-based replacement have been categorized in the tables, like you see to the right, and organized by subassembly. Keep in mind this is a generic list and what I would recommend replacing when doing a major overhaul. Specific makes and models may have some additional small parts that should be replaced that I have either generalized or omitted mentioning.

Cylinder/Piston	
Part	Replacement
Piston	Always
Rings	Always
Wrist Pin	Always
Wrist Pin Bearing	Always
Circlips	Always
Cylinder	Inspection Dependent
Cylinder Base Gasket	Always
Cylinder Head O-Rings/Gasket	Always
Cylinder Head Sealing Washers	Always

Within the cylinder and piston subassembly, the cylinder is the only item that is inspected prior to replacement. Depending on how much use the cylinder has seen and the thickness of the plating, the cylinder can usually withstand multiple honing/deglazing operations before it must be replated or replaced. If the plating has been damaged or is worn out, the choice to replate or replace the cylinder will come down to cost and how quickly you need the cylinder finished.

> **HOT TIP:** For pistons being fit to cylinders that have already had a couple pistons run in them and are closer to the end of their useful life, waiting on selecting the piston until the cylinder has been measured is a good idea. Some aftermarket companies offer pistons in slightly oversized diameters (we are talking 0.0004" or 0.01mm increments) which can be used to achieve the correct piston to cylinder clearances in cylinder bores which are close to their service limits.

Reed Valve Assembly

As long as the engine is equipped with composite reed petals the majority of the components within the reed valve assembly are inspection dependent. Gaskets are the only item in this subassembly that should always be replaced. Older engines that utilize metal reed petals are a different story and it is advisable to replace the petals every rebuild. The consequences of ingesting a metal reed petal verse a composite one are much more serious and detrimental.

Reed Valve Assembly	
Part	Replacement
Intake Manifold	Inspection Dependent
Reed Valve Body	Inspection Dependent
Reed Petals	Inspection Dependent
Reed Stoppers (if equipped)	Inspection Dependent
Reed Valve Gaskets	Always

Power Valve Assembly

Within the power valve assembly any bearings, seals, and gaskets should always be replaced. The power valves themselves and related hardware should be replaced depending on their condition.

Power Valve Assembly	
Part	Replacement
Power Valves	Inspection Dependent
Power Vavle Shafts	Inspection Dependent
Power Valve Bearings	Always
Power Valve Seals	Always
Power Valve Gaskets	Always
Power Valve Governor Spring	Inspection Dependent
Power Valve Retaining Cup	Inspection Dependent

Crankcases

The only bearings which I don't recommend messing with, unless absolutely necessary, are the needle bearings used to support the clutch actuation arm. They are a royal pain to remove and seldom wear out since the clutch actuation arm isn't moving back and forth very quickly.

Crankcases	
Part	Replacement
Crank Bearings	Always
Crank Seals	Always
Transmission Bearings	Always
Auxilliary Crankcase Seals	Always
Crankcase Gasket	Always
Clutch Actuation Arm Oil Seal	Always
Clutch Actuation Arm Bearings	Inspection Dependent

Crankshaft/Rod

Starting with a fresh crankshaft assembly is essential for building an engine with a solid backbone. Whether the crankshaft assembly is rebuilt or replaced will be entirely dependent on the condition of the used crankshaft, part costs, and service costs.

Crankshaft/Rod	
Part	Replacement
Crankshaft Halves	Inspection Dependent
Rod	Always
Rod Bearing	Always
Crank pin & Thrust Washers	Always

Transmission/Gear Shift Mechanism

Most of the transmission and gear shift components are inspection dependent. The one thing I will stress is that if you remove any of the retaining rings from the transmission shafts, they should be replaced with new ones. The reasoning for this will be covered in detail later on.

Transmission/Shift Mechanism	
Part	Replacement
Shafts	Inspection Dependent
Gears	Inspection Dependent
Bushings	Inspection Dependent
Retaining Rings	Always
Shift Forks	Inspection Dependent
Shift Drum	Inspection Dependent
Shift Drum Bearings	Always

Clutch

Clutches are easy to service when the engine is together in the bike. Unless the bike was exhibiting clutch problems before requiring a rebuild, replacing the clutch components can be done on an as needed basis.

Clutch	
Part	Replacement
Clutch Basket	Inspection Dependent
Clutch Hub	Inspection Dependent
Clutch Pressure Plate	Inspection Dependent
Steel Clutch Plates	Inspection Dependent
Clutch Discs	Inspection Dependent
Clutch Springs	Inspection Dependent
Clutch Basket Sleeve	Inspection Dependent
Clutch Basket Bearing	Always
Clutch Pushrod Thrust Bearing	Always
Clutch Hub Lock Washer	Always

Balance Shaft Parts

While uncommon on older two-strokes, balance shafts are making their way back in newer models.

Balance Shaft	
Part	Replacement
Balance Shaft Bearings	Always
Balance Shaft Seal	Always
Balance Shaft Bearing Retaining	Always
Balance Shaft	Inspection Dependent

Right Cover/Water Pump/Odds & Ends

In the last two tables of subassemblies there aren't too many things requiring explanation. One point of interest that may catch your eye are one time use fasteners. Occasionally, a manufacturer will use nuts or bolts that end up getting permanently deformed once used. Manufacturer's should clearly indicate any instances where one time use fasteners are used so you can prepare accordingly. In Chapter 13 Inspection, all the parts within the engine that may wear will be covered in great detail so you can make accurate assessments of the inspection dependent parts.

OEM vs. Aftermarket Parts

Now that you know what all to replace, the next big question on your mind is probably what to replace these parts with? Little did you know, never has a more controversial question been asked! There are a lot of opinions floating around on this subject. Perhaps you've heard of someone saying brand X's part failed in their engine and that you must never use their parts? Or someone used brand Y and then this happened?

Right Cover/Water Pump	
Part	Replacement
Water Pump Bearing(s)	Always
Water Pump Seals	Always
Water Pump Shaft	Inspection Dependent
Water Pump Cover Gasket	Always
Right Cover Gasket	Always
Kick Start Seal	Always
Engine Seals	Always

Odds & Ends	
Part	Replacement
Stator Cover Gasket	Always
Kick Start Gears	Inspection Dependent
Misc Retaining Rings	Always
Misc Seals & O-rings	Always
Misc Gaskets	Always
Drive Sprocket Lock Washer	Always
Air Filter	Always
Spark Plug	Always
One Time Use Bolts or Nuts	Always
Sealing Washers	Inspection Dependent

There are so many variables affecting part life that it is very hard to establish a cause and effect relationship that would single out the manufacturer of the part as the source of the failure. I'm not saying that manufacturers never make mistakes and never sell parts that are faulty, but it is not the norm for OEMs or the aftermarket. If it were, it wouldn't take long for consumers to wise up and alter where they spend money, leaving the offending company grasping for business. More probable reasons for part failures result from assembly error, lack of maintenance, misdiagnosis of the condition of parts when the engine was apart and not replacing all worn parts, and abuse/misuse of the engine by the rider.

OEM parts and aftermarket parts both have their advantages and disadvantages. OEM parts from any of the major manufacturers have the advantage that they are the exact replacement part for a specific machine. Extensive time has been spent designing the parts, they have been rigorously tested, and offer a very high level of quality. There is no reverse engineering going on when making these parts.

The downside to purchasing OEM parts is that the pricing models used to price OEM parts makes the parts very expensive. The way parts are grouped together and priced leads me to believe that a lot of thought went into how the most money can be extracted from the consumer so that dealers, and ultimately the manufacturer, would prosper the most. When shopping OEM don't always expect a piston, rings, wrist pin, and circlips to be grouped together. That would be far too convenient and wouldn't give you the opportunity to spend more and buy all these parts separately!

Aftermarket parts are great because they can be more affordable, be designed for specific applications, and they are much more conveniently packaged. If you need a high strength rod for a performance application, there are several companies to choose from. Likewise, if you want a better reed valve assembly than the OEM option, that can be done too. The possibilities are endless as far as what aftermarket companies specialize in and there are a lot of companies to choose from.

The downside to the aftermarket as I see it is that in some cases aftermarket parts are not tested as rigorously and quality control is not as good. As a result, the aftermarket introduces more problematic parts into the marketplace than OEMs. I want to stress that these instances of imperfection are a rarity and not all aftermarket companies produce bad parts. The majority of aftermarket companies that specialize in specific parts often exceed OEM quality. My personal belief is that larger aftermarket companies manufacturing a high volume of parts by using manufacturing facilities in countries with less developed manufacturing capabilities are more likely to be the culprit of bad parts than smaller highly specialized businesses.

Whether you decide to go with OEM or aftermarket brands for replacement parts in your rebuild should be a decision based on what makes the most sense for you, based on your specific build needs, and your budget. Most of the time what offers the most performance and makes the most financial sense will be a combination of OEM and aftermarket parts.

What tools you use to work on your engine can have a big impact on how well your build goes. Using incorrect tools for various tasks can result in wasted time, broken parts, and a poor quality build.

Prior to tearing into your engine it is important to have a rough idea of what tools will be needed to perform the work. You are probably wondering how you get a rough idea of what you need without actually tearing into it. This chapter is aimed at giving you an overview of all the tools you need to work on most Japanese and European dirt bike engines.

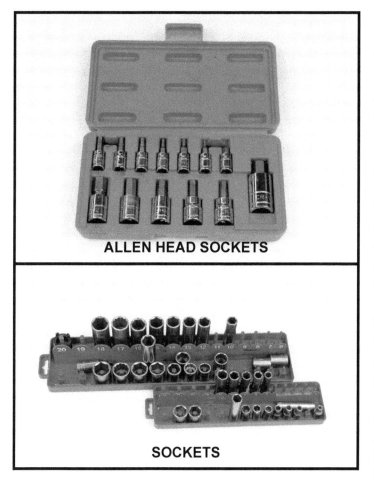

ALLEN HEAD SOCKETS

SOCKETS

An assorted set of allen head sockets is a must for most engines. While allen wrenches are good, they cannot be used for torquing a bolt during final assembly. Kill two birds with one stone and get a set of allen head sockets which can be used for disassembly and assembly purposes. A set ranging from 2mm to 14mm will have you covered for most jobs.

Most modern two-stroke dirt bike engines utilize fasteners with head sizes between 6 and 19mm. This creates a standard of sorts across brands and once you have a socket set capable of dealing with these sizes you are set. There are always a few anomalies though that will require larger sizes, namely the swingarm pivot nut, flywheel nut, and clutch basket nut. These nuts can require socket sizes that at-home mechanics don't have readily available. In some cases, manufacturers choose to use specialty nuts or fasteners which require a special socket to remove them. Nothing is more irritating than progressing through a disassembly only to be brought to a screeching halt because you don't have the right size or type of socket to remove a fastener. These situations can be avoided by carefully scanning through your service manual in advance to pinpoint fastener sizes with which you aren't equipped to remove. Most quality tool stores stock individual sizes where you can pick one up or a quick internet order can be made to get the right tool for the job.

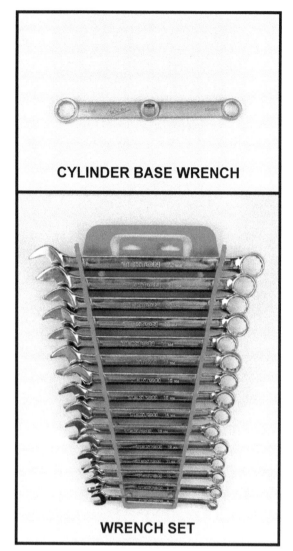

CYLINDER BASE WRENCH

WRENCH SET

The cylinder base nuts on most two-stroke dirt bike engines cannot be removed with a socket, instead a wrench must be used. This means that without a special tool, the nuts cannot be correctly torqued upon reassembly. A purposely designed tool such as Motion Pro's wrench which features a socket adapter in its center should be used. Alternatively, some types of crows feet can be employed.

Similar to socket sizes, most dirt bikes can be disassembled and assembled with a wrench set from 6 - 19mm. A crescent wrench will always work in a pinch if you find yourself without the right size. Just remember crescent wrenches are big and don't always fit into the space surrounding the fastener. Crescent wrenches are also more prone to rounding the edges of the fasteners, so make sure you are careful when using them.

Torque wrenches are imperative when it comes to final assembly. They are the only tool that can ensure all the fasteners have been tightened to their correct torque specifications. Since this is the case, it is equally important that the tool you select for the job is of high enough quality to consistently return accurate results.

There are a few different types and styles of torque wrenches available to the consumer, all of which have their advantages and disadvantages. The three main types of torque wrenches are beam, click, and electronic.

Beam style torque wrenches are notable for their simplicity and low cost. A beam style torque wrench connects the head of the wrench to the handle through a long lever arm. The lever arm has a certain amount of elasticity to it. As the wrench is turned, the elasticity in the handle correlates to the torque gauge at the end of the handle.

The gauge simply consists of a long straight metal pointer and a wide range of torque values the needle will point to as the handle bends. The more resistant the fastener is to turning, the more force is applied to the wrench, the more the lever arm bends, and the more torque is read on the torque gauge.

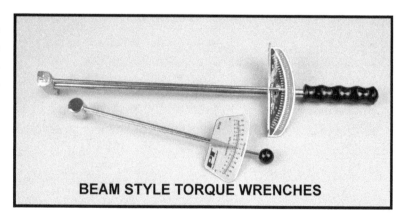

BEAM STYLE TORQUE WRENCHES

The disadvantages to beam style torque wrenches are that they are not easy to use in all situations and not very accurate. While operating a beam style torque wrench with the engine out of a bike is usually not a problem, trying to use one with the engine in the bike can be troublesome. Along with space constraints, in order for the beam type wrench to work accurately the user must be able to view the needle and torque gauge perfectly perpendicular to the face of the gauge. If viewing the needle and face of the gauge from an angle, a parallax error will result giving you an incorrect torque value. Lastly, when using a beam style torque wrench on fasteners that require a great deal of torque, it can be very difficult to keep the wrench steady enough to obtain an accurate reading as you are fighting to pull on the wrench.

The clicker style torque wrench is favored by many due to its ease of use. The wrench is comprised of a spring loaded clutch which is set by the user to the desired torque value. The torque setting is adjusted on the handle of the wrench. As the torque setting is increased, tension on the internal spring is increased, which causes the clutch to engage at a higher torque level. When you are tightening a fastener and the desired torque value is reached the head of the wrench "clicks" and you know when to stop.

While simple to use, the composition of the click style wrench is more complicated. There are many individual parts to a click style wrench. The quality of the materials, accuracy of manufacturing, and how well the manufacturer calibrated the wrench are the major factors which determine its accuracy. Higher end wrenches usually come with a calibration certificate from the manufacturer that details the results of the manufacturer's calibration and lets you know the wrench passed all the calibration tests.

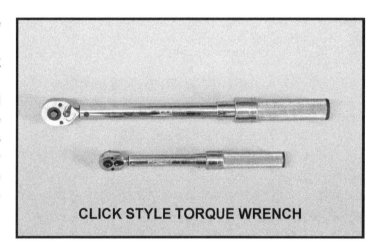

CLICK STYLE TORQUE WRENCH

Clicker style torque wrenches tend to be more accurate in the middle range rather than at the far ends of their range. Usually, for engine and bike work it is necessary to have a couple different clicker wrenches which overlap in range. This will yield the best accuracy. The range covered by the wrench also influences how accurate it will be. A wrench that spans from 0 - 200Nm for example will be less accurate than a wrench that spans from 0 - 100Nm. Just as you get the best performance from your engine by keeping it in its powerband, you will get the best performance from your torque wrench by keeping it in the middle of its range.

As a click style torque wrench is used over time, it will need to be recalibrated. The main reason for this is that the torque spring within the wrench will fatigue. While use does contribute to the spring fatiguing, the biggest reason the spring fatigues is due to users forgetting to take the tension off the spring after they are done using the wrench. Leaving a click style wrench's torque spring tensioned can quickly lead to the wrench requiring recalibration. An adjuster inside the wrench must then be tweaked to make the wrench read accurately again. Calibration is usually done by the manufacturer or an independent tool measurement and calibration business. While this sounds complicated and may turn you off from click type wrenches, it shouldn't. If a click type wrench is properly cared for, it will last a long time before it needs calibration.

Click style torque wrenches range in price significantly which means there are plenty of options available to meet many different budgetary needs. Reading torque wrench reviews from reputable sources is a great way to get familiarized with which wrenches stand out in their respective price ranges. Keep an eye out for brands that are affiliated with the top brands. Companies like Snap-On rebrand so they can offer similar products in different price ranges. The affiliated company may not be able to offer a wrench in the same color scheme or with all the features, but there is a good chance similar care has been taken to produce a quality product. One affiliate brand of Snap-On I want to briefly mention is a company called CDI. CDI offers click style torque wrenches in the medium price range ($100 - $150) and most of them come with a calibration certificate.

The last type of torque wrench I want to touch on is the electronic torque wrench. An electronic torque wrench uses a strain gauge attached to a torsion rod to measure torque. A transducer is used to convert the strain gauge's measurements into useful torque values. From there the values are sent to a screen the user can easily read as the wrench is being used. Most electronic wrenches can also be programmed to emit an audible beep once the desired torque is reached.

Like click style torque wrenches, electronic wrenches are very easy to use. They are fairly expensive though and do require calibration from time to time. While they are great to have on a manufacturing floor for serious assembly jobs, they are probably a bit overkill for the home shop mechanic.

Whichever style torque wrench you choose, be certain it meets your needs, abilities, and is something you'll be comfortable using. In addition, be sure the wrench reads in both inch/foot pounds and Newton Meters. Owning a wrench that doesn't have both scales on it is sure to cause problems at some point in your wrenching career.

Cross-head style fasteners can be found on all Japanese motorcycles. Most people will associate this style of cross-head to a Phillips style bit. This is incorrect. These cross-head Japanese fasteners don't actually use a Phillips style head. A Phillips bit just happens to fit in them and, out of convenience, most people use an appropriately sized Phillips screwdriver to loosen or tighten the fastener. In reality, these Japanese fasteners utilize a Japanese Industrial Standard (JIS) head. JIS screwdrivers and

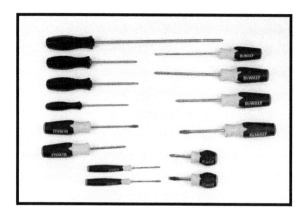

socket bits are readily available and are the correct tool to use when working on Japanese motorcycles. While Phillips bits work in JIS heads, they are not the appropriate style bit to use and are more prone to stripping the screw heads. This is especially true in situations where the screw must be torqued fairly tight. Subtle differences between the profiles of the Phillips bit and JIS head cause the Phillips bit to strip (cam-out in technical jargon) the head in medium to high torque applications.

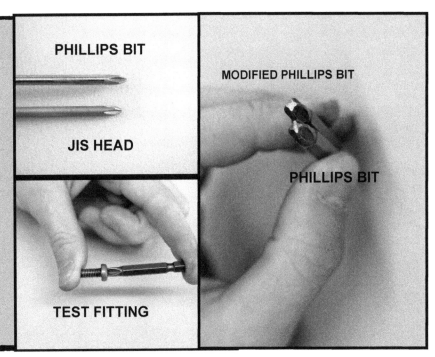

PHILLIPS BIT

JIS HEAD

MODIFIED PHILLIPS BIT

PHILLIPS BIT

TEST FITTING

HOT TIP: Having the correct JIS screwdrivers and socket bits on hand when working on Japanese machinery is always best. Occasionally though you may find yourself in a situation where you just don't have the bit you need. If this is the case you can modify a Phillips bit to fit nicely into a JIS style head by carefully grinding the tip away until the edges of the bit fit tightly into the tapered slot of the JIS head.

European bikes have minor quirks about them just like the Japanese brands. While found occasionally on Japanese bikes, Torx style heads are much more common on European bikes. If you own a European brand having a set of Torx bits in your toolbox is a good idea.

An impact driver is an indispensable tool when it comes to dealing with cross-head fasteners that have a threadlocking agent on them. Bearing retaining plates on the inside of crankcases are one of the most common areas you'll encounter this scenario. Using an impact driver to remove these tricky cross-head fasteners has always worked flawlessly for me and has lessened the likelihood of these fasteners stripping. If you don't have an impact driver, I highly recommend you pick one up.

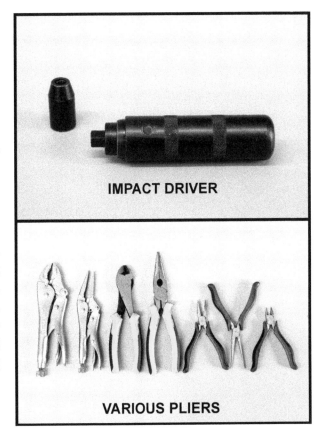

IMPACT DRIVER

VARIOUS PLIERS

Having an assortment of pliers around when working on dirt bikes and engines is always handy. Their uses are almost endless and they are particularly good at aiding in the removal of spring clips, feeding fasteners into hard to reach spots, and grabbing parts that have fallen into black holes. You can never have too many plier variations. Having a small and large set on hand along with a set of vice grips makes for a well rounded toolbox.

Along with the common pliers, having a clutch hub holding pliers is especially helpful. Clutch hub pliers are by far the best and fastest way to lock the clutch hub in place so the nut can be loosened or tightened. The pliers are universal and can be adapted to any motorcycle clutch you encounter, so they are definitely a worthwhile investment.

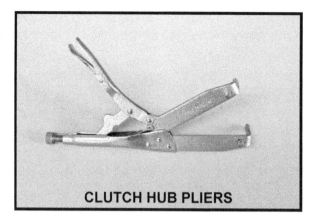

CLUTCH HUB PLIERS

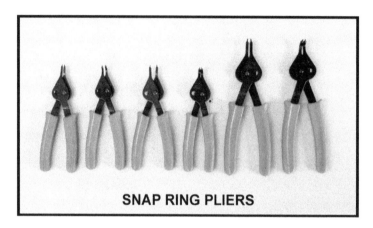

SNAP RING PLIERS

Snap ring pliers are a must when disassembling and assembling transmission shafts. Internal or external retaining rings are also commonly used to retain bearings, idler gears, and power valve components. There really is no substitute to a pair of snap ring pliers when it comes to quickly and correctly removing snap rings. While it is possible to work retaining rings off by using a combination of picks, screwdrivers, and pliers, the possibility of damaging the retaining ring and mating parts is greatly increased. The time and patience involved in using this combination of inferior tools is ridiculous. After attempting this a few times, you'll quickly realize the time you wasted could have been better utilized earning the money required to buy a set of snap ring pliers. Internal and external snap rings usually come in small sizes on dirt bike engines and one pair of snap ring pliers usually won't cover them all, unless you have a pair with adjustable tips. Having two to three pliers with tip sizes from around 0.038" (0.97mm) to 0.070" (1.78mm) should cover most retaining rings found within a dirt bike engine.

The pen magnet is one of my favorite specialty tools. Its ability to retrieve hard to reach magnetic objects or objects that have been accidentally misplaced in the nooks and crannies of an engine's internals make it invaluable (speaking from experience here).

The flywheel puller is an engine specific tool that is mandatory. Each make and model of bike will have its own flywheel puller requirements. If you own four different brands of bikes there is a good chance you'll also own four different types of flywheel pullers. The good news is that they aren't too expensive to buy. If you happen to have a lathe and some extra time, making your own is fairly simple too.

FLYWHEEL PULLER

A strap wrench, flywheel holding tool, or pinned holding tool are types of specialty tools used to secure flywheels in place. The most suitable tool will depend on your engine's flywheel and surrounding geometry. Strap wrenches and flywheel holding tools work great on flywheels that protrude out from the crankcase while special pinned holding tools are required for flywheels that are recessed into the crankcase.

You may be wondering why you'd lock out the flywheel when you could just lock out the primary gears on the opposite side of the engine. If you lock the primary gears in place then use your wrench to tighten or loosen the flywheel nut, a torsional force is introduced across the crankshaft which, if big enough, could twist a pressed fit crankshaft out of alignment. You'd be surprised how little force is actually required to misalign a press fit crankshaft. This would be a huge problem if it happened during reassembly because you would have no way of knowing it happened until the engine starts vibrating excessively when run.

A seal puller will work flawlessly time and again when removing any type of seal from an engine or any other part on a bike. They can be had for less than 10 dollars. Not only is a seal puller a big time saver, it also lessens the chances of damaging the seal bore, which can happen when using screwdrivers to pop seals out.

Most bearings can be removed through the careful application of heat to the crankcases and then tapping them out with a punch. Unfortunately, there are almost always a couple bearing bores that are blind, meaning the bearing can't be tapped out by a punch. Even with the crankcases heated to the maximum safe temperature (more on this later), the bearing bore won't expand enough to allow the bearing to drop out. These

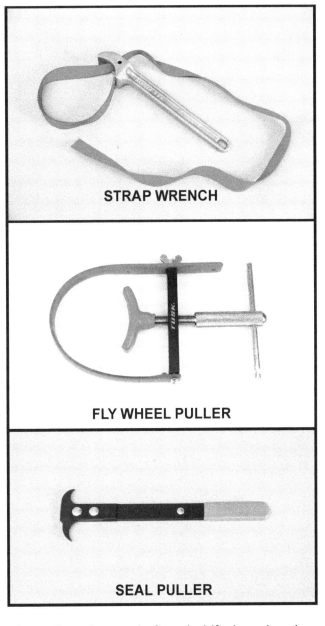

STRAP WRENCH

FLY WHEEL PULLER

SEAL PULLER

bearings are usually found on the left crankcase and are the primary shaft and shift drum bearing bores. A blind bearing puller is the best answer to get these pesky bearings out. A blind bearing puller and the set of associated puller heads for dirt bike engine maintenance are definitely an investment. If you don't do enough engine work to warrant spending around 120 dollars on a set of blind bearing pullers, you may want to check out your local auto parts store. Some auto parts stores rent blind bearing pullers which can be an economical option if you'll only be using the tool occasionally.

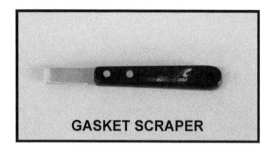

GASKET SCRAPER

A gasket scraper tool is by far the best choice for removing old gasket material left on sealing surfaces. Chisels, razor blades, sandpaper, or steel wool may all be tempting options, but they should be avoided. Chisels are far too sharp and can easily gouge the gasket surfaces. Razor blades face similar problems but are more prone to leaving deep scratches instead of gouges. Sandpaper or steel wool will round the edges of the surface. This rounding of the edges will ultimately leave less surface for the gasket to seal against in the future. Gasket scrapers are made in a variety of widths and have a blunt hardened blade ideal for freeing up old stuck gasket.

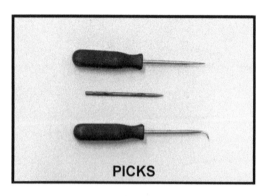

PICKS

Having a couple different types of picks around will greatly help when removing circlips. Keeping a straight pick and a pick with a 90 degree bend at the end will be all you need to accomplish most tasks. Thinner dental type picks can also come in handy when inspecting parts and feeling for subtle grooving in shafts.

A cylinder hone is used to restore the surface finish of an engine's cylinder bore. The hone can be used when the cylinder bore is not damaged or outside the manufacturer's recommended service specifications. If the cylinder is damaged or out of spec, alternative methods such as replating or replacing the cylinder will be necessary. Reconditioning of the cylinder bore should be done any time the piston and rings are replaced. As an engine is run, the surface finish of the cylinder bore changes from a cross-hatch finish to a polished finish due to the reciprocation of the rings and piston against the cylinder bore. The polished finish creates two problems that must be addressed before an engine is put back together. First, a polished surface finish on the cylinder wall does not allow oil to easily be retained on the cylinder bore. A nice cross-hatch finish allows oil to be retained on the cylinder wall and is very beneficial to piston/ring lubrication. Second, new piston rings must wear a minuscule amount against the cylinder bore in order to create a gas-tight seal. This cannot happen when the rings slide across a polished surface.

CYLINDER BRUSH HONE

If you intend on reconditioning the cylinder bore yourself, a cylinder hone will be necessary. Performing the honing operation may sound complicated and unfamiliar, but you may warm up to the idea after learning more about honing later in this book.

Cylinder hones come in different styles, types of materials, and different grits. There are three types of deglazing hones available: the ball hone, the brush hone, and the spring loaded stone hone. My preference and recommendation for anyone learning how to deglaze the bore of a two-stroke cylinder is to use a brush hone. I believe brush hones are more forgiving than stone hones, remove less material, and don't run the risk of damaging port edges which can occur with ball and stone hones. Selecting the right hone material and grit is dependent upon the material of the rings and cylinder bore. Fortunately, the surface finish requirements for most rings found in dirt bike engines are very similar. This means there is very little legwork to do on the consumer's end and honing products offered by companies such as Wiseco can be tailored to the application.

Honing tools vary in price depending on the bore size you require. For large bores (500cc range) hones top out in price at about 115 dollars. In addition to the hone, honing oil should be purchased to lubricate the hone. To operate the hone, an electric drill capable of speeds up to about 600 RPM will be required. Post-honing, automatic transmission fluid and cotton swabs should be on hand to aid in cleaning the honing grit out of the cylinder bore.

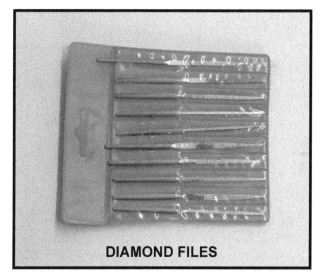

DIAMOND FILES

Diamond files can be a real asset when perfecting small parts. The diamond files work well for setting piston ring end gap, deburring circlips, and correcting small flaws on gasket surfaces. A set of small diamond files can be bought for less than 10 dollars and will last you a long time.

For completeness, piston ring compressors are worth mentioning; however, I have not encountered a two-stroke engine where the rings could not be installed by hand. For this reason, I don't consider them a mandatory tool to have on hand. Should you decide you want them anyway, ring compressors are either adjustable with a one size fits all function or are designed for a specific range of bore diameters. I personally have no experience working with the adjustable type and have never seen them used in the industry. The ring compressors that I'm familiar with and have seen used the most are the type which have different sized compressor rings for very specific bore sizes. These compressors typically come with six or more compressor rings so that a fairly wide range of bore diameters are covered.

A DIY piston ring compressor can quickly be made if the need arises from common hardware store items. A roll of plumber's pipe hanging tape and an appropriately sized hose clamp will work for this.

DIY RING COMPRESSOR

An oven and a freezer are very helpful when it comes to building an engine. The most common use for the oven and freezer combination is to help facilitate the installation of parts that have interference fits. An interference fit occurs when one part is slightly larger than the part it is supposed to fit into. The relationship between the crankcase bearings and crankcases is a great example of this. In order for these parts to fit together, either a force would need to be applied (such as using a hydraulic press) or the bearing would need to be cooled while the crankcases would need to be heated. The heating and cooling would allow the parts to expand and contract due to thermal expansion/contraction, thus allowing the bearings to drop right into their respective bores without requiring any force at all. This method of installation is great because little to no stress is put on the crankcases and the bearing bores have no chance of marring or getting damaged as the bearings are installed.

While I don't see any reason you need an oven dedicated specifically for building, I must warn that if the crankcases are not cleaned thoroughly, they can create quite a stink in the kitchen. Burning oil is the leading cause of the smell. Even with meticulously cleaned crankcases you can expect the baking to cause the room to smell. It definitely won't smell like your grandmother baking your favorite cookies, but it is not completely unbearable. With a little ventilation and window opening, the smell usually leaves the room in an hour or two. The easiest thing to do is to bake your crankcases when your wife/husband, girlfriend/boyfriend, mom/dad, or roommates are out of the house!

Punches are handy for all sorts of tapping exercises. Some prime examples are separation of engine covers, bearing removal, and bearing installation. Having steel punches in ⅛", ¼", and ⅜" sizes is handy. Having a couple punches made of a soft material such as brass can be handy for delicate situations.

ASSORTED HAMMERS

Having a couple types of hammers for the build is also important. A metal hammer will be required for many tasks. In addition to the metal hammer, it is necessary to have either a plastic or rubber hammer on hand for situations which require more finesse. The soft hammers are great for situations where it is necessary to tap directly on metal surfaces.

Catch containers are a pretty standard requirement when doing any sort of automotive work. A nice wide, flat, engine oil drain pan will be beneficial to catch oil. When draining coolant just about any sort of container will work. I personally like to repurpose a large drink container which has measurement markings along the side of the container so I can easily keep track of the volumes coming out and going in.

CATCH CONTAINERS

Many engines are designed to utilize an interference fit between the crankshaft and crank bearings. Care must be taken with these engine designs when removing and installing the crankshaft. A crankcase splitting tool is the only way to easily separate crankcases utilizing this design.

The case splitter attaches to the crankcase half with three bolts. The bolts are installed into three existing threaded holes on the crankcase. A center bolt on the splitter is turned against the end of the crankshaft which forces the crankshaft from the bearing. This configuration is great because force is applied in the right locations and the crankpin is not stressed.

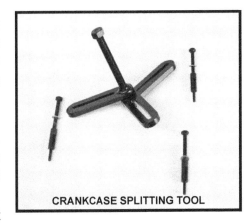

CRANKCASE SPLITTING TOOL

When a crankshaft with an interference fit is installed into the crank bearings there are three ways to install it. First, the inner race of the bearing can be warmed with a torch so that it expands and the crank can be cooled in a freezer so that in shrinks. This will allow the crankshaft journal to slip through the bearing. In the event heat cannot be applied to the inner race or heat doesn't expand the inner race of the bearing enough, the best way is to install the crankshaft into the bearing is to pull the crankshaft through the bearing. To do this, a special

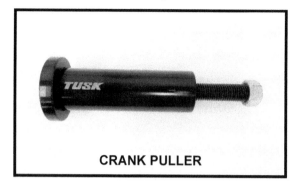

CRANK PULLER

tool is used which attaches to the end of the crank and pulls against the inner race of the bearing or the crankcase. A universal tool can be bought which has a variety of options for attaching to the end of the crankshaft; however, a much cheaper option is to create this tool out of common hardware store parts (more on this later).

The third option is to use a crank jig. The crank jig is adjustable in size and fits between the crank webs. Once the jig is installed, the crankshaft is pressed into place. This method is less desirable because force is applied across the crank webs which could cause the crankshaft to come out of alignment if the jig is improperly installed. The best and easiest ways are to shrink or pull the crankshaft through the bearing because these methods don't put any force on the crank pin and there is no risk of misaligning the crankshaft.

Measurement tools are a very special breed of tool. They are extremely important when building an engine since they determine if parts are still usable or require replacement. Often times measurement tools are operated by feel. This means the accuracy of the tool is not only dependent on the quality of the tool, but also on the operator's ability to proficiently use the tool. Measurement tools take time to master and practice is essential in order to obtain meaningful repeatable measurements.

Investing in measurement tools is also a relatively expensive affair. Buying new name brand measurement tools usually results in a significant rousting of one's wallet; however, there are

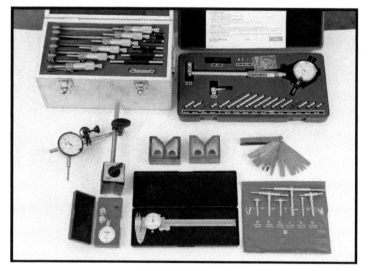

alternatives for the home mechanic. One of the great things about measurement tools is although they are expensive, they are always used delicately so they seldom wear out. This means that some great deals can be had on used name brand measurement tools. Searching Craigslist for high quality measurement tools turns up scores of deals. Often times a retiring machinist will be dumping an assorted lot of high quality tools that can be picked up at bargain prices. As more companies have entered the precision measurement industry, a greater selection of tools are also available now. Lesser known brands have emerged with some pretty accurate tools at more reasonable prices than what the name brands have to offer. If you don't use the tools every day and don't mind calibrating them a little more frequently than what you would a top brand tool, these can be a good buy for the home mechanic.

Ultimately, determining whether it is worthwhile to learn the skills required to accurately operate precision measurement tools and to invest in them will be a personal decision. At the bare minimum, a home mechanic should have a 0-1" and 0-2" micrometer, set of lash gauges, and a caliper at their disposal when building an engine. This will allow inspection of the bulk of the components. For the other important inspections, a professional engine builder or machinist should be summoned to help with the build. If you are interested in performing your own inspections and measurements, Chapter 8 has been dedicated to the subject.

While not what you may consider tools at first glance, lubricants are extremely helpful throughout a build. A dedicated parts washer is very handy if you frequently do heavy duty cleaning work; however, for most, a simple wash basin and a couple spray cans of brake cleaner will do wonders. Spray cans of brake cleaner or parts cleaner can be found at just about any automotive store and are inexpensive. Just remember when working with harsh cleaners to take the proper precautions to protect yourself from those nasty chemicals. Wearing protective gloves, long sleeves, and eye protection is a must when working with these cleaners.

VARIOUS LUBRICANTS

Thread-locking compounds are used to secure bolts which are likely to work their way out. A manufacturer's service manual will specify specific locations where thread-locking compound needs to be applied to a fastener. One common spot where a locking agent may be used is on bearing retaining bolts. Make sure you buy a high quality locking compound as they are not all created equal and some are not compatible with all types of materials. Locking a zinc plated bolt into aluminum does not create a favorable environment for locking agents to work so make sure you have one that can handle all scenarios. One of my personal favorites is Loctite 243.

Anti-seize is another lubricant that at times can be worth its weight in gold. The most common situation where anti-seize is used is in high temperature environments when a fastener must be able to be easily removed. Consider the interaction between the spark plug and cylinder head as a prime example. Another popular use for anti-seize is to help protect fastened joints from corrosive environments. Aluminum fasteners threaded into aluminum holes is a good example where corrosion could become a problem and anti-seize should be used.

Silicon grease is great for helping gaskets seal and not stick to either of the parts' mating surfaces. Nothing is more annoying and time consuming than having to scrape away baked-on gasket material from an engine cover. By simply rubbing silicone grease into both sides of the gasket this problem can largely be eliminated. Both packaged silicon grease or 100 percent silicone dielectric grease can be bought. I have found that 100 percent silicone dielectric grease is more readily available.

Grease can also be used to pre-lubricate rubber engine seals. A multi-purpose lithium based grease is great for seals because it has no effect on the rubber. Depending on the composition of the seal, some petroleum based greases can actually be harmful to the seal. Multi-purpose grease is also used on other areas of the bike and is great to have around.

Assembly lube is extremely important because it provides a means of lubricating the engine during the build and before startup. After an engine has been disassembled, cleaned, and put back together, oil circulation via the premixed fuel takes time to disperse to the engine's bearings and cylinder bore. Similarly the gearbox oil requires a short time to disperse within the gearbox. If components are not lubricated during the build they can run dry and accumulate noticeable amounts of wear. This wear is completely avoidable by correctly lubricating while assembling the engine.

In the assembly portion of this book, the when and where to use assembly lube will be covered in detail. Anyone familiar with OEM service manuals can attest to seeing the molybdenum disulfide grease symbols or callouts throughout the manual. For the most part, molybdenum disulfide grease is synonymous for assembly lube. Most modern assembly lubes provide similar or better wear resistant properties than traditional molybdenum disulfide grease and can be used in their place. If you are wondering what type of assembly lube to buy, Red Line manufacturers a high quality assembly lube which is used throughout the industry and is my personal favorite.

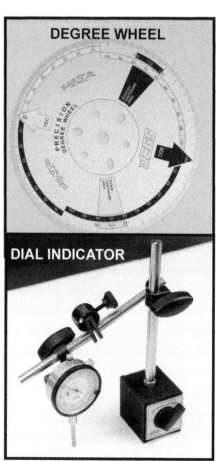

DEGREE WHEEL

DIAL INDICATOR

Having gearbox and two-stroke oil on hand during the build is also necessary. Like assembly lube, these oils are used to pre-lubricate parts during assembly. Keeping a small amount of each oil in a little bottle makes dispensing the oil easy.

For those that want to build a race engine or complete a build to race engine quality, I'm going to bring to light some additional tools that will be necessary. While engines come equipped with timing marks to align the flywheel, crankcase, and stator plate to time the engine, these markings are not designed to help check port timing. To measure the exact port timing the engine must be carefully timed using a degree wheel or the port heights must be measured with a caliper. Both of these options will be detailed later.

A dial indicator or a piston stop will be needed to find and confirm TDC. The most convenient way to fix the indicator is to use a magnetic base and fabricate a plate that can be bolted to the top of the cylinder.

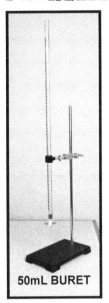

50mL BURET

A 50mL buret with 0.1mL graduations is ideal for checking the compression ratio of racing engines. The buret meters fluid into the combustion chamber when the piston is at TDC. The volume of fluid displaced correlates to the combustion chamber volume. Once the chamber volume has been found, calculations can be performed to determine the real compression ratio of the engine.

Solder varying in thickness between approximately .040-.118" (1-3mm) is required to check the squish clearance. The squish clearance is simply the distance between the top of the piston and combustion chamber when the piston is at TDC. Hollow core solder closely matched in diameter to the estimated squish clearance is best so that it is not flattened excessively when the clearance is checked. The required solder diameter is highly dependent on the specific engine being worked on.

So how much does it cost to equip yourself with all the necessary tools to rebuild an engine? A table consisting of all the tools previously mentioned was created to help answer this question. The tools selected for the table were picked with budget in mind; however, they are not the cheapest options. Many of the tools listed I own, so I can also attest to their quality. Lastly, for the sake of transparency, I'm not affiliated in any way with the selling process so my endorsement of these tools is not financially driven.

General Assembly & Disassembly	Tool	Brand	Price	Source
	2-14mm Allen Head Sockets	Anytime Tools AT200979	16.95	Amazon
	1/4" Drive Socket Wrench	69 Piece Metric Socket Set, Stanley 92-824	57.99	Amazon
	3/8" Drive Socket Wrench			
	6 - 19mm Socket Set			
	Breaker Bar	Neiko 15" Breaker Bar B01FOQJIDY	12.59	Amazon
	6 - 19mm Wrench Set	Tekton 18792 (8-22mm)	44.99	Amazon
	22mm	Performance Tool W32222	7.09	Amazon
	27mm	TEKTON 47779	8.88	Amazon
	5/8 socket	TEKTON 14203	5.99	Amazon
	JIS Socket Bits or Screw Drivers	Hozan JIS-5	36.15	Amazon
	Torx Bit Set	Bosch CC90396	3.99	Amazon
	20-150 in.lb (2.5-16Nm) Torque Wrench	CDI 1502MRMH	109.99	Amazon
	10-100 ft.lb (13.5-135Nm) Torque Wrench	CDI 1002MFRMH	148.35	Amazon
	Flat Head Screwdriver Set	Craftsman 9-47137 (5 piece)	14.95	Amazon
	Impact Driver	Lisle 29200	30.64	Amazon
	Needle Nose Pliers	Stanley 84-079 (6 piece)	12.99	Amazon
	Diamond Files	10 Piece Mini File Set SE 73810DF	8.98	Amazon
	Steel Punches	18 pcs Brass/Steel Punch Set 40105	15.78	Amazon
	Brass Punches			
	Hammer	Stanley 51-616	6.79	Amazon
	Rubber Mallet	Rubber Mallet 2259323	9.54	Amazon
	Catch Container	rubbermaid 30621	9.29	Amazon
	Oil Pan	Lumax LX-1632	19.60	Amazon
		Total	**581.52**	

Specialty	Tool	Brand	Price	Source
	Clutch Hub Pliers	Motion Pro 08-0008	21.59	Amazon
	Snap Ring Pliers	OTC 4512	61.78	Amazon
	Pen Magnet	Master Magnetics 07228	2.01	Amazon
	Flywheel Puller	Model Specific	10.00	RMATVMC Amazon
	Strap Wrench	OTC 7206	29.26	Amazon
	Flywheel Holder	Tusk 1479350001	19.99	Amazon
	Seal Puller	Lisle 56750	11.01	Amazon
	Blind Bearing Puller	Tusk 1219080001	94.98	RMATVMC Amazon
	Gasket Scraper	Tusk 1604130001	10.99	RMATVMC
	Picks	TEKTON 6943 (4 piece)	9.67	Amazon
	Cylinder Hone/Deglazing Tool	Wiseco 1427060002 (57-70mm)	77.95	RMATVMC
	Cylinder Base Nut Tool or Crows Feet	Motion Pro 1271480001	13.49	RMATVMC
	Crankcase Splitter	Pit Posse mx170692351700	58.77	Amazon
	Crank Installer (Optional)	Tusk Crank Puller/Installer Tool 17-8667	61.41	Amazon
	Timing Light (Optional - Model Dependent)	Performance Tool W80578	51.19	Amazon
		Total	**534.09**	

Lubricants	Tool	Brand	Price	Source
	Parts Cleaner	CRC Brakleen Brake Parts Cleaner	3.47	Amazon
	Medium Strength Locking Agent	Loctite #243	17.13	Amazon
	Anti-Seize	Permatex 80071	5.56	Amazon
	Silicon Grease	Versachem 15339	9.49	Amazon
	Multipurpose Grease (Lithium Based)	Lucas Oil 10533	7.95	Amazon
	Assembly Lube	Red Line 80319	16.19	Amazon
	Hone Oil	Brush Research Flex-Hone Oil	11.99	Amazon
	Two-Stroke Oil	Owner's Choice	NA	NA
	Gearbox Oil	Owner's Choice	NA	NA
		Total	**71.78**	

Measurement	Tool	Brand	Price	Source
	0-1" Micrometer	Anytime Tools AT201876 0-6" set	154.95	Amazon
	1-2" Micrometer			
	3-4" Micrometer			
	0.002 - 0.015" Lash Gauges	Lang Tools 1610	19.81	Amazon
	Telescoping Gauges	Anytime Tools AT201862	22.85	Amazon
	Dial Bore Gauge	Fowler 52-646-500-0	250.39	Amazon
	Caliper 0 - 6"	Anytime Tools AT203185	35.00	Amazon
	V Blocks	HHIP 3402-1006	52.20	Amazon
	Dial Indicators	Grizzly G9849 (Magnetic Base Included)	23.95	Amazon
	Magnetic Base			
	Dial Test Indicators	HFS 16679	45.99	Amazon
		Total	**605.14**	

Race Engine Building	Tool	Brand	Price	Source
	Degree Wheel	JEGS 81622	20.99	Amazon
	50mL Buret	Eisco CH0233B	16.79	Amazon
	Solder	1mm - Model Dependent, NOR KMG TK-704	2.30	Amazon
		Total	**40.08**	

Grand Total				**1,832.61**

As you can see, the total cost to become well equipped to build engines is fairly reasonable. The total price indicated includes all optional tools and assumes none of these items are already on hand. The lubricants selected would last for many builds and it should be noted some tools are packaged as sets. For most, only a portion of the listed items would actually need to be purchased in order to get set up for engine building. Taking into account the costs associated with having a shop rebuild the engine, it would only take a handful of rebuilds to justify the investment of purchasing the necessary tools.

Lastly, I want to talk about one tool in particular you should try to avoid. The impact wrench. Impact wrenches are a pretty common tool amongst mechanics and home shop enthusiasts. Impact wrenches make removing bolts easier, speed things up, and overall seem like a good tool to have; however, they should be used sparingly when working on motorcycles and especially engines. An impact wrench works by storing up energy in a rotating mass. The rotational energy is transferred to the shaft of the impact wrench where the socket is attached in quick successive bursts. This allows the wrench to apply high torque loads to the nut or bolt being loosened or tightened. As dirt bike owners the problem we face is that the our machines are comprised of small hardware with fine threads, often times secured in soft metals such as aluminum and magnesium. The scenario of fine threaded fasteners secured into soft metals is not an ideal situation for using an impact wrench.

Consider a practical example where an impact wrench is used to assist in the removal and installation of crankcase bolts. What could go wrong here? First, the likelihood of the aluminum crankcase threads being damaged by the steel bolt as it is removed is increased since it is unlikely that the operator can refrain from applying pressure to the bolt as it is coming out at an elevated rate of speed. The pressure being applied to the bolt threads, speed at which the bolt is making its way through the threaded hole, and difference in hardness of materials may damage the aluminum threads. If the bolt is corroded or stuck in place then the high torque load applied to the bolt to free it may strip the threads in the crankcase making for a real mess.

Upon reinstallation of the bolt, using an impact wrench to start the bolt increases the chance of cross threading the bolt and ruining the crankcase threads. This is mostly due to the speed at which the bolt is rotating and the lack of feel of thread engagement the operator has. Using the impact wrench to fully tighten the crankcase bolt can also lead to disaster since a finite amount of torque should be applied to the bolt and an impact wrench has no way of metering torque in the fine increments required for tightening bolts. Without knowing how much torque is being applied to the bolt by the impact wrench, the manufacturer's torque spec can easily be exceeded potentially resulting in stripped crankcase threads.

The only places you may consider using an impact wrench are on highly torqued fasteners which thread into other steel parts. Often times, it may be necessary to use an impact wrench to remove the crank primary gear fastener or clutch hub nut. This is especially true if the previous owner of the bike used an impact to tighten these fasteners. Always try using conventional wrenches first before resorting to the impact wrench.

CH 7 | SERVICE MANUALS

All the tools discussed thus far are extremely important; however, nothing is more important than having an Original Equipment Manufacturer's (OEM) service manual to guide you through your build. How important you ask? Well, as you can see I've devoted an entire chapter to it! Now if you're a seasoned vet you already know this, but I know there are a lot of folks getting started with engine building who need to learn about service manuals and how to use them.

The manual I'm talking about isn't the owner's manual you get with the bike, but the actual manual that professional mechanics use. These mechanics work at OEM dealerships or other shops and they reference these manuals to work on bikes day in and day out. There is no substitute for an OEM manual in terms of completeness. While other companies attempt to recreate OEM manuals in whole or in part, or combine many different model years together, I personally have not seen an aftermarket manual that rivals an OEM manual in quality, accuracy, and completeness.

Getting your hands on an OEM manual shouldn't be too hard. There are several ways to go about this. First, If you visit your local dealership, most of them will be happy to sell you a service manual. Some dealers will even be able to offer you the manual in print or pdf form. Print manuals usually run from $25 - $100 dollars, depending on the manufacturer selling the manual. The age of the machine also has an influence on price and for older models the manuals can be a bit cheaper.

The internet is your next best friend for getting your hands on a manual. While I don't condone piracy, there are plenty of legitimate options on the internet for obtaining a manual. Almost all manufacturers have a dedicated page or website devoted to service and owner's manuals. These sites will either have options to buy, download, or point you in the right direction so you can get one. In addition to the manufacturers' sites, try searching sites such as Ebay and Amazon. Usually manuals in either print or digital format will turn up on these sites and can be purchased from a private party.

Once you have your manual, figuring out how to efficiently use it is your next challenge. Luckily, regardless of manufacturer, service manuals all come in the same basic format. The manual will be divided into sections which might look something like the table on the following page.

> HOT TIP: Occasionally you may find a typo in the manual while you're working through a specific subsystem. Cross referencing between the subsystem section and the information in the general information section may help to clarify the discrepancy.

VEHICLE SYSTEM	TOPIC	SECTION
	GENERAL INFORMATION	1
	TECHNICAL FEATURES	2
	FRAME/BODY PANELS/EXHAUST SYSTEM	3
	MAINTENANCE	4
ENGINE AND DRIVETRAIN	FUEL SYSTEM	5
	COOLING SYSTEM	6
	ENGINE REMOVAL/INSTALLATION	7
	CYLINDER HEAD/CYLINDER/PISTON	8
	CLUTCH/KICKSTARTER/GEARSHIFT LINKAGE	9
	CRANKCASE/CRANKSHAFT/TRANSMISSION	10
CHASSIS	FRONT WHEEL/SUSPENSION/STEERING	11
	REAR WHEEL/SUSPENSION	12
	BRAKE SYSTEM	13
ELECTRICAL	ELECTRICAL SYSTEM	14
	WIRING DIAGRAM	15
	TROUBLESHOOTING	16
	INDEX	17

There are a handful of sections that I think are commonly overlooked. The "General Information" section is one of them. This section is packed full of vehicle specifications, service specifications, torque values, lubrication and seal points, cable routings, and other helpful information. This section is like a pocketbook of knowledge which can quickly be referenced when you are working on the bike. I find this section the most helpful once I've familiarized myself with the bike I'm working on and just need a quick refresher on something. Finding what you need in this well organized section is usually much quicker than sifting through each specific subsystem section.

The technical features section is fascinating if you're an engineer or like to understand how things work. This section isn't included in all manuals nor is it completely necessary to read. If you are the type that likes to understand some of the specific technologies that have gone into your bike and how things work, this is a fantastic section to read through.

Familiarizing yourself with the maintenance section is a must. In this section you'll find a plethora of relevant maintenance info to keep your bike running in tip top shape. The information provided usually includes basic tasks such as oil changes, cable adjustments, etc. Along with these basic tasks you may also see information which will help you set the bike up, tune the bike, and tweak suspension settings.

Tables will be provided with maintenance intervals as well. The maintenance intervals will cover everything from when to change the gearbox oil to when to replace the piston. It has been my experience that these suggested interval periods should be taken with a grain of salt. Usually, the manufacturer will base the maintenance interval schedule on the regimen of a top level motocross racer. This makes sense for the manufacturer as it constitutes a worst case scenario of abuse. Essentially they are covering their tail and don't want racers risking injury by running parts within an engine longer than they should. From a monetary standpoint the manufacturer also stands to do well by keeping maintenance intervals short as consumers may think they need to replace parts more often than they do. The problem for the majority of the riders in the world is that very few are riding at a level where the bike is being used and abused as harshly as a factory backed professional rider. This makes some of the manufacturer's service interval recommendations irrelevant. One example of this recommendation being erroneous would be for someone who does light trail riding to replace their piston every 15 or 20 hours as some manuals suggest. The amount of wear on the piston, rings, and cylinder bore after 15 hours of light use would not warrant a piston and ring replacement, it would cost the consumer a lot of money, and is completely irrational. As I've stated in prior chapters, service intervals should be tailored to an individual's riding and how the bike is used. Simply use common sense when rationalizing the data you see in the manufacturer's service interval tables and then decide how applicable it is to your riding habits.

The troubleshooting section is a great section to study when, you guessed it, you are having trouble with the bike! This section provides a handful of good things to try when you can't quite pinpoint your problem. The cause-effect relationship in most troubleshooting sections is helpful and the suggested workflow through the potential problems is too. If you are new to wrenching, this section is definitely worth a look.

The remainder of the sections are categorized by subsystem and each section goes through in detail the correct maintenance procedures/orders to follow when disassembling, inspecting, and reassembling the subsystem. These subsystems are where you will spend the bulk of your time. Since the manual has no way of predicting what your specific task may be, nor was it designed to give specific step-by-step instructions from start to finish, you will find that you have to bounce around a lot. Consider it an advanced adult version of a pick-your-own ending book.

For example, if you jump to the section on "Crankcases" you would see right away it assumes you have already taken the engine out of the frame, disassembled it, and are ready to take the cases apart. Right at the beginning of the section it will kindly remind you what you need to do before you can perform the work in that section and point you to the subsequent sections to perform the preceding work. While you may slyly think you can get away with performing a task without doing all the preceding tasks suggested by the manual, this is rarely the case. It does happen occasionally, but the majority of the time you will end up having to admit defeat and do as the manual suggests. After being defeated a time or two you will quickly realize it is more efficient to do as the manual recommends.

CH 8 | PRECISION MEASURING

The world of measuring is so complex by nature that one could get wrapped up writing an entire book on the subject and still not cover it all. This is not my intention with this book. My aim is to provide you with the principles of how measuring works, what the most important takeaways are on the subject of measuring, and an overview of how to use the tools correctly. Once informed, you can then delve further into the intricacies of measuring depending on your own needs.

There are three terms which are important to the fundamental understanding of measurement. These terms are often mixed up, confused as meaning the same things, or used incorrectly. These terms are accuracy, precision, and resolution. Understanding these three terms will go a long way in ultimately understanding measuring and the capabilities of individual measurement tools.

ACCURACY
Accuracy is how close a given measurement is to the "true" value of an object. For example, if a cylinder bore was exactly 2.6772" (68.00mm), accuracy would quantify how close the measurement tool was to the true value.

PRECISION
Precision is a measurement of repeatability. For example if an object was measured five times, precision would quantify how close the five measurements are to one another. Another way to think of precision is the finiteness of which a measurement tool can be read repeatedly and reliably.

RESOLUTION
Resolution is the smallest distinguishable value of a measurement tool. An example being if a ruler is divided up into tenths of an inch then the resolution of the ruler is one tenth of an inch. A micrometer that can be read to one ten thousandth has a resolution of one ten thousandths of an inch. Just because a measurement tool, such as a micrometer, has a very fine resolution doesn't mean it will be accurate or precise to that resolution. This will be explained in depth later in this chapter.

Distinguishing the difference between accuracy and precision is most easily done with a set of pictures. Four scenarios can occur when measuring.

1. **A measurement can be both accurate and precise.**
2. **A measurement can be accurate but not precise.**
3. **A measurement can be precise but not accurate.**
4. **A measurement can be neither accurate nor precise.**

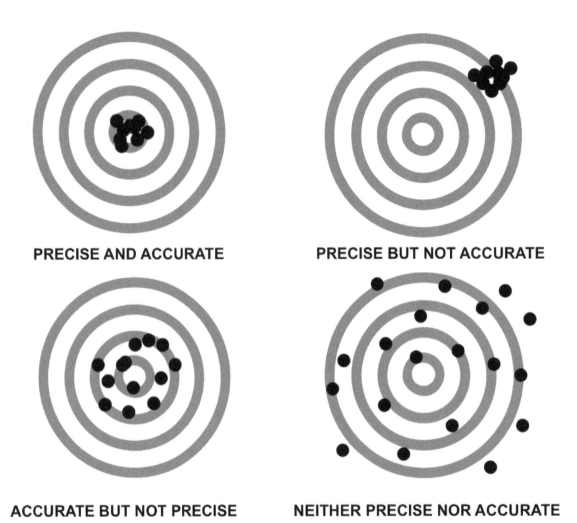

PRECISE AND ACCURATE   **PRECISE BUT NOT ACCURATE**

ACCURATE BUT NOT PRECISE   **NEITHER PRECISE NOR ACCURATE**

Notice that if the bullseyes were taken out of the pictures, like on the following page, there would be no way to reference if the shots were accurate. If we removed the bullseyes from the "accurate but not precise" and "neither precise nor accurate" scenarios, it would be easy to tell the measurements didn't yield meaningful results. However, the "precise but not accurate" scenario's results could be misleading for someone measuring. This is exactly why it is important to calibrate measurement tools before using them. By calibrating a measurement tool, you ensure it is accurate prior to measuring an unknown object.

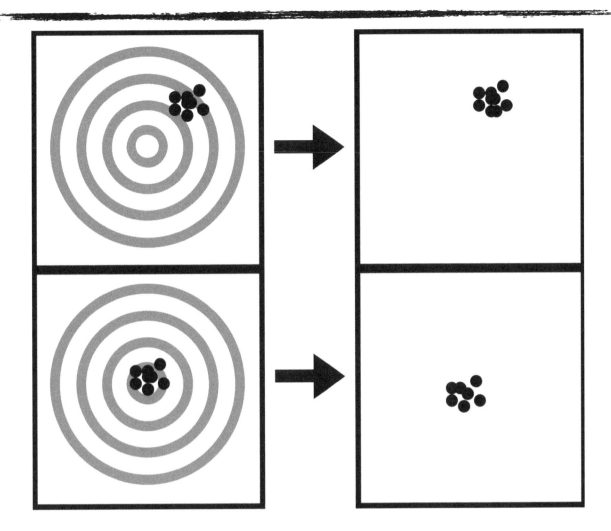

WHAT AFFECTS ACCURACY AND PRECISION?

Now that the key parts of accuracy, precision, and resolution have been outlined, how do they apply to measuring tools and measuring? I want to go over three factors that lead to variation in accuracy and precision when working with measurement tools.

Type of Tool and Tool Quality

Different types of measurement tools will have different ranges of accuracy. For example, a digital 0-6" caliper is usually accurate to 0.001" (0.025mm); however, it will have a resolution of 0.0005" (0.0127mm). Just because the resolution of the tool is 0.0005" (0.0127mm) doesn't always mean the tool will be accurate to the same value. For a 0-1" micrometer the accuracy is 0.0001" (0.0025mm) and so is the resolution. Be sure to keep accuracy and resolution in mind when using and shopping for measurement tools. Decent measurement tools should have the manufacturer's accuracy specified in the tool's description.

Using a caliper to measure the bore of a cylinder is a good example of using a measurement tool which is not accurate enough for the task at hand. Most dirt bike cylinder bores have a diametric range in the neighborhood of 0.0006" (0.0152mm), taper limit of around 0.0004" (0.0102mm), and out of round limit of around 0.0004" (0.0102mm). As you can see a caliper is off an order of magnitude in accuracy and is thus not capable of doing the job.

Temperature

The temperature at which a measurement is taken can have a large effect as well. A standard has been set for the temperature parts are measured and inspected at in the engineering and metrology worlds. That standard temperature is 68°F (20°C), which is what you should strive for when you are precision measuring parts.

The reason temperature is important is due to the concept of thermal expansion. In a nutshell, thermal expansion explains how an object's volume will change as temperature changes. As volume changes so does length, which is what matters in this case. Equations for linear expansion will be used to show the role temperature plays on the diameter of a cylinder bore at two extremes: 32°F (0°C) and 100°F (37.78°C).

Consider a cylinder that has a bore of 2.6142" (66.400mm) - typical of a 250cc engine. At 68°F we will say the cylinder measures exactly 2.6142" (66.400mm). What happens when the same cylinder is measured at 32°F (0°C) and at 100°F (37.78°C)?

Let's work it out. The formula for linear expansion is:

$$\Delta L = \alpha \times D \times \Delta T$$

Where:
ΔL = change in diameter of the cylinder bore
α = coefficient of thermal expansion for aluminum (11.8 x 10^-6) in/in °F
D = original diameter of the cylinder
ΔT = change in temperature (Final Temperature - Initial Temperature)

α = (11.8 x 10^-6) in/in °F
D = 2.6142"
ΔT = 32°F - 68°F = -36°F

Now it all gets put into the equation and solved:

ΔL = (11.8 x 10^-6) in/in °F x 2.6142" x -36°F = -0.0011"

ΔL = -0.0011" (0.028mm)

So the 2.6142 inch cylinder has now shrunk to 2.6131 " (66.372mm).

A 36°F (20°C) change in temperature has caused the aluminum cylinder bore to change by 0.0011" (0.028mm)! In terms of cylinder measurements, this is a big change and illustrates just how important it is to measure engine components in the right environment.

A similar change can be seen when the cylinder is measured at 100°F (37.78°C).

$$\alpha = (11.8 \times 10^{-6})\ \text{in/in °F}$$
$$D = 2.6142"$$
$$\Delta T = 100°F - 68°F = 32°F$$

Now it all gets put into the equation and solved:

$$\Delta L = (11.8 \times 10^{-6})\ \text{in/in °F} \times 2.6142" \times 32°F = 0.0010"$$

$$\Delta L = 0.0010"\ (0.025mm)$$

So the 2.6142 inch cylinder has now grown to 2.6152 inches (66.425mm).

As you can see, if you work in environments that are at one extreme or another on the temperature spectrum you are guaranteed inaccurate measurements. The scenario where measurements are precise but not accurate would be a good illustration for how temperature affects measuring.

User Error

Lastly, the person doing the measuring also has an effect on the precision of the measurement. Another example is the most effective way to illustrate my point. Consider a situation where an inexperienced measurer measures a part five times and returns five different measurements. Next, a seasoned measurer measures the same part five times and returns the exact same measurement all five times. Both people measuring used the same measurement tool and carried out the measurements at the same temperature. The only variable that wasn't the same was the person doing the measuring. This variation of measurement between people isn't that uncommon and happens all the time. Even two different seasoned professionals who inspect and measure parts daily can end up with different measurements for the same part. It is very likely though that the variations in the professionals' measurements will be much more precise when compared to one another.

How do I know my Measurements are Accurate and Precise?

Alright we're starting to get into the more interesting, I mean practical, aspects of measuring! Hopefully the last few sections haven't bored you or deterred you from wanting to measure your own engine components. I assure you, with practice and patience you can become a well versed measuring machine!

I want to touch on some practical ways to determine if measurement tools are working correctly. If you went out and bought a cheap or expensive set of micrometers with measurement capabilities ranging from 0-6" how would you know they were accurate right out of the box? Is the manufacturer responsible for insuring they are accurate? Do they ever lose accuracy? Does the fact they were either cheap or expensive matter? The answer to all these questions is that prior to use, regardless of price or quality, most measurement tools will require calibration.

Calibration is the practice of checking or setting the accuracy of a measurement tool to a known value. For measurement tools such as calipers and 0-1" micrometers simply ensuring the tips of the tool are clean, closing them together, and making sure the tool reads zero may be all that is necessary. This is a fairly easy method of calibration for these two tools, but isn't possible for measurement tools where the tips don't close together all the way (ex. 2-3" micrometer) or the tool has tips that extend outwards (ex. dial bore gauge). For these situations measurement gages are necessary for accurate calibration.

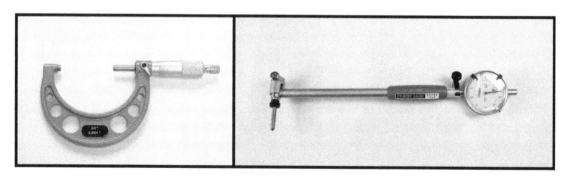

Calibration gages (sometimes called standards) come in several varieties depending on tool application. The most common and applicable to engine inspection are gage blocks and ring setting gages. Gage blocks are small blocks of steel (more expensive variants come in other materials) which have been finished to extremely tight tolerances. Gage blocks are toleranced into several different classes. For engine inspection the most accurate measurements that must be made are to 0.0001"(0.025mm). In the measuring world the rule of thumb for calibrating tools is to use a standard which is at the minimum four times as accurate as the tool itself. So for a micrometer which is accurate to 0.0001" a gage block with an accuracy of at least +/- 0.000025" should be used.

What the measuring world does and what the at home engine builder can feasibly do are two completely different standards. For the majority of us, our measuring abilities will get in the way of our accuracy long before the gage block used to calibrate the tool has any effect. For this reason I would suggest that using the standards which come with the tools will be fine instead of splitting hairs over not knowing the exact accuracy of the standards.

HOT TIP: If you are shopping for a 0-6" set of micrometers most decent sets will come with standards. The standards will usually come in 1, 2, 3, 4, and 5 inch sizes so all the micrometers can be calibrated at any time.

Ring setting gages are similar to gage blocks and are also used for calibrating measurement tools. They are, as the name suggests, rings that have been machined to very fine tolerances. Usually instead of having a tolerance range that the ring falls into, the ring will be stamped with the exact diameter it was machined to. A measurement tool such as a dial bore gauge is then calibrated to the exact diameter of the ring setting gauge. Ring setting gages are generally quite expensive as they are challenging to make accurately.

"Okay, I Understand the Importance of Calibrating My Measurement Tools. What About Making Precise and Repeatable Measurements?"

Precision gets complicated pretty quick because you have to factor in the measurement tool, temperature, and user taking the measurements. These three variables are difficult to separate completely. However, out of the three variables the user is usually the most likely variable to have a large influence on the precision of the measurement tool. In order to make precise and repeatable measurements it is important to do as many things the same as possible. Below are some recommendations to make sure your measurements are as precise as possible.

1. Make sure the temperature in the room you are measuring is at 68°F (20°C). If the parts being prepared for measurement originated in a room that was warmer or cooler than the room used for measurement, ensure the parts being measured have had adequate time to reach equilibrium.

2. Try to perform measurements of a part or set of mating parts in a short time period. There's no need to rush the measurements or to measure all the parts in one day. It's not that critical, but for example don't measure the diameter of the piston one day and then wait to measure the bore of the cylinder the next day. That doesn't make sense.

3. When using micrometers, use a micrometer stand to secure the micrometer in place. Not only will this make positioning the part easier and the micrometer easier to read, it will also keep the heat of your hands from warming the micrometer. Remember thermal expansion? Believe it or not, there are actually studies out there detailing how body heat makes a micrometer expand in length. It's a minuscule amount, but still worth mentioning!

4. A lot of measurement tools are operated by feel. When working with these tools try to be as consistent as possible when turning the handles. The amount of pressure you apply can have a big effect on the final measurement. For example, the difference between a part that drags hard through the tips of the tool versus one that drags but is soft in feel could be several ten thousandths of an inch.

5. Use your fingertips and a light grip. The fingertips are one of the most sensitive parts of the human body. As such they can be utilized to feel subtle variations in measurement.

6. Instead of just taking one measurement take 3 to 5 measurements. This is something you should definitely do when calibrating your measurement tools. By taking multiple measurements you'll quickly get a feel for how precise your measuring is. If you are all over the board there is a good chance your technique is inconsistent. If you are within a ten thousandth or two each time you are onto something! For important measurements like cylinder bore diameter, taper, and out of roundness take 3 to 5 measurements. Then take the average of these measurements and use the average as your final measurement.

7. If you are struggling to determine if your measurement tools are working properly, compare them to another known good set. If the two sets are not reading close to identical there is probably a problem with the unknown set.

8. Compare your results to those of someone with a lot of measuring experience. If a seasoned machinist can get your measurement tool to repeat to a ten thousandth of an inch it is probably not the tool. If you have the opportunity to get help from a machinist or someone fluent with measuring, watch them carefully. Ask them questions, study how they work the tools, and learn from them.

9. Be patient and take your time. Rushing the measurement process is not a good idea and can lead to silly mistakes. You need to be in a state of mind where you don't feel rushed and don't mind taking the time to do a thorough job.

10. Write your results down! Write down everything clearly from the calibration measurements, any calculated averages, and measurements of specific parts. By writing things down, you can easily work backwards to see if a mistake has been made somewhere.

HOW TO USE MEASUREMENT TOOLS

It's finally time! Hopefully you feel like you have an understanding of the world of measuring and are ready to start working with the tools. Each measurement tool in this section features a description of appropriate uses for the tool and a step-by-step tutorial on how to use it. This section was designed as a reference so you can easily come back to it at any time.

> HOT TIP: Make sure your measurement tools are at room temperature prior to measuring. If you brought your tools from a warmer or colder room they will need time to adjust to the temperature.

Calipers: Digital & Dial

Calipers are one of the most versatile measuring tools due to their ability to take internal, external, and depth measurements. Calipers are also able to take some of the widest ranges of measurements. Most calipers have a measurement range from 0 - 6 inches (0 - 150mm). For these reasons, every engine builder should have a caliper at their disposal. Calipers can come with dial, digital, or Vernier scale readouts. Personally, I would avoid the Vernier type as they are cumbersome to read, instead choose either a digital or dial caliper.

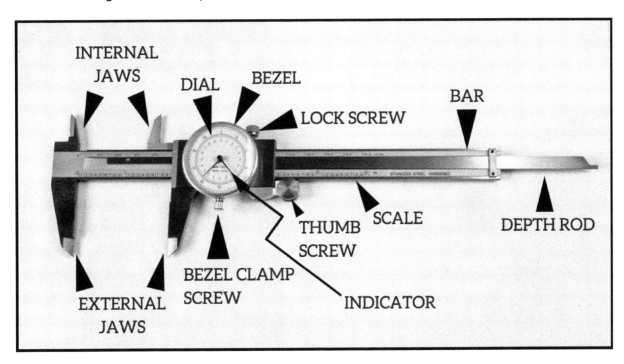

Where to use: Some examples include power valve components, clutch spring length, clutch disc thickness, and shift drum slots. Calipers are not the most accurate measuring tool and should not be used where extreme accuracy is required. Most calipers have an accuracy of about 0.001" (0.025mm).

Reading Dial Calipers: A dial caliper consists of a scale which runs along the bar of the caliper. Depending on the type of caliper you have, the scale will either be inch or metric based. On an inch caliper the scale will be in tenths of an inch, while a metric scale will be in millimeters. To read the scale, simply line up the edge of the jaw with the closest whole value.

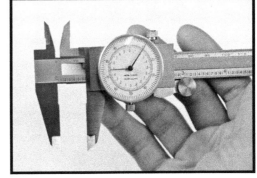

Once the whole value has been found, move to the dial. The dial will be broken into thousandths of an inch or hundredths of a millimeter. Simply add the value indicated by the pointer on the dial to the value previously recorded on the scale. In the photo to the right, the caliper incorporates both inch and metric scales. The caliper reads 0.610" (15.49mm).

Reading Digital Calipers: The value shown on the digital readout is the total value. Most digital calipers have a button which can be pressed to cycle between inch and metric units.

Calibration For External and Internal Measurements

1. Start by ensuring the jaws are free of dirt or debris. Clamp a piece of paper between the jaws and slide the jaws past the paper.

2. Close the jaws completely. On a digital caliper simply press the "zero" button to zero the caliper. On a dial caliper loosen the bezel clamp and rotate the dial face so that the "0" aligns with the pointer.

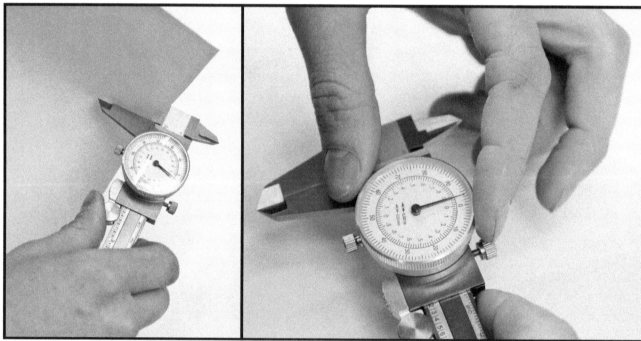

3. Slide the caliper open and closed a few times to confirm the caliper consistently reads "0". If for some reason the caliper does not repeatedly read "0" try re-calibrating the caliper.

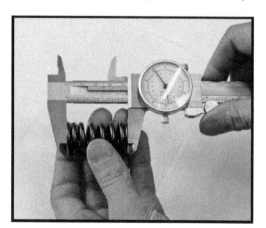

How To Use - External Measurements

1. Position the part to be measured between the jaws as close to the bar of the caliper as possible. The further out the part sits in the jaws, the more likely the jaws are to flex, resulting in a less accurate reading.

2. Make sure the part sits squarely in the jaws of the caliper.

3. Apply a moderate amount of pressure to the outer jaw. This is one of those Goldilocks situations where it can't be too loose or too tight. Too loose to the point where the part can fall out of the jaws will result in an oversized reading. Too tight and the jaws will flex, or if measuring springs they may compress which will result in an undersized reading. Acquiring the feel to determine the correct pressure to put on the jaws will come with practice.

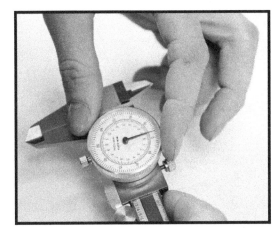

4. Once finished measuring, return the jaws back to zero and make sure the caliper zeros. For situations where utmost accuracy is required, take a few measurements to confirm repeatability.

How To Use - Internal Measurements

The process for obtaining good reliable internal measurements is the same as that of the external measurements. Simply utilize the internal jaws when measuring. Remember to make sure the jaws sit squarely in the bore as you measure and to keep a moderate amount of pressure on the part.

Calibration For Depth Measurements

1. Extend the depth rod out from the end of the caliper.

2. Slowly lower the end of the caliper down retracting the depth rod until the end of the caliper sits flush with the flat surface. Make sure to keep the end of the caliper square to the surface as it is lowered.

3. Once the end of the caliper is sitting flush with the flat surface, zero the dial.

4. Extend and contract the depth rod a few times against the flat surface making sure the dial zeros each time.

How to Use - Depth Measurements

1. Square the end of the caliper up against the surface the depth measurement will be taken from.

2. Extend the depth rod down until it touches the measurement surface. Make sure the depth rod is only extended far enough so that it sits flat. Extending the rod too far and the end of the caliper may not sit flat or the depth rod could flex.

3. Confirm both the end of the caliper and depth rod are square and take the reading from the caliper.

4. Remove the caliper, stand it on end against a flat surface, and double check the depth rod still reads "0".

Remember due to the limited surface area available for positioning the end of the caliper, having to keep it square, and the flexibility of the depth rod - depth measurements are difficult to get accurate. Other measurement tools specifically designed for measuring depths accurately are much more suitable in instances where a high level of accuracy is required.

That sums up the three ways you can utilize a caliper. Remember the cleaner your caliper is, the longer it will last, so keep it in its case when not using it. A caliper usually ends up ruined by being dropped on the floor. A floor drop can result in the fine edges of the jaws getting nicked and damaged as well as wreaking havoc on the internals of the tool. Take care not to let them plummet to the ground!

Lash Gauges (Feeler Gauges)

Lash gauges are used to measure the clearance between two parts. Their design and function is simple. The gauges consist of long thin pieces of metal varying in thickness. The gauges are inserted between two parts to determine the clearance between them. Different thickness gauges are selected until the gauge fits snugly between the two parts. The thickness of the gauge correlates to the clearance between the parts.

Having a nice set of lash gauges can save a lot of time and headaches when engine building. Find and use a set of lash gauges which have both standard and metric graduations,   incrementally increase in thickness by 0.0005" (0.013mm), and are fairly long. Having more thickness options available will make it much easier to determine the clearance between two parts.

Watch out for angle errors. In a perfect world lash gauges would be inserted between the clearanced parts perfectly flat. This rarely happens. Make sure when you work with the gauges that the tip of the gauge is parallel to the surfaces it is being fit between. When working in tight spots which don't allow the gauge to be inserted flat, either press down firmly on the middle of the gauge so that the gauge flexes or bend the gauge tip so that it can be inserted parallel.

How To Use

1. Start by selecting a gauge thickness which will fit between the two parts.

2. Work up in thickness until a gauge is found that just passes between the two parts. The gauge should not require a great deal of force to push through the parts nor should it slide in and out easily. An appropriately sized gauge should drag just slightly between the two parts.

3. Once a gauge is found that drags slightly between the parts, that gauge then corresponds with the clearance between the two parts.

Where to use: Examples include rod big end side clearance, piston ring end gap, and spark plug gap.

HOT TIP: If you'll be using your lash gauges to aid in finding and setting port timing be sure to pick up a set that features tips that narrow.

Outside Micrometers

During an engine build outside micrometers are the most commonly used precision measurement tool. As the name implies, outside micrometers are primarily used to measure outer dimensions of parts. Both inch and metric versions of the micrometer are available with high quality inch and metric variants having resolutions of 0.0001" and 0.002mm respectively. A 0 - 6" or 0 - 150mm set is ideal and will provide an engine builder with all the micrometers needed to accurately measure dirt bike engine parts.

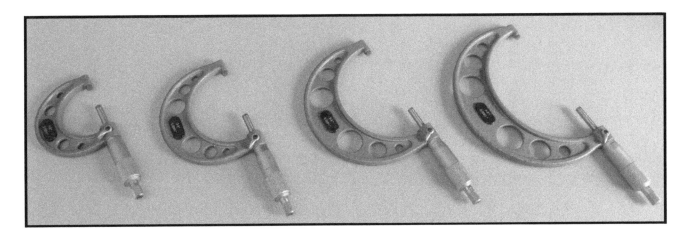

A good set of micrometers will come with their own checking standards. The checking standards are similar to gage blocks. The standards are important as they are the finely machined lengths of metal which are required to calibrate each micrometer. For a 0 - 6" set the set should come with a 1, 2, 3, 4, and 5 inch standard so each of the five micrometers which don't close completely can be calibrated before use. A good set of micrometers should also come with a lock. The lock is used to clamp the spindle in place so a measurement isn't lost before it can be read.

Micrometers are offered with or without a ratchet stop. A ratchet stop is handy for beginners because it regulates the pressure being applied to the measured part leading to more consistent readings. While used less often by seasoned professionals, I personally like the ratchet stop feature and think anyone just starting out should utilize a set with ratchet stops.

Where to use: Examples include the piston skirt, gear shafts, and power valve components.

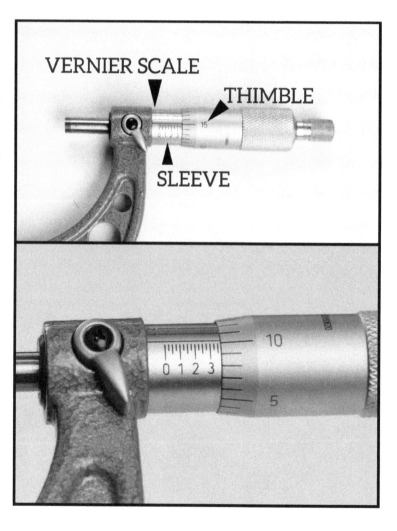

Reading Micrometers: Micrometers are easy to read as long as you understand the three parts of the measurement system found on the micrometer. The three parts of the system are the sleeve, the thimble, and the Vernier scale

On an inch-based micrometer the sleeve features graduations of 0.025". The sleeve of the micrometer is always read first. Keep in mind only whole fully visible lines can be counted. In the picture to the right the micrometer sleeve reads 0.350".

Next comes the thimble. The thimble is divided into 25 graduations of 0.001" inch increments. This makes sense because one full revolution of the spindle would be equal to one increment on the sleeve (0.025"). To determine the value on the thimble simply line up the the horizontal hash mark on the thimble with the horizontal line on the sleeve. In the picture above the thimble reads slightly more than 0.010". The value obtained from the thimble reading is then added to the value from the sleeve, so far totaling 0.360".

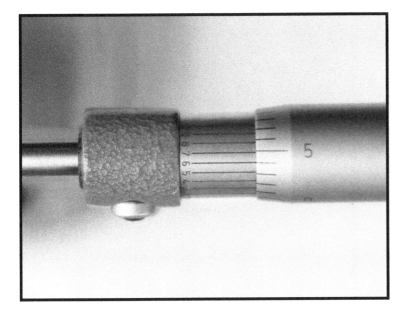

Lastly, the Vernier scale comes into play. The Vernier Scale consists of 10 horizontal lines. Each line represents 0.0001". When all ten lines are added together the sum equals 0.001" which is equivalent to one increment on the thimble. To read the Vernier scale simply look for the set of horizontal lines that match perfectly. The corresponding value associated with the matching lines is the number of ten thousandths which must be added to the sum of the sleeve and thimble value. Make sure to read the value on the Vernier scale and not on the thimble when reading the 0.0001" measurement.

In the photo above the line corresponding to the "6" on the Vernier scale matches perfectly to the line on the thimble so we know to add another 0.0006" to the measurement. The total measurement is 0.3606" (0.350" + 0.010" + 0.0006"). Unbeknownst to you, this is a 2-3 inch micrometer so 2" must be added to the measured value to arrive at a total of 2.3606".

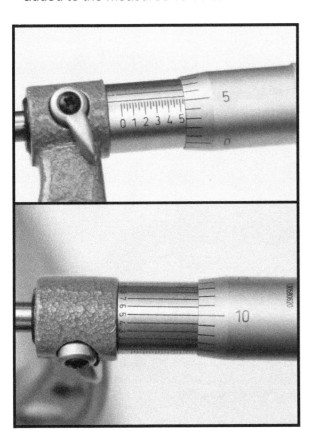

Let's try another example:

In the picture to the left the sleeve reads 0.525".

As you can see in the above picture to the left, the thimble shows a little more than 0.005". So far our measurement is 0.530" because we add the value from the thimble to the value from the sleeve.

Last, we look at the Vernier scale in the lower picture to the left. The horizontal line on the thimble matches perfectly with the fifth line on the Vernier scale so we must add 0.0005" to the sleeve and thimble readings. This results in a final value of 0.5305" (0.525" + 0.005" + 0.0005"). Again using a 2 - 3" micrometer the total value is 2.5305".

For metric micrometers the process is exactly the same; however, the sleeve is divided into 0.5mm graduations. The thimble features 50 - 0.01mm graduations. The Vernier scale is divided into 5 - 0.002mm graduations.

Calibrating Micrometers

Each micrometer will require calibration prior to use to ensure that it is accurate. A 0-1" micrometer is the easiest to calibrate because when its measuring faces are closed all the way together the micrometer should read "0". For micrometers which measure sizes larger than 1 inch, standards or gage blocks will be needed to calibrate the micrometer. The calibration process for all micrometers is the same apart from the use of standards to calibrate the larger micrometers which don't close all the way.

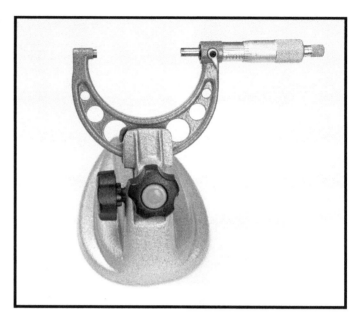

1. Set the frame of the micrometer in a micrometer stand. By using the stand you will free up one hand and won't transfer your body heat into the micrometer.

2. Lightly clamp a piece of paper between the measuring faces (0-1") and slide the micrometer across the paper to clean the measuring faces. For larger micrometers wipe the paper across each of the measuring faces using your fingers.

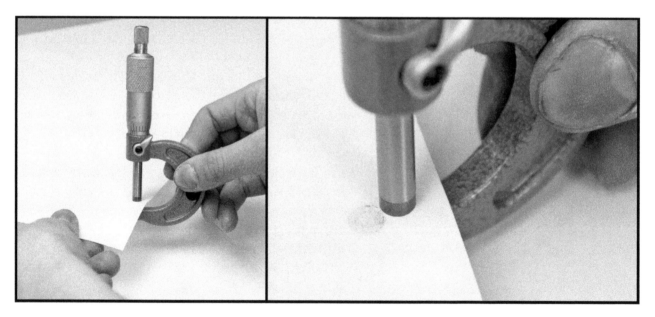

3. Close the measuring faces (0-1") or insert the appropriately sized measuring standard. Read the micrometer and see if the sleeve, spindle, and Vernier scale align precisely at "0". If the micrometer does read "0" open and close the measuring faces a few more times to confirm.

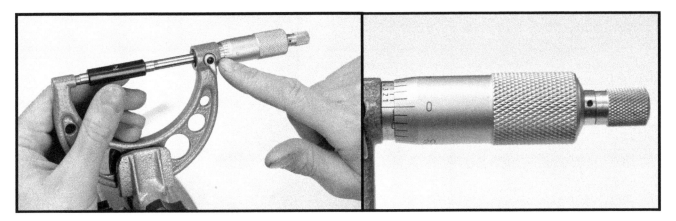

4. If the micrometer does not read "0" it will need to be adjusted. With the measuring faces closed or the standard inserted, follow the adjustment procedure outlined for your specific type/brand of micrometer. Carefully zero the micrometer then tighten any adjusters. Open and close the micrometer a few times to confirm it has been zeroed. Once the micrometer repeatedly reads "0" it is ready to use.

HOT TIP: Sometimes you can find a machinist that is willing to let you check your micrometer and standards against theirs. This is especially useful when checking the accuracy of cheaper micrometer sets. Compare the accuracy of the cheaper set to a high dollar set of Starrett's or Mitutoyo's. This is great for engine building peace of mind!

How To Use:

1. Open the spindle so the piece being measured can fit between the measuring faces.

2. Gently turn the ratchet until the measuring faces start to touch the part being measured.

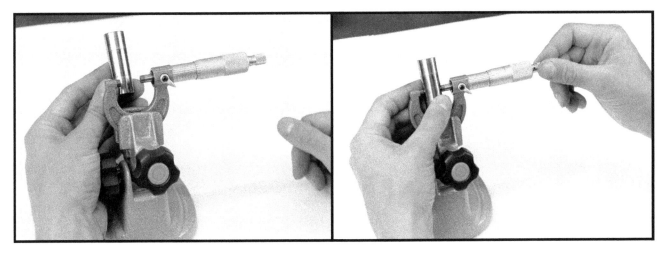

3. Make sure the part is square to the measuring faces. For cylindrical parts, slide the part between the measuring faces to make sure you are measuring the diameter of the part at its widest point.

4. Turn the ratchet stop until it clicks a few times. The correct pressure has now been applied to the part being measured. If the micrometer doesn't have a ratchet stop, turn the spindle until light pressure has been applied to the part. The part should still be able to move between the measuring faces, dragging just slightly.

5. Use the lock to lock the spindle in place.

6. Remove the part being measured.

7. Read the micrometer. Remember to start with the whole number value, then record the value on the sleeve, add the value on the thimble, and finally add the value on the Vernier scale to the sleeve and thimble readings.

8. Don't forget to unlock the micrometer prior to taking another measurement.

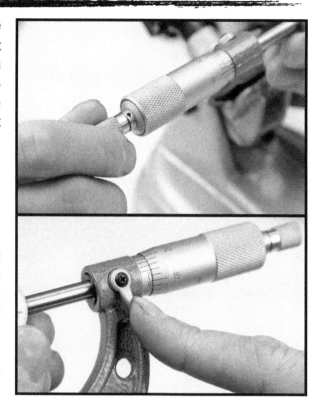

HOT TIP: For measurements requiring the utmost accuracy take 3 to 5 measurements. Then take the average of your measurements and use this value as the measured value.

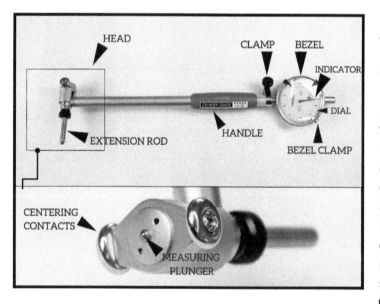

Dial Bore Gauge

A dial bore gauge is a very versatile and accurate tool used to measure internal diameters. The dial bore gauge features a long shaft with a dial indicator affixed to one end and a measuring head attached to the other. Most measuring heads feature interchangeable extension rods so the gauge can be used to measure a variety of different bore sizes. To quickly and accurately measure cylinder bores, the dial bore gauge is the best tool for the job. The dial bore gauge is a comparative measurement tool, meaning that it must be set to a specific diameter prior to measuring.

Dial bore gauges come in different size ranges, accuracies, and resolutions. Dial bore gauges are not a cheap measurement tool so take care to research quality, determine your personal measuring needs, and access your budget before purchasing. For dirt bike engine building finding a dial bore gauge which can measure from 1.4 - 6" (35.5 - 152mm) will cover the majority of applications. If you don't work with any small bores a gauge with a range from 2 - 6" would be fine. The accuracy and resolution of the gauge should be 0.0001" (0.0025mm).

Calibrating the gauge can be done several different ways. The most accurate way to calibrate a dial bore gauge would be to use a ring setting gauge which is close to the bore diameter being measured. While this is the best way, ring setting gauges are expensive and may not be worth the investment if the dial bore gauge won't be used frequently to measure a specific diameter. If you were to build an array of engines all with different bore sizes, it would be necessary to have a ring gauge for each bore size. This would be cost prohibitive and is a difficult cost to justify for the amateur builder.

A more economical calibration method is to use a micrometer to set the diameter of the dial bore gauge. A micrometer is adjusted and set to the bore size being measured and the gauge is calibrated based on the size of the micrometer. One pitfall with this method is that the micrometer must be very reliable and accurate in order for the bore gauge to be accurate.

Special bore gauge setting tools are also available. Bore gauge setting tools work similar to a micrometer; however, one setting tool will usually cover all the sizes the bore gauge is capable of measuring. Most setting tools come with their own setting gauge to ensure the tool is accurate.

One final method worth mentioning involves using gage blocks and plates to set the bore gauge. The gage blocks are added together until they equal the desired bore diameter. Precision ground plates are set at each end of the gage blocks and the assembly is lightly clamped together. The bore gauge can then be calibrated between the ground plates.

Where to Use: Cylinder Bore

Reading Dial Bore Gauges: The gauge face of a dial bore gauge is similar to other dial gauges. The gauge is divided into equal graduations representative of the tools resolution. A needle pointer indicates the tools measurement.

Reading measurements from a dial bore gauge is a little different than other tools. To use a dial bore gauge correctly the tool is rocked back and forth in the cylinder bore. As the tool starts out of square with the bore it will read high, as it becomes square it will read its lowest value, then as it proceeds past square it will

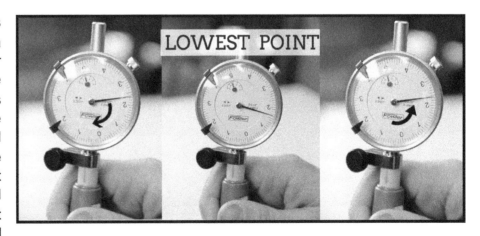

read high again. The correct point to take the measurement from is when the dial bore gauge reads at its lowest value just before the needle starts to change direction.

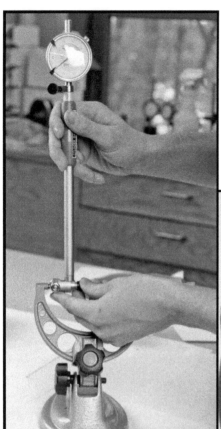

Calibrating a Dial Bore Gauge: Micrometer Method

1. Calibrate a micrometer with a resolution of 0.0001" which is capable of measuring the diameter of the cylinder. See the micrometer calibration section for specific details. Set the micrometer to the desired size and lock it in position.

2. Gently clean the dial bore contact points with your fingertips.

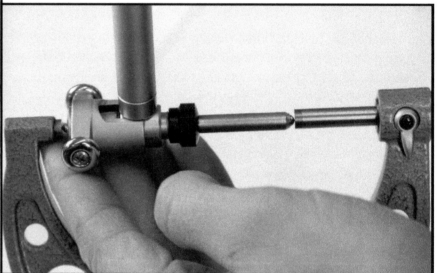

3. Insert the dial bore gauge between the micrometer.

4. Carefully rock the dial bore gauge back and forth. Note the lowest value the needle reads and how far the dial must be turned so the "0" on the gauge face aligns with this point.

5. Rotate the dial face and zero the dial bore gauge to the lowest needle reading.

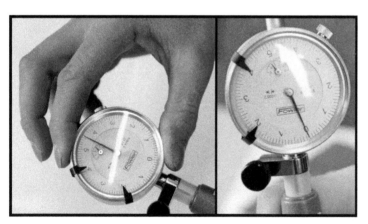

6. Reinsert the dial bore gauge between the micrometer measuring faces. Gently rock the gauge back and forth. Confirm the lowest reading of the bore gauge is "0". If the gauge doesn't quite read "0", remove the dial bore gauge and rotate the dial again. Recheck and repeat this process until the dial bore gauge reads "0" between the measuring faces of the micrometer.

7. Check the calibration for repeatability.

If you're having trouble keeping the dial bore gauge tips between the measuring faces of the micrometer, try slipping a quarter inch piece of tubing over the end of the micrometer. The tubing won't affect the measurement but will help to keep the dial bore gauge positioned.

If you don't have a micrometer stand but you have a vice, the micrometer can be gently set in the vice. Use a rag to pad the micrometer ensuring the micrometer won't be damaged by the jaws of the vice.

Alternatively, the dial bore gauge could be carefully clamped in the vice and the micrometer left free to rock back and forth during calibration.

HOT TIP: Use a micrometer stand to hold the micrometer while calibrating the dial bore gauge. This makes the process much easier and frees up an otherwise busy hand to assist with calibration.

Calibrating a Dial Bore Gauge: Ring Setting Gage Method

The process for calibrating a dial bore gauge using a ring setting gage is similar to that of calibrating the gauge using a micrometer. Simply follow the steps outlined for calibrating the gauge using a micrometer, but enjoy the fact that you don't have to first calibrate the micrometer! The dial bore gauge will also be much easier to center in the ring setting gage and you won't need a third hand.

How To Use

1. Insert the dial bore gauge into the cylinder bore. Set the end of the contact head at the desired height in the bore and gently touch the plungers to the bore.

2. Slowly pivot the handle of the bore gauge so that the contact head and handle start to become square with the bore.

3. Simultaneously, while pivoting the gauge watch the indicator.

4. Once the gauge is square to the bore the dial gauge should read at its lowest value.

In the photo above the needle is at its lowest point. The bore gauge reads 0.0019" larger than the calibrated size.

5. As the gauge passes through the point of being square the gauge needle will change directions indicating the length of the gauge is starting to get longer.

6. The point at which the needle reads the lowest value just before it begins to change direction is the point at which the measurement should be taken.

7. Record the measurement.

8. To determine total bore size either add or subtract the measured value from the calibrated value of the micrometer or ring setting gauge. Consider an example where the micrometer was set to 3.0710" (78.0034mm) and the dial bore gauge was calibrated to this value. Once the bore gauge was inserted into the cylinder the gauge needle changed directions at the positive value of 0.0019" (0.0483mm). By adding 3.0710" (78.0034mm) and 0.0019" (0.0483mm) together the final bore diameter ends up being 3.0729" (78.0517mm).

9. Don't forget to take a few measurements when measuring critical dimensions of parts.

HOT TIP: For comparing taper and out-of-roundness, simply compare the measurements taken from the bore gauge to one another. There's no need to add the calibrated bore diameter into the mix.

Dial Indicator

A dial indicator measures variations in height by utilizing a plunger which travels up and down. As the plunger travels a dial gauge records the amount the plunger has moved. For engine building purposes a dial indicator is a handy tool to have when measuring crankshaft runout, piston position, and finding top dead center.

There are a wide range of dial indicators on the market. Choosing the best one for engine building may be daunting if you're not familiar with them. There are two main features you want to look for when selecting an indicator. The amount of travel the indicator has and the resolution of the indicator. Choose an indicator with around 1.0" (25mm) of travel which has a resolution of 0.001" (0.025mm). This type of indicator will work well for engine applications.

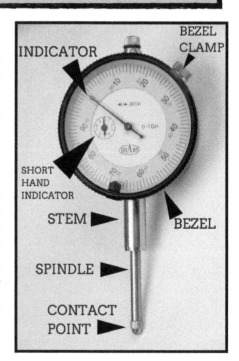

In addition to the indicator, getting a few accessories for the indicator will be beneficial. Most indicators are not sold with a base. Magnetic bases are really handy when setting the indicator up and provide a means of securing the indicator so it can't move. Even when working with aluminum parts (ex. cylinder) a magnetic base can be utilized by bolting a flat piece of steel to the aluminum part.

Dial indicators usually come equipped with rounded contact points which are ideal for measuring flat surfaces. Occasionally you may encounter a setup which requires a different contact point. A variety of contact points are offered for indicators and having an assortment never hurts.

Tip extensions are a must have if you plan on doing any deep depth work with the indicator. One situation which may require a tip extension is when using the indicator to find top dead center with the cylinder head on (think setting or adjusting ignition timing post build on certain engines). Tip extensions can be bought in multiple lengths.

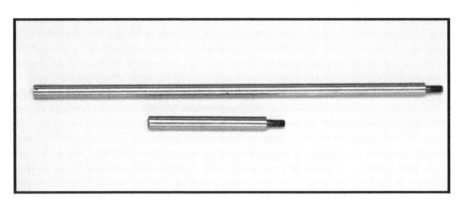

Where to use: Examples include crankshaft runout, setting ignition timing, and finding top dead center.

Reading Dial Indicators: Reading a dial indicator is very similar to reading a dial caliper. The only difference is the dial indicator's gauge face is equipped with a second smaller dial face. For an indicator with a resolution of 0.001" the small face is divided into 10 graduations. Each graduation represents a tenth of an inch. The outer dial face is divided into thousandths of an inch. Each time the outer needle rotates one revolution around, the second small needle tallies a tenth of an inch. This eliminates the need for the user to keep track of how many times the needle has gone around.

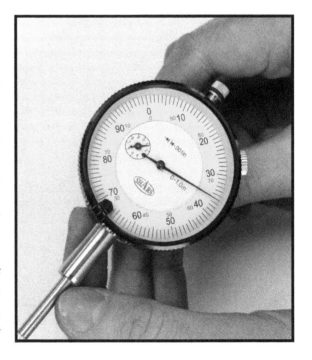

The total measurement is comprised of the number of tenths of an inch the smaller needle is indicating plus the number of thousandths the large needle is indicating. In the picture to the right the dial indicator reads 0.136".

For metric and other resolutions of dial indicators the reading process is identical to the above. Take note of the units and resolution and proceed to read the indicator accordingly.

Calibrating Dial Indicators

Checking and adjusting the accuracy of dial indicators usually can't be done easily in one's own shop. For dial indicator calibration the indicator would have to be sent to a calibration lab. Fortunately, the applications an indicator is used for when building engines doesn't require the utmost accuracy, so calibration is seldom a problem.

How To Use

1. Clean the contact point of the indicator and the part which will be indicated.

2. Carefully set the indicator up so that it is fixed to a sturdy base which can't move

3. The amount of travel in each direction you will need depends on the specific application you are measuring. Consider the motion and travel of the part you want to measure and set the indicator accordingly so that it doesn't run out of travel halfway through measuring.

4. Square the spindle of the indicator being measured. The more square the indicator spindle is to the part the more accurate the readings will be. If the indicator is set at an angle to the direction of travel of the part the indicator will not read accurately. Keep this in mind and always try to set the indicator spindle as square as possible to the part being measured.

5. Zero the indicator by rotating the gauge face so the outer needle aligns with "0". For example when measuring runout the zero point may be a low or high point.

6. Move the part being indicated a few times returning it to its starting position each time. Check to make sure the indicator consistently reads "0". If it doesn't then carefully adjust the gauge face to realign the needle.

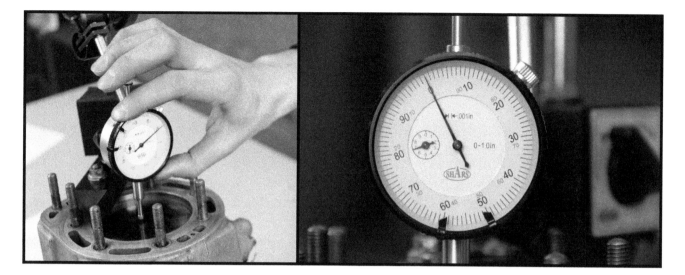

7. Once the indicator has been zeroed proceed to move the part being indicated and take measurements.

8. After measuring return the part to its original position. Occasionally an indicator can get bumped or something can happen during the procedure. This is a good way to confirm one last time that the indicator is still zeroed.

Dial Test Indicators

Dial test indicators are very similar to dial indicators; however, their primary function is more as a comparative tool than a measurement tool. The main difference between a dial indicator and dial test indicator is the dial test indicator uses a contact point which pivots instead of a plunger that travels up and down. This pivoting action results in an arcing path instead of a straight up and down path. The test indicator is best suited for taking comparative measurements and zeroing runout. For engine building purposes this makes a pair of dial test indicators well suited for measuring the runout of a crankshaft.

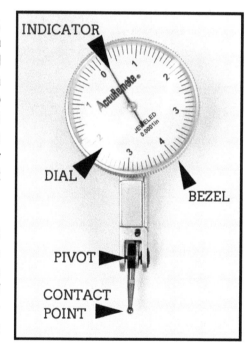

Just like dial indicators, test indicators are made with different lengths of travel and different resolutions. The most suitable resolution for crankshaft truing and inspection purposes is 0.0001" (0.0025mm). Most test indicators with a resolution of 0.0001" will have a travel of 0.008" (0.203mm) or 0.010" (0.254mm) which will be suitable for crankshaft inspection.

The test indicators will require fixturing so having a pair of bases, stands, and clamps is necessary. Fortunately, the test indicators use similar mounting systems as dial indicators so if you have fixturing for dial indicators you are all set to mount the test indicators.

Where to use: Examples include crankshaft inspecting or truing.

Reading Dial Test Indicators: The gauge face of a dial test indicator is symmetrical. The face is divided into graduations based on the resolution of the test indicator. Each side of the face represents half of the total travel of the test indicator. Reading the gauge is simply a matter of determining how many graduations the needle has moved from its starting point to its ending point.

Calibrating Dial Test Indicators

Like dial indicators, calibrating dial test indicators is usually done by a professional calibration lab. As long as the test indicator is well cared for the need for calibration should be infrequent.

How To Use

Since the contact point of the test indicator travels in an arc the way the indicator is set up has an impact on measurement. This is the main reason test indicators can't be relied on heavily for taking measurements and instead are used for comparing.

1. Clean the contact point of the indicator and the part which will be indicated.

2. Carefully set the indicator up so that it is fixed to a sturdy base which cannot move.

3. Most test indicators function best when the contact point is perpendicular to the direction of travel of the workpiece. Some indicators differ slightly and should be set at a slight angle, so confirm with the instructions supplied with your test indicator to attain the correct orientation.

4. The majority of test indicators work best when the contact point is preloaded. As a rule of thumb a $\frac{1}{10}$ to $\frac{1}{4}$ revolution of the needle is about right for setting preload. Instructions supplied with individual indicators may have specific preload instructions.

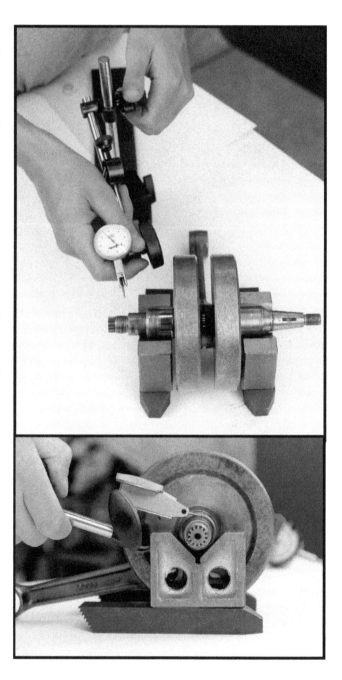

5. Rotate the part to find the high or low point. Zero the indicator by rotating the dial face so the needle aligns with "0".

6. Move the part being indicated a few times returning it to its starting position each time. Check to make sure the indicator consistently reads "0". If it doesn't then carefully adjust the gauge face to realign the needle.

7. Once the indicator has been zeroed proceed to move the part being indicated and take measurements.

8. After measuring return the part to its original position. Occasionally an indicator can get bumped or something can happen during the procedure. This is a good way to confirm one last time that the indicator is still zeroed.

Transfer Gauges

Transfer gauges are measurement tools which don't yield a direct measurement. They are simply tools which can be used to transfer the dimensions of something requiring measurement to a measurement tool. There are two types of transfer measurement tools commonly used in engine building, small hole gauges and telescoping gauges.

Transfer gauges can be tricky to use accurately for a couple reasons. First, they introduce a second source for error. Instead of taking a direct measurement the measured part must first be sized using a transfer gauge. Then the gauge must be measured by a measurement tool such as a micrometer. It is easy to see how mistakes can accrue in this situation. Second, transfer gauges rely heavily on feel to obtain accurate measurements. If the user of the gauge is unskilled, the transfer measurements could be all over the board.

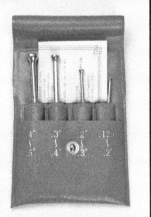

Taking these points into consideration transfer gauges can still be incredibly helpful when measuring engine parts. Transfer gauges are one of the most relied on methods of accurately measuring internal diameters.

Small Hole Gauges

Small hole gauges are used to transfer internal measurements usually less than ½" in diameter.

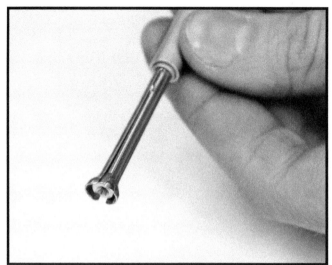

A small hole gauge has a split in its head which allows the head to expand or contract to the size of the part being measured. An adjustment knob at the end of the handle is turned to expand or contract the head. The head on the gauge can either be a full or half sphere design. The half sphere designs have the advantage of being able to measure blind holes.

Small hole gauges are usually sold in sets capable of measuring from around 0.125 - 0.500" (3.175 - 12.4mm). Each set is comprised of around four gauges with each gauge being able to measure a certain portion of the set's total range.

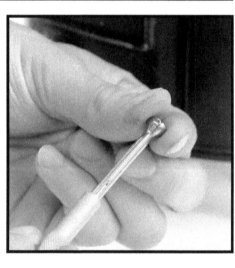

Where to use: Examples include power valve shaft bores and other small features. Small hole gauges may be most applicable to small displacement two-strokes.

How to use

1. Clean the bore of the part to be measured and the head of the small hole gauge with your fingertips.

2. Slowly turn the adjustment knob on the gauge expanding the head of the gauge inside the bore of the part being measured.

3. Simultaneously, gently rock the gauge back and forth and fore and aft inside the bore until the head of the gauge just starts to drag on the bore of the part. As you rock back and forth make sure the handle of the gauge passes through the point where the handle is square to the bore.

4. Remove the gauge.

5. Use a micrometer to measure the diameter of the gauge to determine the diameter of the part's bore. Since the gauge can easily be compressed little to no pressure can be applied by the measuring faces of the micrometer

6. Slide the gauge back and forth and fore and aft as you delicately tighten the ratchet or thimble of the micrometer. An accurate reading will be obtained when the micrometer just starts to drag against the gauge. Remember to measure perpendicular to the split in the gauge.

7. Lock the the spindle of the micrometer and read the micrometer to obtain the bore diameter.

Telescoping Gauges

> **HOT TIP:** Since this is partly an exercise of feel, take multiple measurements until the measurements start to yield the same results. This way you can be certain the measurements are accurate.

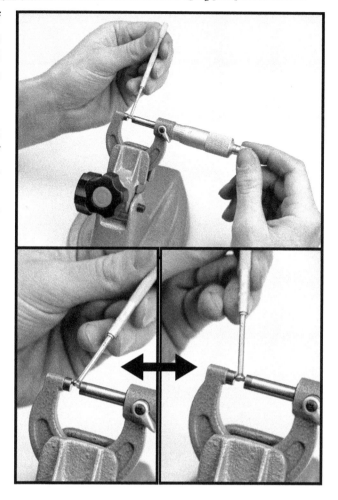

Telescoping gauges are the big brothers of the small hole bore gauges. Telescoping gauges are shaped like a "T". A tightening knob is situated at the handle end and it controls one or two spring loaded plungers (dependent on gauge type). Once the knob is loosened the plunger(s) expand outwards to capture the diameter of the bore being measured. The plunger ends are convex so the gauge can be rocked back and forth to obtain the measurement.

Telescoping gauges are usually sold in sets capable of measuring from around 0.3125 - 6.0" (8 - 152.4mm). Each set is comprised of around six gauges with each gauge being able to measure a certain portion of the set's total range.

Where to use: Examples include cylinder bores and wrist pin bores.

How to use
1. Clean the bore of the part to be measured and the ends of the plungers on the telescoping gauge.

2. Set the gauge inside the bore with one plunger touching the side of the bore.

3. Slowly loosen the adjustment knob on the gauge handle expanding the plungers of the gauge inside the bore of the part being measured.

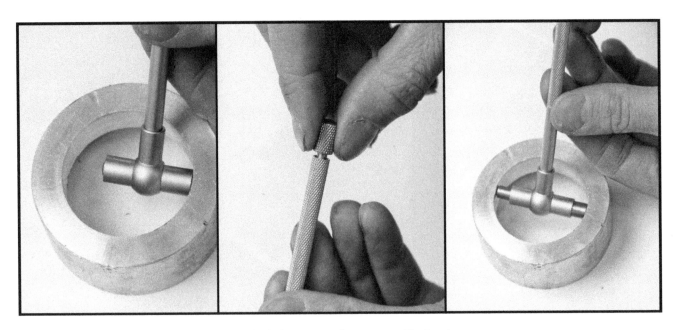

4. Set the gauge up so that the handle is just out of square with the bore.

5. Tighten the adjustment knob down.

6. Gently wiggle the gauge back and forth while passing the gauge through the bore. Only pass the gauge through the bore once. This will center the gauge and set the plungers to the diameter of the bore.

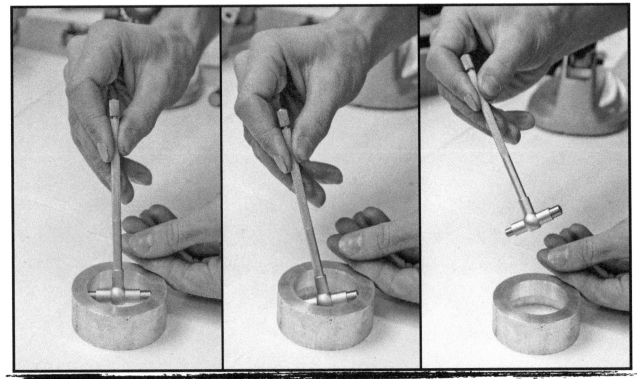

7. Clean both measuring faces.

8. Use a micrometer to measure the diameter of the gauge to determine the diameter of the part's bore. Since the gauge can be compressed, little to no pressure can be applied by the measuring faces of the micrometer.

9. Slide the gauge back and forth and fore and aft as you delicately tighten the ratchet or thimble of the micrometer. An accurate reading will be obtained when the micrometer just starts to drag against the gauge.

10. Lock the the spindle of the micrometer and read the micrometer to obtain the bore diameter.

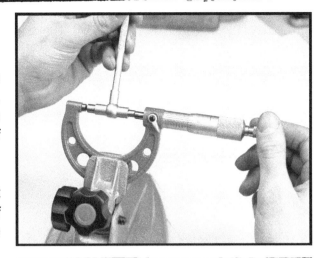

HOT TIP: Since this is partly an exercise of feel, take multiple measurements until the measurements start to yield the same results. This way you can be certain the measurements are accurate.

V-Blocks

A V-block is a large precision machined metal block with a V in it. During an engine build V-blocks are used primarily for checking runout of cylindrical parts such as the crankshaft.

When shopping for V-blocks a precision ground matched set should be purchased. Fancy versions may come with magnetic bases, multiple Vs, clamps, or rollers. While some of these features are nice they certainly aren't necessary and add to the cost.

That concludes the majority of precision measuring tools you will encounter as you build engines. Just to reiterate, learning how to properly utilize precision measurement tools takes time, effort, and practice. The methods I have laid out here in this chapter are sure to help you along the way, but ultimately your keen eye and attention to detail will bring you the most accurate results.

I like to compare building an engine to performing open heart surgery. The precision and organization that goes into open heart surgery is exactly the mindset you need as you begin to rebuild your engine. Just like an operating room, I require my workspace to be as clean as possible. In the industry, companies have dedicated rooms just for engine building equipped with dust management systems, precise temperature control, and spotless work surfaces. I don't expect the at-home mechanic to have this extensive of a setup, but you should aim to have the cleanest work area possible.

The area you are working in should be clean and free of dirt. Use a vacuum to suck up dirt from work surfaces and the floor. Occasionally you'll drop a part on the floor and the last thing you want is for it to wind up covered in dirt. This should go without saying, but don't try building an engine where metal is being ground or cut.

The temperature of your build area is also important. As mentioned before parts are designed, manufactured, and inspected at 68°F (20°C). This means that in order for you to correctly measure a part during your build, it should be at the standard temperature of 68°F. As long as you are close to 68°F you'll be fine; however, building an engine in a cold unheated garage in the dead of winter may not yield accurate results. Conversely, measuring parts in an unairconditioned sweatbox of a garage will not work that well either.

Let's move on to other aspects of the workshop that are important. Until recently, my workbench was old and the work surface wasn't the smoothest or cleanest. I got to work and added fresh ¾" plywood and then finished it off with a few coats of paint. It is always difficult to get all the dirt out of the plywood, so I like to line it with paper or cardboard then replace as often as necessary throughout the build to ensure cleanliness is kept up. This practice ensures I'm not working on a dirty surface and exposing parts to unnecessary dirt which could cause scratches or damage. If you have the luxury of working on a laminate countertop or other hard smooth surface, more power to you. Just remember to wipe the surface clean as you go to keep dirt to a minimum.

Lighting is one area that can be overlooked for many home mechanics. Make things easy on your eyes and be sure you have a good source of lighting where you are working. This way you'll easily be able to see the wear in used parts, accurately read measuring equipment, and correctly assemble new parts. I prefer good overhead lighting when available, but when unavailable, good portable lighting can be just as effective. Portable lights affixed to stands that can be raised above shoulder level work well.

Tool storage and how you choose to handle your tools throughout the build comes down to personal preference. My tools are stored in a two level rolling toolbox. I can easily roll my toolbox from the motorcycle lift to my workbench once the engine has been removed. Instead of putting tools away after I've used them for a given task, I like to leave them out. By keeping them neatly organized I don't have to go digging for them. The tools I frequently use are then set either on my workbench or on a rolling cart so I can quickly grab them throughout the build.

Allocating space to set parts aside as they are disassembled is important. Laying out and keeping a completely disassembled engine organized requires some room. A 3' x 4' area dedicated to storing disassembled engine parts will usually work. Alternatively, a rolling cart with multiple levels is a handy option as it allows better organization and you can wheel parts around with ease. Make sure you are storing parts on nice smooth soft surfaces. Laying out parts on something like a grated metal work surface wouldn't be a good idea as the parts could be damaged when they contact the surface. This is especially true of gasket surfaces on covers which mar fairly easily. Another must is to never stack parts on top of one another. Make sure the area you have chosen to lay out parts is dirt and dust free throughout the build.

CH 10

RACE & PERFORMANCE ENGINE BUILD CONSIDERATIONS

With so many aftermarket parts, add-ons, and doo-dads available to you, determining if any of them are worthy of your hard earned dollar can be challenging. The way aftermarket parts are advertised and presented leads one to believe adding extra horsepower to an engine is a simple bolt-on affair. While this may be true in some instances, there are a lot of other factors which you should be aware of before planning a build. Building a racing engine is an exercise of harmoniously linking all aspects of the engine together so that all parts of the engine function in unison with each other, resulting in the biggest performance gains possible for the given application.

Many considerations, besides making the engine's systems work well together, must be weighed when deciding how the engine will be built. Contrary to what many people believe, horsepower is rarely the sole focal point when building a racing engine. A good engine builder will tailor the engine in a specific way based on the following factors:

THE ABILITY LEVEL OF THE RIDER

Ideally, every engine would be designed to suit a given rider's ability level and style of riding the bike. This would allow each rider to excel regardless of ability level by allowing them to ride a bike with an engine which has had its power characteristics optimized for their needs. As an example, performance and power curve requirements are vastly different for beginners and experts. An engine tailored to the needs of a beginner may actually incorporate modifications which reduce the peak power of the engine and spread the power of the engine out across a wider RPM range so that the beginner rider has an easier time keeping the engine in its usable power range. On the other hand, an advanced rider who is very good at controlling power delivery and moderating power will be able to achieve faster lap times by incorporating engine modifications which sacrifice useable power for peak power.

THE PURPOSE IN WHICH THE ENGINE WILL BE USED

Desired engine characteristics will vary significantly depending on how the engine will be used. A desirable power curve for a motocross racer will be very different from what a hare scrambles racer would want. Unfortunately, it is not possible to design an engine to be good at everything. You can blame the laws of physics and gas dynamics for this unpleasant truth. Since this is the case, engine components must be selected based on their ability to provide certain desirable attributes to the overall scheme of the build. For example, if an engine was being built for an expert motocross racer, a ported cylinder with additional exhaust duration may be used which would increase peak power and reduce the useable portion of the power curve. While this is a good design choice for the motocross racer, an expert hare scramble racer would cringe at the thought of having a narrowed power curve.

DURABILITY REQUIREMENTS

How long does the engine have to last? Believe it or not, some race engines are only designed to last a race or two before they must be serviced. This sort of servicing regimen requires an enormous amount of time, manpower, and money to keep the engine running at peak performance. There is always a trade-off between increased performance and durability of the engine. This is something many people don't understand and it is important to consider when deciding how to build a performance engine. Especially if you are a privateer (as most of us are) who don't have the luxury of sponsors, full time mechanics, a lot of money to spend, and the needed time to devote to taking care of the engine.

RACING RULES

Engine design considerations contingent on the racing rules may include a variety of limitations. Racing rules may specify things such as:
- Displacement limits
- The type or octane rating of the fuel that can be used
- Which parts can be modified within the engine
- The number of engines you are allowed to use within a racing season
- Materials which cannot be used to make engine parts
- Acceptable alterations which can be made to the engine's Ignition timing or ECU

BUDGET

While professional racing organizations have seemingly unlimited budgets to build and develop their engines, the average Joe doesn't. Before spending a huge chunk of change on engine parts, carefully consider your overall budget. By establishing a budget, design choices can be made and parts selected which meet your budgetary requirements and yield the most value for your money. While it pains me to say this as someone who loves engines, upgrading and improving a bike's suspension is far more beneficial in terms of reducing lap times and improving handling than increasing the power of the engine. If you have not dialed in your suspension, it would be foolish not to do this first before making modifications to the engine. As one of my personal heroes, Frits Overmars has said many times, "Increasing speeds through the slowest parts of the track is far more important than increasing the overall top speed down the longest straightaway".

I've purposely picked examples which are at the extreme ends of the performance engine spectrum to highlight my points and I realize that many of you are not looking to create a fully optimized professional level engine. I'm not trying to scare you off from upgrading your engine, nor am I implying all upgrades will result in a loss of durability. My point is that when considering how to improve the engine many additional things, besides power improvements, should be considered. All too often a lot of people actually reduce the ridability of their bike by implementing engine modifications which make the bike more difficult to ride. This is something that is easily avoidable by understanding your specific needs and ability level.

After carefully considering your specific needs and determining what you want out of the engine, you will encounter two more hurdles. First, while I may be able to provide general advice on areas in which you should focus your efforts, I cannot provide you with a blueprint outlining your unique needs, tell you exactly what parts to install, and how to build your engine. Determining which parts to install on your engine and which modifications to make will require research on your end. Learning about and understanding how various component upgrades such as ported cylinders, pistons, cylinder heads, exhaust, and intake systems function is essential. Once you have an understanding of how these parts work and interact with one another, you can then begin to peruse the available aftermarket options.

Unless you have an experienced background in tuning two-strokes and the necessary facilities to undertake research and development work, it is unlikely that you will be discovering a new hot setup on your own. Luckily, it is not necessary to reinvent the wheel. If you research what other credible builders are doing to achieve the performance results you desire, the majority of the development work can be bypassed. While this methodology is not good enough for the factory teams, the majority of us are not participating at that level. If you can put together an engine package catered to your needs and optimize the suspension of your bike, you will have a huge advantage over the majority of your competition.

Finding and speaking with a professional engine builder who specializes in your make and model is one of the best ways to explore your options and learn about setups that will work best for you. When it comes to putting together a good engine package there honestly is no substitute for experience. Not all builders will share their secrets with you since that is how they make their living, but perhaps you can offer an incentive for their help. There are a few ways to show appreciation for a builder who is forthcoming and helpful in coming up with engine optimization solutions for you. One way is to purchase parts through them. Another option is to hire them to perform some of the more complicated tasks throughout the build such as any necessary cylinder porting or engine tuning, whether it be rejetting the carburetor or remapping the ECU. Don't expect a professional builder to reveal his tuning secrets, knowledge, and give up his time in exchange for a warm handshake and a pat on the back.

Performance gains are widely advertised by aftermarket part manufacturers, but rarely do you see any information pertaining to how their parts affect service intervals or the life of the engine. Experienced builders work with these aftermarket parts on a daily basis and should have good insight into how various components affect performance and durability. This alone is another good reason to strike up a relationship with a professional builder if you plan on making serious engine modifications. In addition to this, professional builders can be a gold mine of specialized knowledge when it comes to knowing how to improve existing components. A good example of this specialized knowledge would be a builder who implements their observations and experiences to dial in the port geometry of a cylinder to a level most others cannot.

Once you have selected the parts, made any necessary modifications, and built your engine, you still must tune the engine to ensure it will perform at its prime. Most engine modifications will affect and require alterations to the amount of fuel the engine is receiving in different parts of the RPM range. In addition to fueling modifications, ignition timing alterations may also be necessary to get the most out of the engine. Depending on the combination of parts chosen and the degree to which the engine has been modified, the amount of time and effort required to tune the fuel delivery and ignition timing of the engine will vary. If minor modifications have been chosen using a common combination of parts, predetermined fuel and ignition settings may be readily available from the aftermarket company. If the engine is fuel injected, a new fuel map and ignition map may be able to be programmed into your ECU or you may have to buy an additional aftermarket ECU programmer. Carbureted bikes are simpler and specific jets and needles may be recommended by the aftermarket manufacturer. You may still need or want a programmable ignition system to get more performance out of the engine.

On the other end of the modification spectrum it may be necessary to create custom fuel and ignition maps or jetting and ignition settings to optimize engine performance. This must be done on an engine dyno by an experienced engine tuner. Again, an aftermarket programmer or specific software will be necessary to tune fuel injection systems, or plenty of carburetor parts will be necessary to tune carbureted engines. Regardless of the extent to which you modify your engine, you need to be aware of the fact that any serious modifications will require alteration to the fuel delivery and potentially ignition timing. Be sure to have money set aside for dyno time, aftermarket ECU programmers, jets and needles, and ignition systems. Failure to alter the fuel or ignition system after adding performance parts can be a recipe for disaster and destroy an engine in short order.

Now that you have an overview and undoubtedly a lot of things to consider let's get more specific. I want to go into detail and discuss how individual engine components affect power, influence each other, and the common modifications which are made to them. Before I get started I just want to reiterate the importance of looking at the engine as an entire system. The easiest way to consider an engine's function is to look at it as an air pump. In order for the air pump to work efficiently, the air going in must roughly equal air going out. Small gains may be achievable by altering only one part, but the largest gains and most harmonious engine is created when the entire system is improved together so there are no imbalances in airflow throughout the entire engine.

THE CYLINDER

The ports found within a two-stroke cylinder in combination with the exhaust system have the greatest influence on power, torque, and the RPM at which maximum power is created out of the various engine subsystems. Typically when a new engine is designed the port characteristics are one of the first parameters to optimize. With this being the case they are also one of the first things anyone planning on altering an existing engine should consider improving or tailoring to their specific application.

A two-stroke cylinder consists of exhaust, transfer, and occasionally inlet ports (true inlet ports are only found on piston or rotary valve controlled engines). The port heights, widths, areas, directions they flow, and relationships to one another all have a significant influence on how the engine will behave. The cutaway of the cylinder shown adjacent details the port arrangement and common nomenclature.

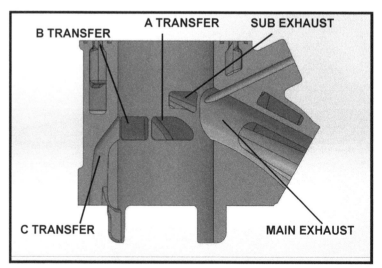

PORT NOMENCALTURE

The inlet port delivers air into the engine's crankcase, most commonly through a reed valve, on a dirt bike engine. On older engines, a rotary valve or the piston may also be used to control the opening and closing of the inlet port. On modern machinery, the inlet port simply connects the reed valve to the cylinder or crankcase. In this case, the primary restriction in the inlet port is the reed valve and as such the valve's geometry and flow capabilities often dictate the inlet port performance.

The transfer ports are responsible for moving fresh air and fuel up from the crankcase into the cylinder. This occurs as the piston travels downward after the cylinder has fired. Once the piston uncovers the tops of the transfer ports the blowdown phase is complete, at which point much of the exhaust gas has been expelled from the cylinder. As the transfer ports begin to open, the exhaust pipe sucks fresh mixture up through the transfer ports into the cylinder. To a lesser extent, the downward motion of the piston also aids in creating a pressure differential between the crankcase and cylinder The shapes and flow capabilities of the transfer ports play a big part in how effectively the cylinder can be scavenged of exhaust gases and filled with fresh air and fuel. The transfer ports also help cool the piston.

The exhaust ports dictate how much and how well exhaust gases depart the cylinder. Similar to the transfer ports, the duct shape, angle, length and volume have a large influence on how well gases can flow through the port. Typically, dirt bike engines commonly feature bridge port or triple port designs.

General insights into a cylinder's performance can be made by characterizing attributes such as the timing of the exhaust and transfer ports, the port widths, and the directional flow angles, but a deeper analysis is required to truly optimize a cylinder. Today, tuners and designers rely on computer software which computes a port's specific time area (STA). As defined in the EngMod 2T software suite, "STA provides an indication of the effective port window area that has to be open for a certain length of time to allow enough gas to flow through the port to achieve the target power at the target RPM for the given engine capacity". STA values are used to quantify the exhaust, transfer, and inlet port geometry as well as the blowdown phase of the two-stroke cycle. The blowdown phase occurs between exhaust port opening and transfer port opening and is one of the most important parameters in predicting engine performance.

By manipulating STA values and subsequently the height, shape, and size of the exhaust, transfer, and intake ports, an engine's power characteristics can drastically be altered. Port modifications can be made which allow more air to move through the cylinder, ultimately increasing the power of the engine. Conversely, ports can be filled or welded and reshaped which tame the engine and provide less peak power but a broader spread of power. Simple modifications to the ports can also be carried out which improves the air or exhaust gas flow through the port yielding better cylinder scavenging.

Unless you have a deep passion for two-stroke tuning, are willing to spend money on software and porting equipment, and are comfortable throwing away botched cylinders, I would recommend having a reputable professional carry out any desired port modifications. Experienced tuners have developed a number of porting combinations that will work well for various makes/models and riding applications which will take the guesswork out of the situation and provide you with a good performing cylinder.

THE EXHAUST SYSTEM

Adding a performance exhaust system can be a great way to increase power and/or alter the power delivery of an engine. I would also argue that optimizing a two-stroke engine's exhaust system is equally as important as ensuring the cylinder's ports are correctly designed for the given application. Not all exhaust systems are designed to do the same things, and much like cylinder port design, exhaust designs are intended to alter power in specific ways. Having a basic understanding of how an exhaust system works can go a long way when it comes to selecting the right exhaust pipe for your engine.

Two-stroke exhaust design is complicated and there are many different variables that must be considered when designing a pipe. I don't intend to go into all of them, but will share a few of the most critical.

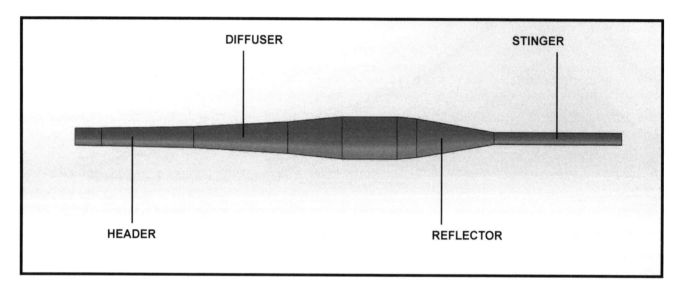

Each time the exhaust port opens to release spent combustion gases, pressure pulses are created. Modern pipe designs harness this pulse energy and use it to help scavenge and fill the cylinder. The process starts when a positive pressure pulse is created once the exhaust port opens and combustion gases leave the cylinder. The positive pulse travels down the pipe until it reaches the diffuser, at which point, part of the pulse is inverted and reflected back towards the cylinder as a negative wave. This negative wave is very beneficial in pulling spent exhaust gases out of the cylinder and fresh mixture up through the transfer ports. The remaining positive pulse continues on its journey towards the end of the pipe where it encounters the reflector. The reflector acts as the name implies and forces the positive pulse back towards the exhaust port. Once reflected back, the pulse remains positive and, if the pipe is designed correctly, it will reach the exhaust port just as the piston is about to close off the port on the compression stroke at the desired RPM for maximum power. Any fresh mixture which has escaped out the cylinder will be forced back in by the positive pressure pulse.

The tuned length of the pipe is dictated by the exhaust port timing, RPM of max power, and the speed of sound. Pulse length and amplitude are governed by the angles of the diffuser and reflector. Generally, steeper cone angles create pulses with more amplitude but shorter duration. Shallower angles generate pulses with less amplitude but longer duration. Given these variables, it is easy to see how a pipe could be tailored for specific applications. An engine converted for road racing may utilize a pipe designed for peak power which incorporates steep diffuser and reflector cone angles so that pulse amplitude is not sacrificed. This peak power would likely come at the expense of a narrowed range of power. An engine tailored for woods riding may feature a pipe with shallower cone angles resulting in less pulse amplitude but a broader spread of power.

The last parameter I want to touch on is how the tailpipe, which is sometimes referred to as the stinger, influences the pipe. The tailpipe creates a flow restriction in the pipe which allows the pipe to have a certain amount of back pressure. Enlarge the tailpipe and the back pressure decreases, make it smaller and the back pressure increases. As back pressure increases or decreases, so does temperature and ultimately the speed of sound. As the speed of sound changes, so does the resonance RPM of the pipe. If the tailpipe is sized too small, cylinder scavenging will be inhibited. When this happens, the cylinder, fresh mixture, and piston will all be overheated.

While engineers and tuners can estimate starting pipe dimensions and tuned lengths, a great deal of trial and error testing is usually still necessary to fine tune the exhaust pipe and optimize the design. Unless you intend on building your own exhausts, this work will have already been done for you.

Contrary to what aftermarket pipe advertising leads you to believe, sound and looks are not the main reasons you should think about dropping a big chunk of change on an aftermarket exhaust system. Sound alone does not win races and if you are at all worried about the looks of your exhaust system, you better not ride your bike after it has been installed! When selecting an exhaust system, you need to focus on how the exhaust alters the power curve. Exhaust systems are tailored to deliver more bottom end performance, top end performance, or performance throughout the power curve. Selecting which system is right for you will depend on how you want your engine to perform. If you've chosen to modify your cylinder ports, installing an exhaust system that compliments the porting can be very beneficial.

You might be wondering about slip-on mufflers. If you've followed along with my explanation of how exhaust pipes work, you'll notice I made no mention of the muffler. While the muffler can have a small effect on performance, it is not the primary factor. Upgrading a muffler is a good way to reduce weight, but there won't be a slip-on out there which significantly increases power.

THE CYLINDER HEAD

On a two-stroke engine, the cylinder head plays a couple of key roles. First, in part with the deck height of the cylinder, the cylinder head is used to alter the compression ratio of the engine. Second, the combustion characteristics are driven by the head design. The head design influences the engine's susceptibility to knock, through a variable called the squish clearance, and also through the shape of the combustion chamber itself. Engine's tailored for different purposes will have different cylinder head design requirements.

In order to modify the cylinder head, a tuner or machine shop must reshape the head using a lathe or mill. Occasionally, welding may also be required to add material to the combustion chamber so that there is enough material to machine away. The combustion chamber shape is something most tuners have dialed in from experience with the given engine and application, but they may require some dimensions from your engine so they can correctly set the squish clearance.

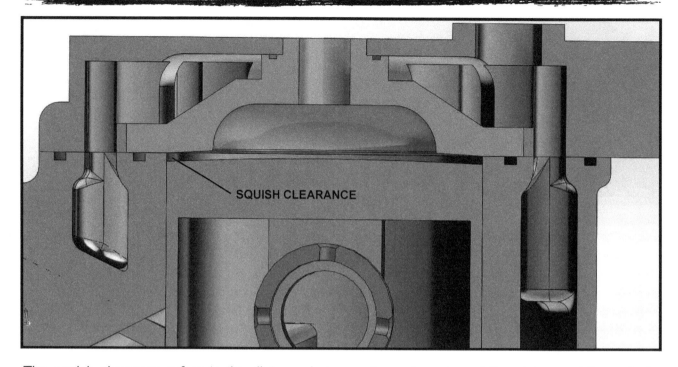

SQUISH CLEARANCE

The squish clearance refers to the distance between the outer edge of the piston and the cylinder head. It should be checked after the cylinder base gasket has been set and adjusted to yield the desired port timings. Once this is done, solder can be used and installed on the top of the piston, the head installed along with any gaskets, torqued down, and the engine rotated through TDC so that the solder is compressed (more detail on this procedure to follow in later chapters). Once this is done, any necessary adjustments can be recorded and given to the machinist who will be reworking the head so that both squish clearance and compression ratio are accurately set.

What's all the fuss about squish? Between the squish clearance, squish area ratio (squish area compared to bore area), and RPM, a squish velocity can be estimated which is an insightful indicator into how much turbulence will be present in the combustion chamber. Turbulence helps increase flame speed which improves power and reduces the thermal load on the engine. In some modern designs, tuners are setting the squish at the mechanical limit of the engine. This is the minimum safe height the cylinder head needs to be from the piston in the event of an engine overspeed. By altering the squish area in combination with the squish height, the maximum squish velocity can be optimized for a given engine RPM and ignition timing.

Once the squish parameters have been established the compression ratio can be tailored for the application. This is done by changing the size and shape of the combustion chamber to so that the chamber volume is either increased or decreased.

The compression ratio defines how much the original air/fuel mixture which was sucked into the engine is compressed. The following equation shows how an engine's compression ratio can be calculated.

$$Compression\ Ratio = \frac{Swept\ Volume + Clearance\ Volume}{Clearance\ Volume}$$

The swept volume is the volume that the piston displaces as it moves through its stroke. Mathematically this volume can be determined using the following equation.

$$Swept\ Volume\ =\ \pi\ x\ \frac{Bore\ Diameter^2}{4}\ x\ stroke$$

The clearance volume is the volume of the combustion chamber when the piston is at top dead center (TDC). While manufacturers specify what the compression ratio should be, due to subtleties in manufacturing, parts vary slightly from engine to engine so finding the exact clearance volume of your engine actually requires measuring the clearance volume. Finding the clearance volume will be covered in later chapters.

Undoubtedly, you have probably heard that raising the compression ratio will increase the power of an engine. This is definitely true; however, you should be aware of the other consequences that come along with this.

The more the air/fuel mixture can be compressed before it is combusted, the more energy which can be extracted from it. The reason for this is due to thermodynamic laws. In summary, the temperature difference between the combusted mixture when it is hottest and coolest determines the power and efficiency of the engine. The hottest point of the mixture will arrive shortly after the mixture has been ignited and the coolest point will occur around the point where the exhaust port opens. Since the temperature of a gas increases as its volume decreases, it is easy to see how increasing the compression ratio increases the overall combustion temperature. Something less obvious is that because the gases are compressed more, they will expand more and actually be cooler by the time the exhaust port opens.

If increasing the temperature of the compressed mixture is good, you might be wondering what keeps us from raising it higher and higher. Detonation, which is a by-product of the additional heat and pressure in the combustion chamber, is the main reason the compression ratio can't be increased beyond a certain point. Detonation occurs after the spark plug has ignited the air/fuel mixture. Normally, once the spark has ignited the mixture, the flame will propagate outwards from the spark plug evenly in all directions. When detonation occurs some of the remaining air/fuel mixture situated towards the edges of the combustion chamber spontaneously combusts before the flame reaches it. When this happens a large spike in combustion pressure occurs. If severe enough, detonation can cause engine damage in the form of pitting on the piston crown, broken ring lands, and scuffing of the piston from overheating.

To combat detonation there are a few different parameters which can be tweaked to help alleviate the problem. The air/fuel ratio can be altered along with the engine's ignition timing to change the peak combustion temperatures, a fuel with a higher octane rating can be used which will be more resistant to detonation, and upgrades to the cooling system can be carried out to help keep the combustion chamber cooler.

Along with increasing the likelihood of detonation as a result of increasing the compression ratio, the engine will also produce more heat. The cooling system must absorb this additional heat and be able to adequately cool the engine, otherwise overheating and detonation may be problematic. Radiator size, thickness, and the speeds at which you ride at all play a big role in how efficiently the cooling system operates. Further discussion on cooling system optimization will follow shortly and may be something you should consider if you are going to increase the compression ratio. Now that you have an understanding of how compression ratio affects performance, you can consider if this will be a good modification for you.

Adjusting the squish height and area is one of the most beneficial modifications that can be made to a two-stroke dirt bike engine, in part because many of the head designs originated during a time when head optimization was less understood. This improvement alone will make jetting the bike much easier and make it less susceptible to detonation. For racers looking to extract all the power from their bike, altering the compression ratio is one of the things that will be necessary. Notice I did not say raise the compression ratio. Raising or lowering the compression ratio is dependent on the engine and whether or not improvements have been made to the cylinder and pipe. It can actually be beneficial to reduce the compression ratio in some high performance engines. This may seem strange, but since the engine is scavenging more efficiently there is actually more air being trapped in the cylinder which yields a denser mixture. If you do a lot of tight woods riding, hare scramble racing, or enduros where low speeds are the norm, you may want to shy away from raising the compression ratio as the cooling system may have difficulty dealing with the increased heat at low speeds where airflow is limited.

THE CRANKCASE

Typically modifications made to two-stroke crankcases are made for two reasons. Either to improve airflow within the crank cavity or to alter the volume of the crankcase which leads to a change in the crankcase compression ratio. An experienced tuner can make flow improvements in the crankcase by modifying the case geometry leading into the transfer ports. The amount of work that can be done in this area is largely dependent on the engine and whether it is equipped with a crankcase or cylinder reed valve. Similarly, the ducts of rotary valved vintage engines can also be improved.

The crankcase compression ratio compares the volume of the crankcase when the piston is at TDC and at BDC. As an aside for technical accuracy, most tuner's and designers exclude the transfer port volumes from the crankcase compression ratio calculation because they are accounted for in other calculations. This makes physically measuring the crankcase compression ratio slightly more difficult, but still doable.

The crankcase volume is important for several tuning reasons. First, the crankcase is the place that the exhaust pipe will pull fresh mixture from. Its volume determines how much of a pressure drop there will be in the crankcase during the transfer phase. Larger crankcase volumes allow for a lower pressure drop which means the mixture will be delivered to the cylinder with a higher average pressure. This higher average pressure correlates to a mixture with a higher average density. Sizing the crankcase volume is a balancing act though. If it is sized too large, the flow velocity inside the case will drop to the point where the fuel and air separate.

Second, the crankcase acts as a Helmholtz resonator. Helmholtz resonance is a type of resonance which applies to air within a cavity. Naturally, it also has an influence within an engine's airbox and the exhaust system. Helmholtz resonance within a two-stroke crankcase is complicated, difficult to predict, and its effectiveness dependent, in part, on the type of intake (reed, rotary, piston port, etc). The case volume is one factor which directly influences at what RPM the crankcase resonates. This is beneficial because when in resonance, additional air can be moved through the engine.

An easy way to alter crankcase volume is with reed valve spacer plates. Depending on the engine, these spacer plates can also help airflow up the rear transfer port. This is not a bad modification to play with because it is reversible. For more serious irreversible modifications, I would recommend working with an experienced tuner.

THE PISTON

Two-stroke pistons used in performance applications are heavily thermally loaded. For this reason it can be necessary or beneficial to upgrade the engine's piston. Before I share upgrade options, I want to discuss one of the problems designers face. While aluminum is almost always used for performance two-stroke pistons due to its relatively good strength and density properties it does have downfalls. One of the big challenges with using aluminum for pistons is that aluminum loses strength as its temperature goes up. This means engineers must be very careful when selecting the alloy which will be used because different alloys have different strengths when they are at temperature. Different aluminum alloys also expand at different rates as their temperature increases so this expansion must be accounted for in the piston design.

The manufacturing process used to produce the piston also has a bearing on the alloy selection process. The normal methods for making a piston are either by forging or by casting it. Alloys that are suitable for casting are rarely ideal for forging, so two distinct types of pistons end up on the market, those that are cast and those that are forged.

In my opinion, cast pistons are usually better suited for high performance two-stroke engines than forged pistons. First, alloys used for cast pistons often offer better strength at temperature than forged pistons. Second, alloys used for cast pistons usually have lower coefficients of thermal expansion so they don't expand as much. This is beneficial because the piston clearances can be designed so that they are tighter at running temperature than what could be achieved with a forged alloy. They will also be tighter when cold or getting up to temp which helps prevent piston slap. Lastly, casting alloys usually (not always) have more silicon content than forging alloys. The silicon in the aluminum is beneficial because it provides wear resistance. Its presence also plays into how big or small the coefficient of thermal expansion will be for the alloy.

Many manufacturers cast their pistons for the reasons I've previously listed, so how much opportunity there is to upgrade depends on what you are trying to do with the engine. If you are on a budget, I would suggest selecting a good quality cast piston no matter the application. If you are one of the few looking to get every bit of performance out of the engine, working with a tuner who has experience with making/sourcing custom pistons tailored to the application would be a good plan. Custom pistons can be refined to a level mass produced pistons cannot. Parameters such as top ring land clearance and piston profile can be tailored to the specific engine and application which is beneficial for extracting more power from the engine.

THE ROD

Upgrading the connecting rod is a wise decision anytime the RPM of the engine is increased or the mass of the piston is significantly increased. When engineers design connecting rods, the design is primarily based on the weight of the piston assembly and the maximum RPM the engine will be operated at. These two variables play a huge role in the amount of force that will be exerted on the rod. Contrary to what a lot of people believe, in a high performance gasoline two-stroke engine the biggest force exerted on the rod is an inertia force caused by the piston assembly accelerating upward and occurs around TDC, not from combustion. To get a better picture of this think about the piston moving upwards, then think about what the rod does once the crankshaft rotates through TDC. The piston will continue traveling upwards while the rod will have started moving downwards. The piston will try to pull the rod up while the crank pulls the rod down, effectively stretching the rod. As RPM and piston mass increase the force exerted on the rod by the piston also increases. Luckily for the two-stroke, the effect of compressing the fresh mixture and firing each stroke counteracts the inertia force lessening it to some extent.

Once the designer has determined the amount of force exerted on the rod, it can be designed to be just a little stronger than the maximum force it will have to cope with. This extra bit of strength is called a safety factor. Depending on the application, safety factors can range from around 1.3 - 1.6 for production applications and as little as 1.1 for racing applications. Another way to think about it is that an additional 30 to 60 percent of strength will be designed into the rod so that there is no doubt that it will be able to handle the maximum force exerted on it.

By establishing design parameters for the rod, it will be as light as possible for use in the given application. Trouble arises when modifications are made to an engine which put more force and subsequently stress on the rod. Depending on the original design specifications of the stock rod and what level of alterations have been made to the engine, it is easy to see how the margin for safety can be cut very thin or even become non-existent. When this happens, major engine failures are likely to occur.

Aftermarket rods are available as off-the-shelf parts or they can be custom made based on an engine's specific needs. The most common way to improve upon the original rod design is to use stronger alloys and, if necessary, add material to the design. If you are building a high RPM engine or adding substantial weight to the piston assembly, as may be the case with some big bore kits, upgrading the rod to a stronger design will be a good idea.

THE CRANK

Crankshaft modifications for two-stroke engines are typically done for a few reasons. First, to alter the balance of the engine. Second, to change the inertia of the crankshaft. Finally, to alter the crankcase volume or to improve airflow through the crankcase.

Unless the engine has a counter balance shaft, crank balance modifications can be useful in tuning the angle at which the engine vibrates. Tuner's often refer to a term called "balance factor" when analyzing the balance of the crankshaft. The balance factor quantifies the percentage of the reciprocating mass that has been balanced. When working with balance factors it is always assumed that 100 percent of the rotating mass has been balanced. Mathematically the balance factor can be expressed as follows.

$$Balance\ Factor\ =\ \frac{Amount\ of\ reciprocating\ mass\ balanced\ on\ the\ crankshaft}{Total\ reciprocating\ mass}\ x\ 100$$

A crank with a balance factor of zero would result in engine vibration which is aligned with the cylinder axis. A crank with a balance factor of 100 percent would eliminate the vibration along the cylinder; however, it would introduce strong vibrations 90 degrees to the cylinder axis. Thus balance factors between 0 and 100 percent proportionately reduce the vertical vibratory forces in proportion to the balance factor. For example, if the engine's balance factor is 50 percent the vertical vibratory forces are reduced by 50 percent. The best value to use is largely dependent on the application.

Most manufacturers do a good job choosing the correct balance factor for the engine, but there are still a few good reasons to check and potentially adjust it. First, when the engine is going to be used for a different application it is often necessary to change the balance factor. For example, when a dirt bike engine is used in a karting application the balance factor is often increased. This allows the vibration from the engine to be more in line with the stiffness of the kart chassis. Subtle weight variations between parts caused by manufacturing tolerances facilitate checking and fine tuning the balance factor as well when building high performance engines. Lastly, when the mass of any reciprocating components, such as the piston, are increased it can be beneficial to correct the original balance factor to suit these weight increases. The most common example of this situation is when a big bore engine is built.

Inertia quantifies how resistant an object is to changes in its acceleration. In the case of a crankshaft, moment of inertia calculations can be performed which will assess how resistant the crank is to acceleration changes. Crankshafts with high inertia, i.e. cranks that have more mass for their given radius, will be more resistant to acceleration changes than cranks with lower inertia.

The crankshafts inertia and weight can be tuned for specific applications. For example, for tight technical or slippery conditions it can be advantageous to use a crankshaft with high inertia. The high inertia crank aids traction and can tame power delivery. On the other hand low inertia cranks can be beneficial in road racing applications. Ultimately, rider preference will determine what is best. Unless an engine is being built at a high level, more often than not altering the crank for inertia reasons is not commonly done. Most people choose to alter the weight of the flywheel because it is often cheaper and easier.

Depending on the design of the crankshaft, modifications intended to alter the crankcase volume or airflow around the crank can be carried out. Naturally, these two variables are linked. One of the most common modifications is to "stuff" the crankshaft in an effort to reduce the amount of mixture that can go into the crank cavity. Thin sheet metal shrouds are often used, as well as epoxy solutions. Stuffing can also be done with the sole goal of reducing the crankcase volume. Whether this is desirable or not is engine specific.

THE INTAKE SYSTEM

The intake system consists of all components used to move or guide air before reaching the crankcase. Commonly upgraded or modified components include reed valves, manifolds, carburetors/throttle bodies, air filters, and the airbox. The goal with improving any of the intake components is to increase the flow of air into the engine.

When engineers design an intake system they determine the size of the reed valve, rotary valve, or piston port, along with the carburetor/throttle body (we'll refer to this as the choke from now on) based on the amount of air that can flow through the cylinder and its associated ports. Based on this analysis, the choke and intake system's flow capability is usually sized to match closely with the flow capabilities of the cylinder (there are some instances where it will be sized smaller). Restrictions in the intake system like the butterfly valve in a throttle body, surface roughness, or mis-matches between parts which reduce flow make it necessary to size the intake system slightly larger than the flow capabilities of the cylinder since the restrictions reduce the effective flow area in the intake system.

I mentioned that the intake system won't always be sized large enough so that the cylinder can flow unrestricted. The diameter of the choke plays a big role in how quickly air will move through the intake system. The larger the choke size, the more slowly air will move. This is not a problem when the engine is sucking hard at high RPMs, but at lower RPMs when the engine isn't operating as efficiently the reduced velocity can slow the amount of air entering the cylinder. This in turn reduces the amount of power that can be made at lower RPMs. If the engine's bottom end is lacking too much, a smaller choke may be used to improve the bottom end performance in exchange for a slight loss of top end power.

Intake system improvements or modifications may be necessary any time the flow capabilities of the cylinder are improved. These improvements to flow are caused by exhaust pipe improvements, changing the port timing within the cylinder, or improving the airflow through the ports so they flow more efficiently.

The original intake system design will largely dictate if any alterations to the intake system are required after modifications to the cylinder or exhaust are made. If you are building an engine which incorporates significant changes to the port timing or the exhaust, I would recommend speaking with the builder who made these alterations for you and listen to their suggestions in regards to altering the size of the intake system. In some cases, the original intake system may be sized to accommodate improved flow, while in others, enlarging the choke may be necessary.

For builders not altering the cylinder in any way, small gains may still be possible by making minor alterations to the intake system. Correcting mismatches between parts like the airbox and choke, choke and manifold, and manifold and cylinder/crankcase can improve airflow through the intake system. Occasionally, the airbox or air filter can become restrictions in the intake system. Air filters which flow better can be installed and the airbox inlet can be enlarged to allow more air to enter.

If more bottom end performance is desired, a smaller choke can be installed or a sleeve installed inside the choke which reduces flow through the choke. This modification will increase air velocity and improve cylinder filling at low RPMs. Thus bottom end power will be improved in exchange for a slight loss of top end performance.

REED VALVE

Two modifications can be considered for engines which feature reed valves. First, the entire reed valve assembly can be upgraded. Second, the reed petals can be replaced or upgraded.

The open area, which is the effective area of the reed valve when the petals are at full lift, determines how much air can flow into the engine. When building high performance engines, looking at reed solutions which increase the open area can be beneficial. Increasing a reed's open area is most commonly done by altering the reed block design. This is usually accomplished by upgrading from a two sided reed block to a four sided block. Alternatively reed blocks from other engines can be adapted which are larger.

Petal modifications come in the form of changing petal material or petal thickness, both of which ultimately result in a change in petal stiffness. The petal stiffness influences how the reed valve opens. Stiffer reed petals will require a larger drop in crankcase pressure before they open than softer reeds. Since a larger crankcase pressure drop is created with stiff reeds, a stronger suction pulse pulling mixture from the carburetor also results. Thus, whenever reed petal stiffness is changed, the carburation will also need to be modified. Petal stiffness can be partly based on trial and error testing and by calculating the resonance frequency of the petals. For prolonged reed life it is important to ensure that the resonance frequency of the reed petal falls outside of the RPM of max power.

THE FLYWHEEL

Modifying or installing a different flywheel will affect performance by altering the amount of inertia the crankshaft assembly has. The flywheel weight will affect how quickly the engine can rev, tractability, and also how susceptible the engine is to stalling. Unlike most automotive racing applications, installing the lightest flywheel possible isn't always the best choice.

There is no tried and true formula for selecting the best flywheel other than testing, seeing what feels best, and what performs best. As a general rule, lighter flywheels will allow the engine to spin up more quickly, give the bike a little bit of a zippy feel, and make the engine more susceptible to stalling at low RPMs. Heavier flywheels reduce the rate at which the engine can spin up and, as a result, offer a rider better traction when grip is limited. Plus the additional weight of the flywheel will help keep the engine from stalling at low RPMs.

To get you headed in the right direction a lot of hare scramble, enduro, novice motocross, and tight woods riders generally prefer a heavier flywheel. Experienced motocross racers, supermotard riders, and road racers tend to prefer a lighter flywheel. Increasing the flywheel weight when conditions necessitate it can also be beneficial. When conditions are muddy and slippery more traction can often be found by switching to a heavier flywheel.

THE CLUTCH

Putting power to the ground is important and the clutch plays a major role in this department. The clutch system is comprised of the clutch basket, hub, steel plates, fiber discs, pressure plate, springs, and push rod assembly.

An alternating series of fibrous clutch discs and steel plates comprise the clutch pack. The clutch discs have tangs which interlock on the clutch basket fingers (these plates are always rotating) while the steel plates are splined to the inner clutch hub (these plates only rotate when the clutch is engaged). The clutch pack is sandwiched between the edge of the basket and pressure plate. The clutch springs are used to hold the pressure plate and clutch pack tight when the clutch is engaged. When the clutch is disengaged, the pushrod extends outward forcing the pressure plate away from the clutch pack and compressing the clutch springs. This puts a gap between the clutch discs and steel plates, causing power to cease moving through the clutch. The transmission of power through the clutch is entirely dependent on friction. The material the fibrous discs are made from, the number of discs, stiffness of the clutch springs, and type of oil used to lubricate the clutch all attribute to the amount of friction in the clutch pack and how efficiently the clutch will transmit power.

When engine power is increased, the amount of friction it takes to keep the clutch plates from slipping against one another when the clutch is engaged may need to be increased. A variety of aftermarket options are available for accomplishing this task ranging from stiffer springs, clutch discs made from different materials, clutch packs consisting of more fibrous discs, or a completely new clutch assembly.

Clutch upgrades may also be necessary if clutch durability becomes a problem. Most stock clutch baskets and hubs are die cast parts made from aluminum. The aluminum alloys used in die casting tend to be softer than the aluminum alloys used in aftermarket clutch assemblies. Due to their softness, the stock clutch components tend to wear a little bit more quickly than aftermarket clutch components. This is one of the main reasons stock clutch assemblies are swapped out in favor of more durable aftermarket assemblies if clutch wear is an issue.

In addition to traditional clutch upgrade options, slipper or automatic clutches can be a good choice for some riders. Riders who prefer little to no engine braking when decelerating may find that a slipper clutch is a good option. Applications where slipper clutches come in handy are supermotard and road racing.

An automatic clutch can be a good choice for some riders as they allow for clutchless shifting, reduce the likelihood of stalls, and help prevent wheel slippage by moderating power transmission. An automatic clutch can be set up for almost all applications and styles of riding. Beginning motocross racers may find them particularly helpful as they no longer have to worry about clutch modulation as much and can focus more on riding the bike.

THE COOLING SYSTEM

As improvements are made to an engine that increase its power, the amount of heat the engine will create will also increase. Effectively removing heat from the engine and cooling it is very important as the power output of the engine goes up. The cooler an engine runs, the more power it can produce.

There are three major ways that the aftermarket attempts to improve the cooling system of an engine. These three ways are to increase flow through the cooling system, increase the cooling capacity of the radiators, and increase the pressure of the cooling system.

The flow through the cooling system can be increased by installing a water pump impeller designed to increase the flow rate of the coolant. The reason increasing the flow rate of coolant works is because the rate of heat transfer from the engine to the cooling system is directly proportional to the mass flow rate of coolant. This is thermodynamics jargon, but there are two key parts to consider. First, how much coolant is flowing, and second, at what speed the coolant is flowing. The more coolant that flows and the faster it flows will reduce the temperature difference between the point where the coolant enters into the engine and where it exits. This next part is not quite as intuitive. When the temperature difference between the inlet and outlet is reduced, the peak outlet coolant temperature is lowered. When the peak outlet coolant temperature is lowered the engine will run cooler. This is why fitting a water pump, which increases the flow of coolant through the engine, improves cooling.

Radiators consist of a series of tubes and fins which run from the top to the bottom of the radiator. These are often referred to as the radiator's cores. As coolant enters the radiator it moves through the series of tubes and heat is transferred from the coolant to the fins. Air passes over the fins and heat is transferred from the fins to the air. This transfer of heat from coolant to air is how radiators reduce the temperature of the coolant.

Coolant temperatures can be reduced by upgrading radiators in three ways, by increasing the frontal area of the radiators, by making the radiators thicker, or by using materials with better heat transfer properties for the cores. For all practical purposes increasing the radiators' frontal area and improving the core materials is rarely a viable option for dirt bike applications. This is because there is little room for the radiators to begin with and they are susceptible to damage, making the use of expensive core materials a risky affair. Unfortunately, both of these options are better improvements to make before resorting to increasing the thickness of the radiators.

Increasing the thickness of a radiator is not as efficient of an improvement as increasing the frontal area of the radiator. In order for thicker radiators to cool more effectively than their stock counterparts, airflow past the radiators is key. When the thickness of a radiator is increased, air must travel a greater distance through the radiator before exiting. The speed the air is traveling plays a big role in determining how quickly the air heats up as it moves through the radiator. If the air is not traveling fast enough through the radiator, the air temperature will rise and equal the coolant temperature before reaching the end of the radiator. Once this happens, heat transfer stops and whatever portion of the radiator remains will not help with cooling. In order for a thicker radiator to be effective, air must flow quickly enough through it so that the exiting air temperature is at, or better yet, below the coolant temperature. In conclusion, benefits from adding thicker radiators will be more prominent in applications where speeds are relatively high. Whereas in applications where the bike is hardly moving, improved cooling may not be noticeable.

The last alteration to the cooling system that can be made is to install a high pressure radiator cap. As coolant temperature increases, pressure increases inside the cooling system. The radiator cap is designed to be the pressure release point in the cooling system in the event too much pressure builds up. This can occur as a result of overheating or a blown head gasket for example. By designing the radiator cap to be the weak link in the system, other parts of the system, such as seals, don't end up getting damaged from being over pressurized. The radiator cap features a plug and spring on its underside. The spring is designed to compress once a certain pressure is reached, at which point the plug will move upwards and uncover a pressure release hole where excess pressure will be vented.

The coolant's boiling point and ability to conduct heat are necessary factors in understanding why a high pressure radiator cap can help improve engine cooling. Water alone boils at 212°F (100°C) while a 50/50 mix of water and antifreeze boils at 223°F (106.1C). Radiator cap pressure designations are usually advertised in bar, with most stock radiator caps designed to withstand pressures up to 1.1 bar (16psi). The more pressure a fluid is under the more difficult it becomes for the fluid to vaporize and the higher its boiling point becomes. When water is under 1.1 bar of pressure, the temperature water will boil at is 260°F (127°C) while a 50/50 antifreeze mix will boil at 271°F (133°C). By installing a radiator cap designed to withstand higher pressures, an additional increase in the coolant's boiling point will be seen. High pressure caps are usually designed to withstand 1.3 bar (19psi) of pressure. This 0.2 bar (3psi) increase in pressure over the stock system will increase the boiling point of water or antifreeze by 8.7°F (4.83°C). This will then bring the boiling point of pure water or a 50/50 antifreeze mix to approximately 269°F (132°C) and 280°F (138°C) respectively.

While this small temperature increase alone won't do a lot for your engine, coupling a high pressure cap and using coolants with better heat transfer properties can do wonders. Antifreeze (ethylene glycol) alone is not an inherently good conductor of heat. In fact, pure antifreeze conducts heat about half as well as water, while a 50/50 mix of antifreeze and water conducts heat approximately three quarters as efficiently as pure water. This means a cooling system using a 50/50 mix of antifreeze would have to flow faster than a cooling system filled with pure distilled water in order to achieve the same cooling efficiency. What this means for you is significant cooling gains can be made by using distilled water and an additive called "Water Wetter" in place of an antifreeze-water mix. Water Wetter is an additive that improves water's "wetting" abilities (another whole subject), adds corrosion resistance, and slightly increases the boiling point of water. A high pressure radiator cap in conjunction with distilled water and Water Wetter as the coolant is by far the best route to go for high performance applications where freezing is not an issue. For applications which must still be resistant to freezing, the antifreeze-water ratio can be altered in favor of mixtures incorporating more water than antifreeze so that the cooling efficiency of the mixture is improved. Just bear in mind the freezing point of the mixture as it is thinned with water will be reduced, so you will need to pay close attention to the environment you are operating in so that the coolant is never susceptible to freezing. A frozen coolant system can ruin an engine and makes for a very bad day!

THE IGNITION

The ignition system consists of the stator and flywheel, ignition coil, and spark plug. The ECU or CDI box controls spark timing, which will be discussed in the next section. The ignition system has one purpose, to create enough spark energy so that the compressed air/fuel mixture ignites. Upgrades to an ignition system are aimed to increase the spark energy, improve spark, and ultimately increase combustion efficiency. The most commonly upgraded components include spark plugs and ignition coils.

Most performance dirt bike engines utilize an iridium spark plug, however those that don't can see minor improvements in spark quality and performance by upgrading to an iridium plug. The reason iridium plugs offer a slight increase in performance is because their electrodes can be made smaller than electrodes made from most other materials. Smaller electrodes are able to better concentrate electrical energy and as a result spark quality is improved.

Ignition coils can be upgraded to high output units which delivery more spark energy to the spark plug. This additional energy facilitates a better spark and leads to increased combustion efficiency. As a result more power may be able to be created and more aggressive ignition timing can be incorporated.

Dirt bike engines use good ignition components to begin with, so this is one area where you won't get a drastic improvement in power for the money you are likely to spend on ignition component upgrades. If you are building a top tier racing engine, upgrading the ignition system can be beneficial, however for anything less, sinking money into the ignition system should be one of the last places money is spent.

THE FUELING AND IGNITION TIMING

When an engine is modified from stock, the amount of air entering the cylinder changes either at certain portions throughout the engine's RPM range or throughout the entire range. Once the amount of air has changed, the fuel map or carburetor jetting will be off and must be adjusted either by richening the mixture (adding more fuel) or leaning out the mixture (removing fuel). The specific way in which airflow into the engine is affected is based on what modifications have been made. For example, an engine tuned for high power which incorporates a ported cylinder, a performance exhaust, and a modified cylinder head will see an increase in top end performance necessitating additional fuel to be delivered at higher RPMs. In this instance, cylinder filling may be worse than stock at lower RPMs and fuel may actually have to be removed to make the engine run correctly.

Entire books have been dedicated to discussing the intricacies of tuning theory and how fueling and ignition systems can be tuned to improve horsepower, torque, and the power curve. My aim here is not to get too deep into tuning theory, but to present you with the options available to you in regards to how you can optimize your engine's fueling and ignition.

In addition to fueling alterations required after modifying an engine, further performance may be able to be achieved by altering the ignition timing. Ignition timing is primarily dependent on flame speed, which is the speed the flame propagates outwards from the spark plug once the mixture has been ignited. Flame speed of course is dependent on a host of things, including the air/fuel ratio, compression ratio, air trapped in the cylinder which equates to cylinder pressure, turbulence, and piston speed to name a few. Because all these variables change when engine modifications are made, the ignition timing may need to be adjusted. Igniting the mixture at precisely the right time throughout the RPM range allows the most work to be extracted from the combusted mixture.

For carbureted engines, making alterations to fueling is a matter of replacing jets, needles, and setting needle clip position correctly. Ignition timing on carbureted engines is controlled by a CDI box and there are many aftermarket brands which offer programmable CDI boxes. Most of these CDI boxes even come preprogrammed with multiple ignition maps to choose from to cater to specific needs.

For fuel injected engines, a host of aftermarket options are available for making alterations to the engine's fuel and ignition maps. The three most popular options are aftermarket ECUs which allow complete control of fuel and ignition, programmers which piggyback off the existing ECU (these usually only control fuel), and services which reprogram the stock ECU and replace the stock map with a performance map. For serious performance applications, swapping out the stock ECU with an aftermarket unit which allows for complete control of all engine settings is the only way to go. For engines that feature increased performance, but budget is a concern, the aftermarket programmers which only adjust fuel are a good option. Reprogramming the existing ECU can be a good choice if the aftermarket company offering the service knows exactly what modifications you have done to your engine and has tailored a fuel map for those specific modifications. Getting the fueling right is very important in this case since, unlike programmers, no alterations can be made to the fuel map unless it is sent back for additional mapping changes.

The best way to tune an engine and dial in the fuel and ignition is to use an engine dynamometer. Engine dynamometers are great because they can measure horsepower and torque so power gains aren't left to "feel", as they would be by seat of the pants tuning. Depending on how modified your engine is, there are a couple different ways to utilize the tuning advantages of an engine dyno.

Highly modified, high performance engines designed for top tier racing will need to be tuned by an experienced engine tuner in order for them to achieve their full potential. Hiring a competent tuner and paying for dyno time is something that can get costly in a hurry, but is a necessary expense in the quest for performance and racing dominance.

Luckily, paying for a tuner and dyno time to create one off fuel and ignition maps isn't the only route to go. For those with limited budgets, much of the same performance can be gained by using carburetor settings, fuel maps, or fuel and ignition maps which have been created by experienced tuners at aftermarket companies. Aftermarket companies spend an enormous amount of time and resources dyno tuning and creating maps for performance engines that feature common aftermarket components. By building an engine which incorporates many of these same components, the fuel maps that have been created by the aftermarket can be used on your engine with little to no modifications. This is a nice economical route to go if you don't need to squeeze out every bit of power from the engine.

WRAP UP

At this point you should have a pretty good feel for how common modifications affect performance, have some ideas on how you'd like to tailor your engine to your riding needs and abilities, and understand that there are many different factors which influence aftermarket component selection. Perhaps you are still a little overwhelmed and need further guidance on where to start?

I want to reiterate my point that suspension tuning will improve lap times much more drastically than engine modifications and that anyone who has yet to optimize their suspension needs to start there. Choosing the correct springs for your weight, setting sag, and preload correctly are great first steps.

As a bonus these are things that can be done relatively affordably, especially if the stock springs work for you.

Once you've got the suspension working correctly we can discuss a logical approach to engine modifications. My suggestion regarding engine modifications is to first determine how much money you are willing to spend on improvements and establish a budget for your project. Performance parts can add up quick and before you know it you can find yourself sinking a lot more than you bargained for into the engine and still end up with something incomplete or lacking the performance you had hoped for once finished.

I can't stress enough how much your ability level and the type of riding you will do determine which modifications make the most sense. Regardless of this, you should always look at purchasing performance parts which will yield the greatest change or improvement of power for the least amount of money first. Once these parts have been purchased you can spend any remaining money on more expensive parts which have smaller effects on power. Here are some of my closing recommendations on selecting performance parts.

• For racers on a budget keeping the engine stock is one of the best ways to ensure a high level of reliability and performance.

• An engine builder who specializes in your make and model is your friend. Incentivize them to help you pick out the best combination of mods if you are unsure. If necessary, paying for expert advice is far better than buying performance parts that may not work well together. If you are building an all out performance engine, working with an experienced builder/tuner closely and incorporating their suggestions is a must.

• An aftermarket exhaust would be one of the first components I would recommend looking at adding for any type of build. As previously mentioned, the exhaust system has one of the greatest effects on power and power delivery, plus they are affordable, and if you don't like the result you can easily revert back to the old setup. Just be sure to do your homework when shopping for pipes, as some may require additional modifications to the cylinder in order for them to work best. Searching for exhaust pipe reviews performed by magazines and other credible sources is a good way to get unbiased info.

• Modifying the cylinder head by correctly setting the squish clearance and squish band is another affordable modification that will have a drastic impact on engine performance.

• Changing the compression ratio makes sense for performance applications that need additional power and operate at high enough speeds so that there is always enough airflow to shed the extra heat created. For tight technical riding this is one modification I would cautiously consider because the extra power isn't necessary and the additional heat generated can make cooling the engine more difficult.

• Setting money aside so that fuel maps or carburetors can be tuned is important.

• Aftermarket CDI boxes which come with multiple preprogrammed ignition curves or ECUs which come with multiple fuel and ignition maps are a great way to alter power delivery if you have the budget for them.

• A heavier flywheel can be a great affordable upgrade if you ride in tight technical terrain.

• A stronger more wear resistant aftermarket clutch will become necessary if power is substantially increased, however for minor improvements the stock clutch will work okay.

• An automatic clutch can be a great addition for any rider that is a bit overwhelmed with the amount of clutching necessary to keep the engine in its powerband.

• Assuming you are not racing in freezing temperatures, adding a high pressure radiator cap and swapping out the antifreeze for a distilled water and Water Wetter mix is a great way to improve cooling for any type of riding. This is an affordable modification to perform as well. Just don't forget to drain the water from the cooling system when cold weather returns.

CH 11 | AN OVERVIEW OF A BUILD

Just like there are many ways to change a tire, there are many ways to take an engine apart and put it back together. Wrong ways aside, there are still plenty of ways to get from point A to point B correctly. This chapter is dedicated to giving you an overview of the process. There are four stages in a major engine overhaul. The pre-teardown, teardown, the inspection, and the reassembly.

Pre-Teardown

The pre-teardown stage covers any diagnostic work that you may want to do before opening the engine up. Gaining as much information as you can about any problems the engine may have before working on it is always helpful. If the engine is trashed (like a holed piston) you may as well proceed straight to teardown. However, there are plenty of scenarios where learning about the problem you are hankering to fix by performing a compression test, a crankcase leak down test, or another diagnostic test is helpful. By doing this investigation upfront you'll have a better idea of what areas to scrutinize when you inspect the engine.

Pre-teardown is also a good time to thoroughly wash the bike and engine. There is almost nothing worse than working on a bike caked in dirt. It's hard on tools, makes a mess, and is just plain unpleasant. Do yourself a big favor and wash the bike before wrenching on it.

> **HOT TIP:** Prior to turning a wrench, carefully look over the service manual scanning through all the applicable procedures and subsystems. If I'm working on an unfamiliar model, I find it is helpful to jot down a rough outline of the disassembly sequence. This saves me time in the long run as I don't have to rely as heavily on the service manual or continually flip through various sections. Another option is to use post-it notes to bookmark each relevant section in the manual. Mark the post-it notes with numbers or headings so you know where to turn to next.

Teardown

The teardown process involves all steps necessary to get the engine completely apart. From removing the engine from the frame, to pulling covers, to splitting the crankcases. This isn't a time to go willy-nilly taking parts off left and right. Taking the engine apart should be done methodically and carefully. Parts and hardware should be attentively and systematically stored eliminating any possibility of reassembly blunders. If there are any areas which are unclear in the service manual photographs should be taken so you have a better understanding of how the parts go together. During the teardown some inspections will also be made in situ to parts like the cylinder head to check for any signs of leaks.

The exact order of how the engine should be torn down after it is out of the chassis is not set in stone. In fact, it depends a lot on what the service manual suggests. Each manufacturer has their preferred way to instruct the technician for each of its models. You may find that some service manuals suggest you start by taking the top end apart, then removing the engine covers, and finally splitting the crankcases. The alternative route is to remove the covers first, then the top end, and lastly splitting the crankcases.

I want to point out that the initial teardown should not consist of disassembling every single little piece of the engine. It should only consist of taking enough parts off the engine to split the crankcases. If the power valves, transmission shafts, clutch, and other subassemblies with small parts and lots of detail were disassembled at the same time it would make for a mess of parts to keep track of. Care could be taken to do it this way, but even the slightest bump of a bench could send some of these small parts careening. In addition to the challenges of keeping the parts organized, it would be a mental challenge to keep track of how they all went together. The much easier way to tackle the entire engine is to set the big subassemblies aside and wait to disassemble them until you are ready to inspect and assemble.

Inspection

The inspection process is your opportunity to act out your childhood dreams of being Sherlock Holmes. Every inch of the engine should be scrutinized. This will involve a combination of visual inspections as well as measurement of specific parts to ensure everything is still in top shape. If the reason the engine is apart is because it failed, the reason of the failure should be uncovered during the inspection process.

Disassembly and the inspection process overlap in a couple of ways. First, as the engine is being disassembled there are a few points where it makes sense to inspect during the teardown. Second, since some of the subassemblies which were removed from the engine haven't been disassembled yet they will require disassembly prior to inspection.

Before inspection can begin, all the parts will need to be cleaned. This will ensure expensive measurement tools won't be damaged from any dirt, oil, or debris. It will also help make sure the measurements taken are as accurate as possible. It usually works best to clean the large subassemblies first, then to disassemble them. Once disassembled, the individual parts can be cleaned one last time before inspecting, measuring, and reassembling.

Patience and a keen eye to detail are of the utmost importance when it comes to inspection. While it may be tempting to skip some inspections or rush through the process, I can't stress enough the importance of being thorough when building an engine. My tendencies are borderline obsessive compulsive. I'm well aware that I probably inspect and measure more components than most, however, on more than one occasion I have found new parts that have had flaws which could have compromised the build. Personally, I don't understand the logic in spending over $1000 for new parts when building an engine and not inspecting as many of the components as you can. It only takes one overlooked part to turn that $1000 plus of parts into scrap metal. The additional time it takes to carry out measurement and inspection work is negligible when considering how long a well built engine will last and the consequences of skipping an important inspection.

Assembly

Assembly of the engine should be a breeze. Most of the leg work has been done in prior stages in preparation for the assembly stage. All the parts have already been cleaned, everything has been inspected, and all the subsystems have been built up with new or refurbished parts, where applicable. All that is left is to take the larger subassemblies and assemble them into an engine!

For the most part assembly is done in the reverse order of disassembly. Again, the service manual will be your best friend for advising on the right order of assembly. Time and care should be taken to follow specific assembly instructions. Each bolt within the engine will have a specific torque it should be tightened to, some fasteners will require a thread-locking agent or other lubricant, specific parts will require lubrication, and correct alignment of certain components will be critical. While some of these details may seem nit-picky, they are all extremely critical for a high quality build.

Along with the outlined steps, race engines will get further special treatment. For optimum performance many small details must be scrutinized. Tasks such as how to set port timing correctly, check squish clearance, and adjust the compression ratio will all be covered comprehensively.

CH 12   ENGINE TEARDOWN

Now that we've gone through an overview of a build, it's time to dive into the intricate details. In this chapter and the following two chapters on Inspection and Final Assembly, all photos and key points come from three engines. A Yamaha YZ250 engine is featured extensively, while a KTM 380 EXC and Kawasaki KX500 engine are used to show technical variation. Between these three builds all the applicable details, techniques, and variation in engine design for modern two-stroke dirt bike engines are covered. After reading these chapters, you will have a solid understanding of all aspects of the engine and feel confident tearing into it.

One of the most challenging parts of writing this book was determining the layout of the next few chapters. A lot of information will be presented and could be organized in a number of ways. What I feel makes the most sense is to present this information chronologically as the build progresses. This way, if you are using this book in conjunction with a service, manual you won't have to flip through chapters to read up on a technique or inspection detail. Major techniques and learning points found throughout this book can easily be referenced by finding the applicable topic in the table of contents. In some instances, techniques will be used more than once. A detailed explanation will be given the first time the applicable Technical Takeaway is presented. After the first mention of the technique, subsequent mentioning will only be summarized.

Removing the Engine From the Frame

Once any pre-teardown diagnostic work has been completed, the bike has been washed, you've looked over the service manual to familiarize yourself with the steps and processes involved, it is now time to get the engine out of the frame. I'm only going to give a brief outline of these steps and present a few helpful tips on engine removal. I believe the service manuals do a great job illustrating what must be removed in order to get the engine out and there are no truly challenging aspects when it comes to engine removal.

Start by draining both the coolant and gearbox oil. Draining the fluids is necessary no matter what and by draining them first you won't have to stop midway through the process. Plus you won't have to worry about moving tools or parts from the lift and clearing a spot for the drain pans.

Signs of trouble ahead can be observed in both the coolant and gearbox oil as they drain. If large metal particles or chunks come out as the oil drains, you can be certain major problems await. Since the clutch deposits aluminum particles into the oil as it is used, determining the origination of smaller particles coming from places other than the clutch is difficult.

Discolored coolant or particles, which drain out with the coolant, are signs that the coolant has broken down. Parts of the cooling system may have also started to corrode. Dark specks in the coolant are indicative of combustion byproducts from a head gasket leak.

Once all the fluids have been drained, be sure to temporarily reinstall the drain plugs. This is so that the engine doesn't leak any remaining oil or coolant as you remove the engine from the frame and bring it over to your workbench. Now that fluids have been drained, disassembly work can begin. Begin removing the necessary parts from the bike so that the engine can be taken out. The following parts in approximately the order listed will need to be removed from the bike in order to get the engine out.

1. **Seat**
2. **Fuel tank and radiator shrouds**
3. **Side covers**
4. **Muffler and exhaust pipe**
5. **Rear subframe**
6. **Radiators**
7. **Engine guards**
8. **Throttle body or carburetor**
9. **Ignition coil**
10. **Shift pedal**
11. **Engine sprocket**
12. **Kick start pedal**
13. **Clutch cable from engine**
14. **Brake pedal**
15. **Engine mounts**
16. **Swingarm pivot bolt**
17. **Engine out!**

Part Storage

As you remove components from the bike, make sure you carefully keep track of the associated hardware that goes with each part. Develop a system in which you are comfortable for keeping track of parts and hardware. As long as you are able to remember where each fastener goes when it comes time to reassemble, there isn't a specific right or wrong way to keep track of hardware. A few options that work well include: using plastic bags to batch hardware with parts, using several small bins to store hardware next to parts, using tape to secure fasteners in their mating parts so they can't come out, and poking fasteners through cardboard so that the fasteners can be secured in the approximate pattern they are assembled in. The cardboard storage method works especially well for keeping track of bolt orientations on engine covers.

Don't Lose Your Settings

Parts that are set based on rider preference, such as the shift lever and brake lever positions, should be marked before being disassembled. This way you won't be left wondering what orientation they were in before you took them off. To mark the position of the shift pedal use a marker to draw an alignment mark across the end of the shaft on to the pedal. A marker will be less confusing than a scribed line in case of a future change. Just make sure you don't rub the mark away when cleaning the parts!

Depending on the model, the brake pedal may or may not have to be adjusted for removal. Either make a mark on the adjustment shaft to note the original position or take a measurement which you can refer back to later when reinstalling. The kickstart pedal alignment is less critical and usually can only be installed in one or two positions before it will interfere with another part, but mark it anyway.

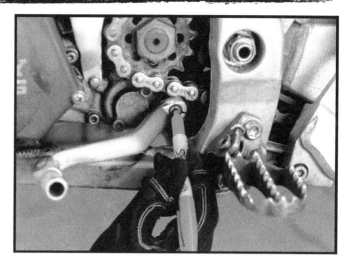

> **HOT TIP:** Pay special attention to the length of fasteners used for each part and where they go. Reinstalling a fastener which is too short for its hole and doesn't have adequate thread engagement can easily strip the threaded hole when torqued. If a part utilizes several bolt lengths, make sure this is noted in some way, whether it be the way the part is stored or writing it down in a notebook.

Plug the Engine

Once the exhaust pipe and throttle body/carburetor have been removed, insert clean rags into the intake manifold and exhaust port. This will keep dirt, tools, and other parts from falling into the engine. This is a good habit to get into especially when servicing the top end.

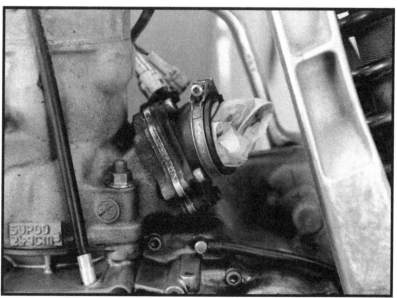

TECHNICAL TAKEAWAY
Be Gentle On Fasteners
Very rarely should a bolt require a lot of pounding in order for it to be removed. In most cases, such as with engine hangers, other bolts which secure the assembly together can be loosened prior to removing the "stuck" bolt.

Once all fasteners have been loosened, the engine itself, or part in question, can be picked up or moved slightly to help better align the holes and take stress off the problematic bolt so that it can be easily slid out.

When resorting to pounding as a last resort, be extremely careful not to damage the threads on the bolt. Don't pound the bolt directly with a hammer, instead use a punch which can be centered on the end of the bolt. That way the threads won't be rounded over or damaged as force is applied. In some instances, a nut can be threaded part way onto the bolt. Then the nut can be tapped on. Just ensure the nut has adequate thread engagement so that the threads aren't damaged.

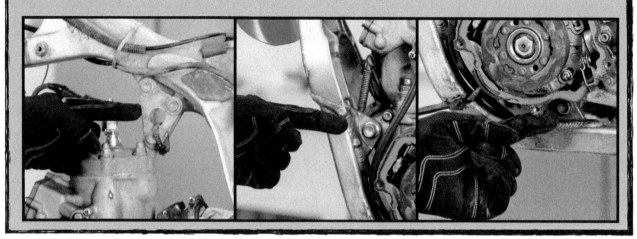

Removing the Swingarm Pivot Bolt

The swingarm pivot bolt can be tricky to remove, especially by yourself. With proper preparation and a solid set up, the odds of a swift removal are in your favor. In order for the pivot bolt to come out with minimal force three things must be properly supported: the frame, engine, and swingarm. By supporting these three components the likelihood that their corresponding pivot bolt holes will stay in alignment with one another as the pivot bolt is removed is much higher.

Start by using a center stand to support the frame. This will set the engine at a pretty workable height for lifting it out of the frame. Lift up on the front of the engine and slide a few wooden blocks under the front of it.

Block the rear wheel up so that the block supports the wheel and swingarm. There is no need to raise the wheel any higher than where it sits with the shock extended. The blocks simply allow some of the load to be taken off the pivot bolt.

Use an appropriately sized punch, rod, or crappy socket and extension to push on the end of the pivot bolt. Pivot bolts which have been properly greased and looked after shouldn't require more than a few gentle taps with a hammer to remove. Pivot bolts which have rusted will require more persuasion to set free.

Removing the Engine From the Frame

Once the pivot bolt is free, it is time to lift the engine out. It is a good idea to take one last look around the engine and make sure all the wires have been disconnected and there aren't any dangling cables which can interfere with removal. Holding onto a heavy engine only to realize you don't have any hands left to remove the wire you forgot to disconnect isn't a fun predicament to be in!

If you haven't already done so, prep your work area where the engine will be moved to. Clear a spot so that you can set the engine down once you have it out of the frame. Disassembling an engine is an oily affair, so take the necessary precautions to protect your work surfaces.

The service manual will state which side the engine should be removed from and have specific instructions for getting the engine out. Whether stated or not, engine removal will get exponentially easier if the swingarm is pulled back out of position. This allows more room to move the engine around and tilt it in order to get it out.

Take your time getting the engine out. Figuring out the necessary steps and positions the engine must be maneuvered into is as much a puzzle as it is a matter of strength. Enlist the help of an unsuspecting friend if the engine weight is more than you are comfortable lifting. The last thing anyone wants is to drop an engine on the ground, or worse their foot!

Once out, set the engine on your workbench. If you have room to store the bike as-is that's great. If not, realign the swingarm pivot bolt and slide it back through the frame so the bike can be easily rolled. Make sure none of the spacers or seals come out as you slide the pivot bolt back through.

Engine Disassembly

Now that the engine is fully exposed on the workbench, take this moment to wipe the engine down before opening it up. Even though all the parts will be cleaned eventually, there is no reason to let excess dirt get into the engine or remain around the workbench. Use a combination of parts cleaner, brushes, and rags to remove any dirt that remains on the engine. The engine externals don't have to be spotless, just make sure any loose dirt on the externals is removed so that it can't fall into the engine when parts are removed.

TECHNICAL TAKEAWAY

A Note On Working With Part Cleaners and Other Harsh Chemicals

Don't forget to take the necessary precautions when working with harsh chemicals, such as parts cleaners, to keep your eyes and skin safe. When using sprayed chemicals or working with compressed air, wearing a pair of safety glasses is cheap insurance in keeping your eyes safe and happy. Some of the chemicals used in various cleaners can have lasting negative effects if they get into your eyes. I personally hate wearing safety glasses, but would much rather deal with the discomfort than lose my vision and no longer be able to ride a bike.

Along with your eyes, chemicals can be absorbed through your skin. Over time and with repeated exposure these chemicals can lead to serious health problems. When cleaning parts or working in oily conditions, wearing chemical resistant gloves is a safe move. Simple throw away nitrile examination gloves or more durable mechanic's gloves are good options for preventing unnecessary skin exposure to harsh chemicals.

TOP END DISASSEMBLY

Before we get into taking the top end apart, I want to cover a technical takeaway that will be applicable throughout the rest of the book.

TECHNICAL TAKEAWAY

Criss-Cross Patterns, Tightening Sequences, and Incremental Steps

In order to understand the importance of criss-cross patterns, tightening sequences, and incremental steps I want to explain how a bolted joint works. As a bolt is tightened to secure a pair of parts, the bolt will stretch a very small amount. The stretch in the bolt creates tension or preload in the joint, which is the force that keeps the joint together. The amount of preload created is dependent on bolt size, bolt material, the torque applied, and the friction between the threads. There are additional variables, however, a discussion on bolt engineering would be very long and not all that exciting! As long as you understand the basics for engine building you can begin to appreciate the importance of correctly tightening fasteners.

As you are well aware an engine consists of many parts fastened together. What you may not consider as much is that the majority of these parts are fastened by more than one fastener. This means that how much you tighten/preload one fastener will have an effect on the surrounding fasteners. This interaction between the fasteners begins to shed light on why tightening sequences are so important.

The evenness of the preload across the bolts securing a part can affect part life. Warpage can occur in parts which are improperly tightened, ultimately rendering the part useless. A prime example of a part that can warp is the cylinder. If the nuts are unevenly tightened over time the cylinder can become permanently distorted. Gasket sealing problems can also occur from improper preloading of bolts across a part. In order for a gasket to seal it must be evenly compressed. If one area of a gasket is highly compressed and tensioned, while another area is not, the gasket can easily leak through the low tensioned area.

Criss-Cross Patterns

Criss-cross patterns are called upon when tightening or loosening parts with a simple square pattern or circular bolt pattern. These basic patterns have been around for a long time and are a proven method for evenly distributing clamping load across a part. Most cylinder heads and cylinders will utilize this type of clamping pattern.

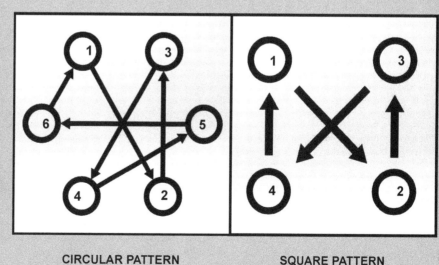

CIRCULAR PATTERN   SQUARE PATTERN

Tightening Sequences

For more complex clamped joints, such as those found on the crankcases, the manufacturer will usually identify a specific sequence for tightening and loosening the fasteners. This sequence is based on testing and the past experiences of the manufacturer.

Incremental Steps

Highly torqued bolts or nuts, such as those found at the cylinder base, are almost always tightened and loosened in incremental steps. An incremental tightening sequence consists of torquing all the fasteners to a specific torque value, then increasing the torque and tightening again, and finally arriving at the final torque value. This sequence is typically performed in two to three steps.

Reed Valve Removal

If the engine is equipped with a cylinder or crankcase reed valve it can be removed at this time. Remove the bolts securing the intake manifold and reed valve. Then remove the manifold, valve, gasket, and any spacer plates.

Power Valve Housing Removal

If the engine you're working on has a power valve, it will likely feature a small housing that must be removed in order to gain access to the power valve mechanism. Follow the procedures outlined for your model and remove the housing. Most housings simply consist of the housing, a pair of bolts, a gasket, and a molded rubber seal.

HOT TIP: When torquing bolts in steps, the change in torque between the steps must be large enough to induce bolt movement. For example, if a bolt was torqued to 35Nm at the first step and the second step was 38Nm, this would not be enough of a change to make the bolt move at the second step. The torque wrench would not overcome the friction of the stationary bolt and would hit 38Nm before the bolt even moves. As a rule of thumb, incremental changes should be no less than 5Nm and if possible should be greater.

Power Valve Linkage Removal

Each manufacturer uses a slightly different linkage system to connect the power valve assembly in the cylinder to the power valve governor located inside the right cover. For this reason, it's important to reference your service manual for specific removal instructions.

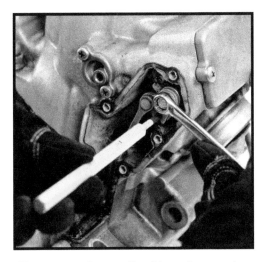

For example, on the Yamaha engine I'm working on, a pin or punch is used to secure the linkage in place while removing the bolt connecting the linkage to the cylinder.

On this KTM a small wire clip must be removed before pulling the ball joint apart.

TECHNICAL TAKEAWAY

Removing Dowel Pinned Parts

Parts which incorporate dowel pins are designed to fit together in a certain way. The dowel pins are used to precisely align the parts so that their features function properly together. The crankcases, cylinder, and engine covers are all examples of parts you will encounter which utilize dowel pins for correct alignment.

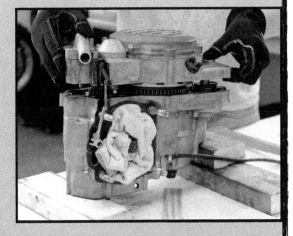

When removing pinned parts, it is important to do so in the correct way for a handful of reasons. The dowel pin hole bores and pins utilize a very tight fit. In order to preserve the tight fit, care must be taken when removing the parts. The component being removed should be pulled up and away squarely from its mating part. As little back and forth rocking as possible should be used to free the parts. Rocking the parts back and forth can cause the dowel pin bores to enlarge, compromising the fit between the dowel pin and pin hole. Pulling the part away squarely is also important, as the dowel pins will bind in their respective bores if removed cock eyed. If the parts are severely cock eyed, the dowel pins can mar the pin bores making the fit very tight the next time around.

Whenever possible, try to remove dowel pins by hand. If stuck, use a needle nose pliers to grasp one wall of the dowel pin and pull straight up. For dowel pins in locations where studs pass through the center, carefully grasp the outer diameter of the pin with a pliers and gently pull the pin up.

RIGHT WAY   WRONG WAY

HOT TIP: For stuck dowel pins that are especially stubborn, heat can be used sparingly. Use a torch to warm the surrounding metal so that it will expand. Then carefully attempt to work the pin out. If a pin is marred upon removal, but still round, a small file can be used to smooth imperfections.

Cylinder Head Removal

Adhere to any loosening patterns or steps outlined in the service manual, then loosen the nuts or bolts securing the head to the cylinder. After the nuts have been loosened, carefully remove the head.

Be sure to keep track of any dowel pins that were used to locate the head to the cylinder.

Head O-Ring/Gasket Inspection

Once the head has been removed, take this opportunity to inspect the cylinder head O-rings or gasket and their corresponding mating surfaces. If the engine you're working on was burning coolant prior to disassembly, it may be possible to see the leak path from the cylinder to the water jacket. Inspect the O-rings for tears. Check both sides of the gasket carefully for signs of leak paths. The leak paths will usually look similar to snail trails. Carbon deposits may also be left around the leak. If a leak path has been identified, look for reasons the leak may have started so the problem can be noted and remedied before reassembly. A few common reasons a cylinder head joint will leak include:

1. **The cylinder head bolts were improperly tensioned.**

2. **The o-rings were not seated correctly in their grooves during assembly.**

3. **Burrs left from the gasket manufacturing process can prevent the gasket from sitting completely flat.**

4. **Either the cylinder head or cylinder mating surfaces are damaged. Damage may include nicks, deep scratches, and other imperfections which keep the parts from sitting flat.**

5. **Old gasket material was left on the head from the previous build, making it impossible for the new gasket to sit correctly.**

6. **Either the cylinder head or the cylinder has warped, making even tension between the two parts impossible.**

7. **An old head gasket or O-rings were reused, instead of being replaced with new ones.**

8. **The cylinder head studs have been installed backwards. This is possible if the stud features two sets of threads with different lengths of threads.**

9. **The cylinder head studs are not fully seated in the cylinder.**

Cylinder Removal

Typically, the cylinder is fastened by four large studs and nuts. The nuts are highly torqued and should be incrementally loosened in a criss-cross pattern, unless the service manual says otherwise. This way tension will be relieved evenly and gradually from the cylinder and crankcase mating surfaces. The cylinder will likely be a very tight fit to the crankcase due to the dowel pins used for positioning the parts. The base gasket may also stick to the cylinder and crankcase, making it harder to separate the parts. Once the nuts have been removed, start by trying to free the parts by hand. If the cylinder won't free itself, it may be necessary to gently tap evenly around the sides of it with a rubber or plastic mallet to persuade it to let go.

Use both hands to work the cylinder straight up away from the dowel pins. Once the cylinder is free of the dowel pins, continue working it upwards.

As the cylinder comes up, the rings will start to show themselves at the sides of the skirt. At this point, position one hand under the piston so that the piston/rod assembly won't slam into the side of the crankcase as the piston becomes free from the cylinder. Gently set the piston assembly to rest against the front or rear of the crankcase, whichever side gravity favors.

HOT TIP: When working on engines suspect of piston, piston ring, or cylinder problems take this opportunity to carefully look over the condition of the piston rings. Note the rings' orientations, check to see if the compression ring(s) are stuck, and look for abnormal wear on the ring faces.

Piston Removal

In order to free the piston from the rod, one of the circlips retaining the wrist pin will need to be removed. Either side will work, so determine which side you'll be more comfortable working from and prepare accordingly.

The easiest way to remove a piston circlip is to use a sharp sturdy pick and small needle nose pliers. The best way to illustrate this is through a series of pictures and explanations on circlip removal.

Insert the pick into the dimple on the piston with your dominant hand so that the pick can be positioned and used to pry the circlip out. Work the circlip out far enough with the pick so that the pliers can be used to grab onto the circlip. Be careful not to scratch the exposed end of the pin bore with the pick.

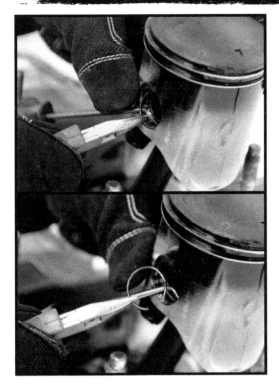

Once the pick has created enough space around the circlip, use your thumb on your non dominant hand to hold the pick in place. Then grab the needle nose pliers with your free hand, grip the circlip, and carefully remove the circlip from the piston.

Use your non dominant hand to support the piston assembly. If TDC isn't the most comfortable position, rotate the crank until you feel comfortable.

Use your middle finger on your supporting hand to press the wrist pin against the circlip. Keeping pressure on the circlip will help to remove it and prevent the piston pin bore from getting scratched by the pick. Scratches on the pin bore can make the pin more difficult to remove and are a huge no-no when assembling a new piston.

HOT TIP: When replacing pistons during a top end rebuild, use rags to cover the crankshaft and crankcase cavity. This way should any circlips go flying they can't end up in the engine.

With the circlip removed, the wrist pin can now be removed. Wrist pins can come out easily or they can take some force. The way the engine was designed has a big impact on how tight or loose the wrist pin is to the piston pin bore, along with how much the piston pin bore has worn, and if the pin bore was previously scratched during installation or removal of the wrist pin. Scratches within the piston pin bore create high spots which cause the wrist pin to become very tight in the bore, making it much harder to remove the wrist pin. This is why I can't stress enough not to scratch the pin bore when working with the pick to remove the circlip.

Start by trying to push the wrist pin out by hand. Use a socket approximately the same size diameter as the pin and an extension to push against the wrist pin. Use one hand to support the rod and piston assembly. If this is all it takes, awesome! If not, you may have to call in the plastic hammer.

If you must resort to tapping with a plastic hammer to get the wrist pin out, I want to stress the importance of supporting the top of the rod with your hand. As the wrist pin is tapped on, lateral forces will be applied to the rod and crank bearings. Crank and rod bearings are best suited for axial loads (like those generated from the reciprocating motion of the piston and rotation of the crankshaft) and minimizing lateral forces on them is considered good practice. To do this, hold the top of the rod and piston assembly firmly so that your hand absorbs some of the blow from the hammer.

Alternatively, if the piston pin is truly stuck, fabricate a pin puller which can be used to extract the pin. This can be created in a similar way as a crankshaft puller out of hardware store parts. Shown below is a simple example consisting of a bolt, socket, and a nut.

I realize if the crank assembly and bearings are going to be replaced this may seem unnecessary, but consider it good practice for when you are only rebuilding the top end of the engine.

Once the piston is free the base gasket can easily be removed. If the cylinder dowel pins stayed in the case, remove them at this time. Set the piston assembly, gasket, dowel pins, and cylinder aside. Wrap rags around the rod to keep it from flopping back and forth as you work on the rest of the engine. Alternatively, if the engine utilizes studs to secure the cylinder and cylinder head, rubber bands can be wrapped diagonally across the studs and around the rod to keep it centered.

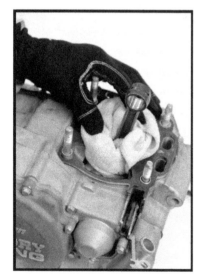

If the rod is left to flop back and forth, after a few hard slaps the impact from the rod into the case can cause the edge in which it slams into to raise up. This can create a leak path between the crankcase and cylinder if not addressed. If the base gasket was leaking previously, this is a common culprit and good spot to look for damage.

Stator Cover, Flywheel, and Stator Removal

Once the top end has been disassembled, unless otherwise specified by the service manual, it doesn't make much difference whether the left or right side of the engine is opened up first. I believe it makes the most sense to remove the stator cover (if not already removed when the clutch cable was disconnected), flywheel, and stator first. This way the stator wires won't get in the way as the rest of the engine is disassembled.

Depending on the design of the engine, the stator will either be housed behind the flywheel and mounted on the crankcase or in front of the flywheel and mounted on the cover. Engines utilizing stators mounted on the crankcase usually feature slotted stator plates that allow for a few degrees of ignition timing adjustment. This is accomplished simply by loosening the mounting screws and rotating the plate clockwise or counterclockwise. Documenting the plate's position is important and will be detailed shortly.

For engines featuring stators mounted on the engine cover, removal can be more challenging. The stator cover will utilize a couple of dowel pins for positioning and will stay right where it's at due to the magnetic pull from the magnets in the flywheel. Cracking the cover open by hand is usually difficult, but should be attempted first prior to using more force. Once the bolts have been removed, grip firmly on the cover and try to pull it straight off.

If the cover won't budge, locate the cast tabs on the cover. These tabs are usually positioned close to opposite one another. During the machining process of the cover, the tabs served as clamping tabs for machine work and now can be tapped against with a punch to help free the cover. Use an appropriately sized punch in combination with a plastic hammer to gently tap on the cover to start working it off. Remember to tap evenly back and forth between the two tabs so the cover is worked off uniformly ensuring the dowel pins don't bind. Once an ⅛ to ¼" (3 - 6mm) gap has formed between the stator cover and crankcase the cover should be able to be pulled off by hand.

Flywheel Removal - Removing the Nut

In order to remove the flywheel, the nut will need to be removed. A strap wrench or flywheel holding tool is essential to performing this task properly. You may be thinking, but wait, surely I could just open up the right side and lock the crank gear in place? This is a fair thought, however, by doing this a twisting force would be exerted across the crankshaft. Once force is applied to the flywheel nut by the wrench, the entire crank half would try to twist around the crankpin. This is the last thing you want to happen on a pressed together crankshaft, because misalignment between the crank halves can occur. The resulting misalignment would cause the engine to vibrate excessively and prematurely wear out crank and rod bearings.

So back to flywheel holding methods it is. There are three ways of strap wrenching that may work for this application. Pictures are by far the easiest way to illustrate the various strapping orientations. Whether or not a strap wrench will be permissible to use will be entirely up to the physical geometry of the engine. In some cases, it won't be possible to get the strap wrench around the flywheel because the flywheel is recessed inside the crankcase.

TWISTING FORCE AROUND CRANK PIN

1. Simple Grab

I don't know if this hold would make me a laughingstock in front of a bunch of plumbers but it has worked well for me in the past. Simply slide the strap around the flywheel and align the tip of the wrench with the elevated timing boss. By biting into the side of the timing boss with the tip of the wrench the flywheel will be less likely to move. The underlying strap will protect the boss from any damage.

2. Thin Walled Grab

As the name implies, the thin walled grab is commonly used on thin wall pipe, which is likely to distort if too much pressure is applied to the wall of the pipe. The same technique can be used to align the tip of the strap wrench with the side of the timing boss, which will yield better bite.

3. Thick Walled Grab

The thick walled grab is the last resort hold. I've always found the thin walled grab to work when flywheels nuts are good and tight, however, I want to present the thick walled grab as one last option. Use this hold cautiously though so you don't end up denting the flywheel.

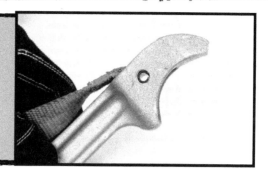

If geometry constraints make using a strap wrench impractical, two types of specialized flywheel holding tools should be considered. For applications where the flywheel protrudes out beyond the crankcase, a pulley clamp style holder can be utilized.

When the flywheel is flush with, or recessed, into the crankcase a pin style flywheel holder is the best option.

PULLEY STYLE CLAMP HOLDER

PIN STYLE FLYWHEEL HOLDER

Flywheel Removal - Pulling the Flywheel

Once the nut has been removed, the flywheel still won't come off on its own since a taper fit is utilized between the flywheel and crankshaft. In order to remove the flywheel, a flywheel puller will need to be used. The flywheel puller is basically a glorified nut/ bolt combo that can be threaded onto the flywheel and then tightened so the flywheel will pop off. Pullers can be bought or, if you are equipped with the right tools, can be made.

Regardless of which route you go, the important thing is to ensure the threads are not damaged during removal. A protective end cap is often included with the puller to eliminate this risk.

FLYWHEEL PULLER

Make sure the flywheel bolt is backed all the way
out so the puller can be threaded fully onto the
flywheel. Once the puller is on, hold the flywheel
in place with your hand and tighten down the
flywheel puller bolt. The bolt will tighten down
onto the end of the crankshaft and will pop the
flywheel off in no time.

Depending on the particular engine you are working on, you may encounter a few different things
behind the flywheel. Part of the engine's counter balance system (if equipped) and the clutch
actuation arm may be housed in the left side of the engine. In most cases, to remove a balance shaft
which spans through the right and left halves of the crankcase, the right side of the engine will have to
be disassembled first before the shaft can be removed. While this isn't applicable on the YZ250 being
documented, the balance shaft will be covered in detail once disassembly of the right side is
underway.

Stator Removal - Housed Behind Flywheel

Prior to loosening the screws securing the stator, carefully mark or note the alignment of the stator
plate to the crankcase. This will ensure that the ignition timing is kept the same once the plate is
reinstalled.

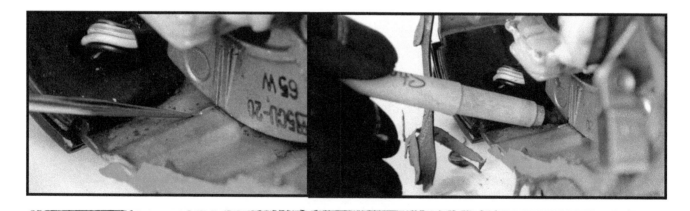

If you believe ignition timing is suspect, don't worry, we'll go through the procedure for checking timing in Chapter 14 during final assembly.

Once the stator plate's position has been documented, proceed to loosen the screws securing it. Next, carefully remove the stator plate.

Stator Removal - Housed in the Cover

If you have an engine that has the stator housed in the left cover, don't feel as if I've forgotten about you. You simply don't have as much work to do. Unless the stator plate features adjustable timing and you feel the timing is suspect, you can simply leave the stator secured to the cover.

RIGHT COVER, CLUTCH, PRIMARY GEAR, BALANCE SHAFT, KICK START, & POWER VALVE MECHANISM REMOVAL

Now that the left side of the engine has been disassembled, our attention can be turned to the right side. The right cover must be removed first. To do so, loosen the cover bolts in the pattern specified in the service manual. If no pattern is specified use a criss-cross like pattern to remove the bolts so tension is relieved evenly.

It is very common for manufacturers to double up bolt functions on the right cover, so make sure you've got all the bolts removed before trying to take the cover off. Usually the clutch cover and water pump cover will feature one or two bolts which are long and thread down into the crankcase.

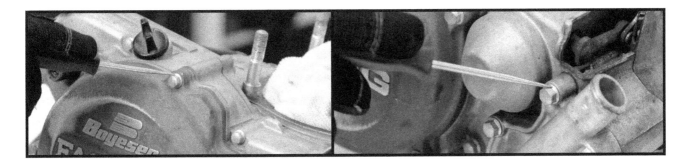

Make sure you have a good method for keeping track of the various bolt lengths of the cover bolts as well. This is a good spot to utilize the cardboard template method as previously described.

In order to easily remove the cover, there are usually four-points of alignment which are important when pulling the cover off. First, two dowel pins are used to locate the cover, then there is the engagement between water pump shaft and crankcase, and finally the kick start shaft must also be kept square upon removal.

THE FOUR ALIGNMENT POINTS

Begin by grasping the cover at both ends and trying to pull the cover away. The gasket may cause the cover to stick, making it harder to get the cover started on its way off.

If the cover won't budge there will be a couple of tabs on the cover which can be lightly tapped against with a punch and hammer. Aim to get a ⅛ - ¼" (3 - 6mm) gap started evenly around the cover.

Once the gap has formed proceed to pull the cover off the rest of the way by hand.

The clutch will be removed first, but before doing so the primary gear bolt and, if applicable, the balance shaft nut should be loosened. This will require both sets of gears to be locked together, one set at a time.

Locking Gears

Gears are made of hardened steel, this means that although they are strong they are also brittle. Usually the contact area between the gear teeth when the gears mesh is more than sufficient to withstand heavy loading so the teeth rarely break or chip during use. When an object is inserted between the gear teeth to lock them in place, the object used has an impact on how susceptible the teeth are to chipping or breaking off.

The hardness of the object and shape of the object are both important to consider before sticking it between the gear teeth. For example, using a screwdriver is one of the worst tools to put between the gear teeth, because it is similar in hardness to the teeth and its profile does not match that of the gear teeth. This can lead to point loading of the teeth and cause the teeth to chip or break off if enough load is applied.

Special gear holding tools made from steel or aluminum which match the profile of the gear teeth are available, however, I don't tend to rely on them as there is an option that makes more cents (pun intended).

Nickels and pennies make good gear holding tools for a handful of reasons. First, their thicknesses allow them to fit nicely between gear teeth. Second, the material composition of both nickels and pennies is softer than that of the gear teeth. Nickels are comprised of about 75% copper and 25% nickel, while pennies are about 95% zinc and 5% copper. The softer composition of the coins is important because it allows them to deform to the shape of the gear teeth as load is applied. As the coins deform and take the shape of the tooth profile, the load is distributed across the tooth instead of just at one point. This helps to ensure that no gear teeth are broken off or damaged when the gears are locked together in order to facilitate the removal of other parts.

Just make sure that once you are done using the coins that you give them a hard whack with a hammer to flatten them back to vending machine condition!

Loosening the Balance Shaft Nut

To loosen the balance shaft nut, insert a penny or nickel between the balance shaft gears to lock them in position. Then use the appropriate tool to loosen the gear.

Loosening the Primary Drive Gear Fastener

The primary gear fastener should be loosened by locking out the primary drive and the clutch driven gear. On engines with balance shafts, one could lock out the balance gears, however, I would strongly advise against this. Since the primary gear bolt is usually highly torqued and the balance shaft gears are usually thinner than the primary drive gear, this doesn't make for a favorable combination. In order to lock out the gear, insert a coin between the primary gear and clutch gear then loosen the primary gear bolt. Once loose, leave the bolt and gear in place for the time being. By loosening the bolt now, the clutch basket won't have to be temporarily reinstalled later on as most manuals call for. This essentially saves you a small step.

HOT TIP: Some engine's utilize a primary gear fastener which features left hand threads. Service manuals will specify this, but if you are in a hurry you can overlook this and spend a long time trying to loosen a bolt you are actually tightening. Don't ask me how I know...

Clutch Disassembly and Removal

Start by incrementally loosening the clutch pressure plate bolts in a criss-cross pattern. Loosening the bolts evenly and incrementally will help keep the pressure plate and bolts centered. As the bolts and springs are removed, check to see if the springs are marked with paint which can help identify the spring. While not done often, occasionally a manufacturer or aftermarket company will use two different sets of springs each with a different spring rate to apply the correct amount of pressure to the pressure plate. If two types of springs are used, it is important to note the pattern of springs and make sure they are installed in the same pattern as they were removed. Typically, if two sets of springs with different rates are used, the pattern will be of even distribution (most likely every other hole). Problems arise when the clutch is reassembled with disregard to spring rate and pattern, leaving the pressure plate with uneven pressure on it.

After the bolts and springs have been removed the pressure plate can come off. Oil usually keeps the pressure plate stuck in place, so lightly pry up on the edge of the plate with a screwdriver. Keep an eye out for the thrust bearing washer, which tends to stick to the back side of the pressure plate.

Pull the washer from the plate if it is stuck. Then remove the thrust bearing, bearing holder/lifter, and clutch pushrod. On some engines a small ball bearing will be used which is usually positioned between the bearing holder/lifter and pushrod. Keep an eye out for the small ball bearing as it can easily come out unexpectedly and go on a high speed excursion across the shop floor.

Once the push rod assembly has been removed, the clutch discs and friction plates can be pulled off the hub. The individual discs and plates which comprise the clutch pack are almost always identical to one another, however, it is a good idea to be observant when removing the clutch discs and plates.

Service manuals should clearly indicate any differences between the discs or plates which must be noted. In case they don't, the usual spot to find a disc or plate which is different from the rest is at the end of the stack. For clarification of what the "end" of the stack is, when removing, this would be the first disc and plate encountered.

When working with an engine I'm familiar with, the easiest way to get all the discs and plates off is to pull them off all at once. Then they can be set aside in the order and direction they came off. On unfamiliar engines, I like to remove the first couple discs and plates just to confirm they are all the same and then pull the entire stack off.

With the clutch pack out of the way, the clutch hub can be secured with a clutch hub pliers so it can be removed. First, there is usually a bent lock washer which needs to be flattened so the nut can be loosened. A screwdriver or a punch combined with a hammer will make quick work of the washer.

I want to stress the importance of using the right tool for the job here, as many good clutch hubs have been lost due to dodgy holding solutions. Wedging screwdrivers or pieces of metal between the clutch hub bolt bosses can best be described as playing Russian Roulette. Most clutch hubs are cast and the aluminum is fairly brittle, so applying a lateral load to the bosses is a bad idea. Locking the primary gear and clutch gear together, then jamming a screwdriver into the grooves on the clutch hub so that the screwdriver locks against the tangs in the basket is also a recipe for disaster.

Loosen the clutch hub nut. Then remove the nut, lock washer, clutch hub, clutch basket washer, clutch basket, clutch basket bearing, and sleeve.

With the clutch removed, the primary gear and, if equipped, the balance shaft gear and assembly can be removed. The order of operations here is not too critical and will depend largely on the specific engine.

Clutch Actuation Arm Removal

Many clutch actuation arms are retained by a bolt that features a pin machined into its end. Simply remove this bolt and then pull out the actuation arm from its bore.

Balance Shaft Removal

For engines equipped with a balance shaft which runs through both crankcases, pay special attention to the removal procedure outlined in the service manual. In many cases the balance shaft will have to be oriented a specific direction in order for it to be successfully removed.

Idle Gear Removal

Usually an idle gear must be used to allow the kick start to rotate the engine in the correct direction and create enough clearance between the kickstart and clutch. Normally the idle gear will either be allowed to float or be retained by a retaining ring. Most idle gears will be offset to one side or another, so pay special attention to the orientation of the gear to avoid any confusion later when reassembling.

Kick Start Shaft Removal

The kickstart shaft assembly is one of the easiest assemblies to remove. The end of the return spring is located in a hole in the right crankcase half. To relieve spring tension, simply pull the end of the spring out of the hole. A stopper plate will keep the kick start shaft from pulling straight out so the shaft will have to be rotated counter-clockwise before it can be removed.

External Shift Mechanism Removal

To start, pull the shift shaft out. There is a washer which almost always sticks to the side of the crankcase, so be sure to grab this before it gets misplaced, then install it back onto the shift shaft. There is also a collar which may or may not stick inside the slot on the end of the shaft arm, as seen below.

Remove the necessary hardware so that the ratchet plate and ratcheting mechanism can be removed. Exercise care and patience when removing this assembly as there are a lot of small parts and the pawls are spring loaded. It is best to try and use the ratchet plate to keep the pawls held in position as the parts are removed. If the assembly does come apart, it is not the end of the world and some pointers on reassembling them will come later.

The shift drum cam bolt will be removed next. Loosen the cam bolt first. Once loose, retain the spring loaded gear position lever so that it is not pushing against the shift drum cam. A screwdriver or punch works well to hold the lever out of the way. Remove the bolt and shift drum cam. A small dowel pin is used to locate the shift drum cam to the shift drum. Make sure to keep track of the dowel pin.

The gear position arm doesn't need to be removed for crankcase separation and it is rarely the cause of any problems, so letting it stay in the crankcase is easiest.

THE DOWEL PIN

Crankcase Separation

At this point all the external components of the engine should have been removed so it is time to separate the crankcase halves! Start by loosening the bolts which clamp the cases together. Follow any specific loosening sequences outlined by the service manual, or similar to the rest of the covers use a crisscross like pattern to release bolt preload evenly. The bolts used to secure the cases will be a few different lengths. Some bolts may even have sealing responsibilities and have copper washers on them. Be sure to keep track of where the bolts came from so they can be reinstalled back into their original locations.

If the clutch actuation arm was secured by a crankcase bolt and bracket, it should be removed at this time.

Pay close attention to the service manual for specific instructions on how to separate the crankcases. Each engine is designed slightly differently and there are several variables which need attention.

Keep in mind which side of the engine should be faced down. This is very important as gearbox shafts are generally much easier to remove/install in one orientation than another.

The fit between the crankshaft and crank bearings utilized by the manufacturer will also play a big part in the ease of disassembly.

While not common among two-stroke dirt bike engines, some crankshafts are designed to have a slight clearance between the crankshaft journals and bearings, allowing the crank to be easily removed and installed. In theory, crankcase separation is made easy this way as the only things to overcome may be sticky dowel pins and the crankcase gasket.

Conversely, and more commonly, many crankshaft journals have a slight interference fit with the crank bearings. This elevates the level of difficulty as the crankcases are essentially stuck together and must be pulled apart in order to be separated. Special tools and techniques must be used to separate the case halves correctly.

There are definite right and wrong ways to separate crankcases which I want to spend some time discussing. First, a few no brainer rules which apply regardless of the crankshaft/bearing fit used.

1. Never use screwdrivers to pry between crankcases. This is a great way to damage the gasket surfaces and end up with leaky crankcases.

2. Never use a metal hammer to tap directly on the crankcases. I think everyone can imagine what can happen when this is done. Instead, if any pounding is necessary, use soft rubber or plastic hammers and only tap in areas which look strong.

3. Avoid any solutions which involve localized heating of the cases as this can cause the cases to distort. The only time this may be absolutely necessary is when the dowel pins have rusted and seized in their bores. Otherwise there are better ways to facilitate separation and bearing removal.

The crankcases will use two dowel pins to locate the halves together, so it is important the halves are separated evenly so the pins don't bind. Once clear of the pins, the transmission shafts, shift drum, shift fork shafts, and crankshaft will have to be navigated as they all play a part in crankcase alignment as well.

Separation of Clearance Fit Crankshaft/Bearing Crankcases

This type of crankcase is not too difficult to separate. Start by trying to pull the cases apart by hand. If this fails use a rubber mallet to tap evenly around the case halves until a ¼" - ⅜" (6 - 10mm) gap forms.

Once the gap has formed block the crankcases up on wooden or plastic blocks, orienting the cases so the correct half faces up. Position your hands near the dowel pins and work the top half the rest of the way off. Turn the case half over and look for any washers originating from the gearbox shafts that have stuck to the bearings. Pull any washers off and install them back onto their respective shafts.

Separation of Interference Fit Crankshaft/Bearing Crankcases

Engine's which utilize an interference fit between the crankshaft journals and bearings will require a crankcase splitting tool to aid in separation. The splitter tool bolts to one of the crankcase halves and a center bolt is turned, which pulls the case half off the crankshaft journal.

In addition to the splitter tool, some manuals call for the use of a crankshaft jig. The jig is fit between the crank webs and helps to keep the crank pin and webs in alignment. While there is no harm in using the jig, it is not absolutely necessary during removal. I personally don't ever use one and think it is an unnecessary tool to own. The forces acting on the crankshaft as the case splitter pulls the case half are limited to the end of the crankshaft and there is no chance the crankshaft can come out of alignment.

Begin by using wooden or plastic blocks to support the crankcases so they can be oriented with the correct half face up. Avoid using any sort of metal blocks as they will scratch the cases.

Install the crankcases splitter into the case half. Aim to use bolt holes on the case that allow the splitter wings to be positioned equal distances from each other.

If necessary, assemble a combination of spacers so that the case splitter is positioned square to the crankshaft in order for the cases to be pulled straight up. Make sure the bolts used to secure the splitter in place have good thread engagement.

As a rule of thumb, good thread engagement is roughly equal to 1.5 times the diameter of the bolt. So for a 6mm bolt the minimum thread engagement would be 9mm. Thread engagement should rarely be a problem, however, it is definitely worth noting.

If there is any concern that the threads on the end of the crankshaft will get distorted when using the splitter consider either reinstalling the flywheel nut or, if one was supplied, using the protective cap that came with the flywheel puller.

Install the case splitter bolt and snug it up against the crankshaft. Slowly turn the bolt and start to pull. Look for gaps which start to form between the case halves. In a perfect world the gap will be uniform all the way around, but this seldom happens. Encourage gap uniformity by pulling by hand or using a rubber mallet to tap against the cases.

Continue to tighten the splitter bolt until the case half is completely separated from the crankshaft. The crank bearing may or may not come out with the crankcase.

Carefully lift the case half away. Turn the case half over and look for any washers originating from the gearbox shafts that have stuck to the bearings. Pull any washers off and install them back onto their respective shafts. Remove the case splitter from the case and set it aside.

Removing the Shift Fork, Shift Fork Shafts, Shift Drum, and Transmission Shafts

The physical task of removing the components housed within the crankcases is not too challenging, but keeping track of all the specific parts and their orientations is important.

Most gearboxes can be dismantled sequentially, however, there are a few instances where the entire assembly must be removed at once. In both cases components and procedures leading up to removal are similar, however, the actual removal procedure for taking all the parts out at once is much more difficult.

Sequential Gearbox Removal

To remove the gearbox the shift fork shafts will need to be removed first. Pull the front and rear selector shafts out.

Depending on the engine either the shift drum or shift forks will need to be removed next. Proceed to tackle whichever necessary. Pay special attention to the orientation of the shift forks. Most manuals have gotten much better about specifying orientation of the forks, but it is a good idea to note any

markings which can be used later to orient the forks. If no markings are present, use a marker to mark the forks.

Since the transmission gears vary in size and are stacked on top of each other the shafts will have to be pulled out as a set. This is most easily done by pushing up on the shafts from the outside of the right crankcase.

> **HOT TIP:** If you are having problems with gears falling off the transmission shafts during removal, try securing a rubber band around each shaft so that the gears can't slide off.

Push up with your non-dominant hand a ½" (12mm) so you can insert the fingers of your dominant hand in and underneath the last set of gears on the shaft.

Pay close attention to the orientation and location of any gears that don't come off in unison with the shafts. The clarity of gearbox assemblies in service manuals varies greatly so it is important to keep track of all the gearbox components. Take photos or draw diagrams if there is any chance the manual will leave you wondering. This way you won't have to fiddle around or second guess assembly orientations when it comes time to reassemble.

Entire Gearbox Removal

In the case of the YZ250 engine the shift forks are secured to their respective shafts so gearbox removal is more challenging because the entire assembly of gear shafts, forks, and the shift drum must be removed at once.

Note any markings on the shift forks, or if necessary, mark them so their positions cannot be mixed up.

I don't have any revolutionary advice for dealing with this cluster of parts other than to be patient and ensure none of the gears or shims get mixed up upon removal. Start the process by pushing the secondary shaft up then work to secure the array of components with your remaining hand. Once you're able to get your fingers underneath the gears, grasp all the components and pull them straight out of the crankcase.

Wrapping Up

For crankshafts which are clearance fit to the bearings, simply pull straight up to remove the crank from the remaining crankcase. For interference fit cranks, you will need to install the crankcase splitting tool into the remaining crank half and push the crankshaft out. Be mindful of preserving the end of the crank.

Carefully remove the two dowel pins which locate the crankcase halves together. Once removed be sure to keep the pins with the cases. Don't set the cases too far away, as they will be the first set of parts to undergo inspection!

Woohoo, we're a third of the way there! Now that the engine is apart, the cleaning, disassembly, inspection, and reassembly of sub-system components can begin. The particular order you choose to follow during the inspection phase doesn't matter, however, I will be presenting the information in the sequence which I personally use.

Crankcases

The crankcases are the foundation of every engine and since they were worked on last, they are likely to be close by. Plus it is very motivating as subsequent work progresses to see a freshly prepared set of cases ready to house the rest of the engine!

Start by choosing a case half to work on. Before cleaning, all the seals and any auxiliary parts should be removed. If any seals were suspect of leaking, an inspection of the seal lip should be performed before removal, because the seal is likely to be damaged during removal. Look over any questionable seals for torn, cracked, or damaged lips. A seal puller works best to remove the seals and minimizes the chance of damaging the seal bores.

If there are any bearing retainer plates in the case, these will need to be removed too. The retaining plate fasteners are usually secured with a thread locking agent, which can make them tough to get out.

An impact driver works best to get these stubborn fasteners moving. Keep in mind that some Japanese manufacturer's use JIS screws to fasten the bearing retaining plates. This means your typical Phillips bit is not going to fit well. Have no fear my fellow engine builder, simply grinding down the end of a Phillips bit, as discussed previously in the "Tools" chapter, can prove to be an easy solution.

TECHNICAL TAKEAWAY
The Importance of Clean Threads

Reinstalling fasteners which are covered in old thread locking agent is a big no-no. The main problem with this is that due to the excess locking compound on the threads, more friction will be present when the fastener is installed. When the fastener is tightened the additional friction present in the threads will cause the torque wrench to reach the desired torque sooner than it should. This can leave seemingly tight fasteners loose.

The chances of cross-threading and damaging threads is also increased by installing goobered up bolts without cleaning them. A wire brush can be used to easily clean bolt threads. Bottoming taps also work well for chasing threaded holes which have old locking agent in them.

The most common bottoming taps required for thread cleaning on dirt bike engines are:
6 x 1.00 mm
8 x 1.25 mm
10 x 1.25mm
12 x 1.25mm
12 x 1.50mm

If there is any uncertainty of the threaded hole size or thread pitch, always compare the tap to the fastener that was removed from the hole before inserting the tap. Alternatively, if available, a set of thread gauges works great too for finding thread pitches.

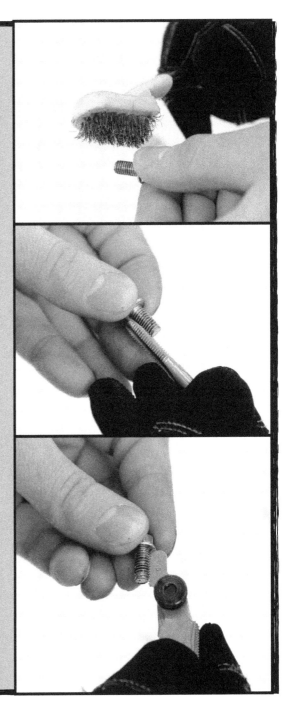

Once the retaining plates and screws have been removed, clean the old thread locking agent off the screw threads and out of the threaded holes in the crankcase.

Carefully clean all the crankcase gasket surfaces using a gasket scraper or a gasket removing solution. As you clean look for nicks, imperfections, and raised edges on the surfaces. If any imperfections are present, they will need to be corrected prior to reassembly.

After the gasket surfaces have been scraped the aftermath can be cleaned up. Use a plastic wash basin or other suitable container so that the crankcase half can be cleaned. Take your time cleaning the case half and do your best to remove all signs of dirt and oil. The cleaner the case half is, the less it will stink up the oven when it comes time to heat it. Disassemble the remaining case half in a similar fashion and enjoy the fun that meticulous cleaning brings!

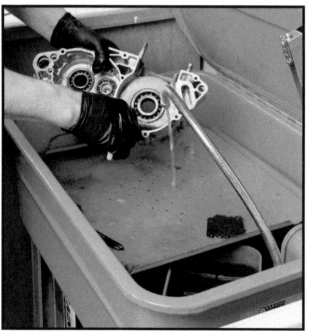

We are fast approaching the point where the cases are to be heated, old bearings removed, and new bearings installed. Investigating and correcting leaking gasket surfaces is best done before these steps. If the engine being serviced had a leak between the crankcase halves, or any other mating surface, the cause of the leak needs to be identified. Now that the crankcases are clean, it is much easier to observe the condition of the gasket surfaces. If any corrections were made to the crankcases, remember to clean any debris produced from the cases so that they remain as clean as possible.

TECHNICAL TAKEAWAY

Correcting Leaking or Damaged Gasket Surfaces On Engine Covers

From time to time corrective action will need to be taken to fix problems with crankcase and cover gasket surfaces. Attempts may need to be made to fix cracks or other damage before throwing in the towel and spending a lot of money on new parts.

Laying each case half or cover on a surface plate or flat surface can help identify any problems and confirm whether or not the parts are warped. The gasket surfaces need to be completely smooth. Raised edges, deep depressions, or leftover gasket material will cause gaskets to leak.

If a raised edge or bur is found, careful filing of the raised edge can remedy the problem. Small flat diamond files work well for this type of work. For cases with deep scratches, depressions, or other abnormalities, JB Weld can be used to correct any depressions.

Crankcases that are found to be warped, usually from welding a damaged area, can sometimes be saved. A surface plate lined with 400 grit sandpaper is the best way to try and remedy warped cases. By carefully sanding the gasket surface the warped section can usually be smoothed and flattened. This is a tedious effort and requires a lot of time and patience.

An attempt can be made to save cracked crankcases and covers as well by welding the damaged area. The aluminum will be oil soaked from the residual engine oil, so the damaged area must be meticulously cleaned prior to welding. Start by using parts cleaner soaked into a rag to clean the problematic area. Once clean, use a rotary burr to create a shallow divot along the area which will be welded. This will expose cleaner metal and make welding a little easier. Prior to welding, if possible, the crankcases or mating parts should be clamped together. All the bolts used to secure the cases or cover should be installed and torqued to their correct specification. Preheat the parts in an oven for 30 minutes at 300°F (149°C). The preheat will raise the temperature of the cases and help eliminate the possibility of distortion caused by welding. Once the welding is complete, let the parts cool completely in their clamped state before disassembling. Check for distortion against a flat surface and take any corrective action necessary.

Replacing Crankcases

If you participate in this sport long enough, chances are high that you will end up in a situation where one crankcase half has been damaged beyond repair while the other half is in good shape. Hopefully, this doesn't come as a result of taking advice from this book! More likely, an out of the ordinary rock strike or other object may inflict irreversible damage to your engine. Replacing crankcases can be an expensive affair and it is important to do your due diligence before shelling out cash for just one half of a crankcase. You may be wondering, folks are selling single crankcase halves all the time so what is the big deal?

The way a manufacturer chooses to make a set of crankcases for an engine will dictate if you are able to replace one case half or you must replace the crankcases as a set. Some manufacturers choose to machine important features of crankcase halves together. They do this by bolting or clamping the cases together part way through the machining process. Then they machine key features into both cases at the same time. Common examples of features machined at the same time include transmission bearing bores, crankshaft bearing pilot bores, and the cylinder deck. As you can imagine, using two different case halves machined at different times can lead to trouble when it comes time to assemble and run the engine. Some manufacturers have established processes which allow crankcase halves to be interchanged with one another. In this case, buying one half of a crankcase is no problem. To determine if the cases need to be replaced as a set or separately, the service manual, OEM dealer, and online subassembly microfiches are good references.

Removing Crankcase Bearings

Since the majority of the bearings housed in the crankcase utilize an interference fit to keep them in place, the best way to remove them is by heating up the crankcases. Heating allows the crankcases to expand, which temporarily reduces or eliminates their interference fit with the bearings. The bearings will expand as well, but since the crankcases are aluminum they will expand at roughly twice the rate of the steel bearings. This phenomena will allow some of the bearings to fall out without any help and minimize the amount of force required to get the remaining bearings out.

There are a few advantages that heating the cases have over conventional brute force methods. First, since the interference fit between the crankcase and bearings is reduced, less stress is put on the cases as the bearings are removed. Second, the possibility of damaging the bearing bores by uneven pounding diminishes. Uneven pounding can cause the bearing to bind in the bore, which if severe enough, can mar the surface of the bore. Third, the likelihood of damaging a bearing by a poorly coordinated strike is reduced. Overall, the heat makes the removal and installation of bearings much easier. I want to address any concerns of how the heating of the cases may affect the material properties and strength of the crankcases. For this discussion I will turn the spotlight over to Jim Buntjer, who is a long time friend of mine and a fantastic metallurgy expert.

The Effects of Heating Crankcases By Jim Buntjer

Most crankcases are made from either ASTM A380, ASTM A360, or ADC 12. The three materials are very similar in chemical make-up and strength. They are typically used in the cast condition which is usually a T3 designation, however to improve strength they can be heat treated to the T5 or T6 condition. This is done based on the loads that may be seen by the crankcase itself. The heat treatment for T3 is done based on a specific cooling rate when the part is cast. The T6 condition is achieved by heat to around 980°F and quenching in water. The parts are then aged at about 325°F for 8 hours. This provides a lot of added strength and does not allow any alloying elements to precipitate into grain boundaries or other detrimental areas of the microstructure. The effects of heating a crankcase to 350°F for a short period of time will have no effect on the part itself. Being that time at temperature is the huge factor here, the part being heated to that temperature for 10 to 30 minutes will have no effect at all. Just try to always stay below 400°F because the higher the temperature, the shorter the transformation time. For example, the same 8 hour process at 325°F can be achieved after only 1 hour at 400°F.

Now that an explanation of why it is beneficial to use heat to remove the crankcase bearings has been presented, there is only one thing left to do - fire up the oven. Set the oven to 300°F (149°C) and let it come up to temperature. Grab a couple old cookie sheets and line them with aluminum foil or line the oven rack directly with aluminum foil. The aluminum foil will do a couple of things. First, it will help protect the crankcase gasket surfaces from getting marred by contacting the oven rack. Second, the aluminum foil will help catch any bearings and oil that drop out of the crankcases. Burnt oil in an oven can be a pretty unpleasant smell so this is a very useful precautionary measure, especially if you have a significant other or roommates to keep happy!

At this point it is best to make preparations for the upcoming bearing removal and installation. It is unlikely that all bearings will drop from the crankcases as they are heated, nor will all of them be able to be tapped out with a punch and hammer. Having a blind bearing puller out and at the ready with appropriately sized puller heads is a good idea. Both the left primary shaft bearing and left shift drum bearing are susceptible to needing help from a bearing puller.

HOT TIP: Most modern engines don't require the crankshaft seals to be installed prior to the bearings. However, for engines which must have new seals installed prior to the bearings the oven temperature should be limited to 200°F (93°C). This will prevent damage to the seals from excessive heat.

It won't be possible to seamlessly remove all the bearings and then quickly reinstall the new bearings because there will be oil trapped behind the bearings. This trapped oil needs to be cleaned from the crankcases before installing new bearings. The bearing bores should be inspected for signs that any of the bearings have spun. This is particularly important for crank bearings and engines which were making squealing noises prior to their disassembly.

Bearing removal and installation plans should also be thought out, as it is never much fun to try frantically removing or installing a set of bearings while being unsure of where they go. The amount a bearing bore will expand is related to the size of the bore. Smaller diameter bearing bores will expand less than larger sized bores. Based on this fact, it is logical to remove the smallest diameter bearings first and work up in bearing size to the largest.

For installation, the small to large bearing rule still applies, however, considerations must be made as to the positioning of the crankcases during the bearing installations. Since the crankcases will be hot and the bearing bores larger than normal, the sequencing of bearing installation is important. If poorly conceived, it is possible to install bearings in one side and have them fall back out of their bores as the cases are turned over so the remaining bearings can be installed! Normally, bearings being installed into the outsides of the crankcases will utilize bearing retainer plates. Once these bearings are installed, the bearing retainer plates should also be temporarily installed so that the bearings can't

Sequence	Left Crankcase	Right Crankcase
1	Counterbalance Bearing* and Retaining Ring	Counterbalance Bearing*and Retaining Plates
2	Primary Shaft Bearing	Countershaft Bearing
3	Shift Drum Bearing	Shift Drum Bearing
4	Countershaft Bearing	Primary Shaft Bearing
5	Crank Bearing	Crank Bearing

*If Equipped

fall out of the crankcases once they are turned over. A typical installation sequence will look similar to the table to the left.

In preparation for installation, the new bearings should be organized into groups based on which crankcase half they will go into and organized in the order of which they will be installed. Some bearings may have seals on one side, notches for retaining plates, or other special features. Referring to the service manual or original installation is important so that the new bearings can be installed correctly. For any bearings which don't require a specific orientation, it is considered best practice to face the letter designations found on the side of the bearing outward so they can easily be read at a later time. Once bearing order and orientation have been determined, an egg carton or storage tray can be used to organize the bearings. After this is done, the bearings should be placed in a freezer so that they have time to shrink. The longer the bearings are allowed to cool the better. Around an hour of freezer time works well.

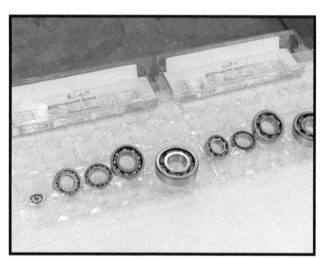

HOT TIP: Very rarely is it necessary to remove the clutch actuation arm bearings. These bearings are very difficult to remove and only wear out if the clutch arm seal has been lost or severely damaged allowing dirt into the bearings. The clutch arm shaft can be used to turn the bearings and feel if the bearings have been damaged. In most cases it is preferable to try and clean these bearings, grease them, and reuse them instead of replacing them.

The work surface that is used during bearing removal and installation can have an effect on how quickly the crankcases cool. Metal work surfaces will suck the heat out of the crankcases much faster than wooden work surfaces. If a wooden work surface isn't available, using wooden blocks to support the cases is a good alternative.

For bearing removal, the crankcases can be heated simultaneously. Once the cases have warmed, pull out the case half of your choice. In the picture to the left I'm starting with the left half. Use a punch and hammer to tap out the bearings.

Since the bearings will not be reused, it makes little difference as to where the bearing is struck as it is tapped out. Please note that this doesn't mean you should go bonkers when pounding out the bearings. Care should be taken to strike evenly around the bearing with the punch and hammer. Strike around the bearing in a circular or back and forth pattern so that it doesn't bind as it is tapped out. Also be careful that the punch doesn't strike the side of the bearing bore, creating a raised edge. If this happens, the edge must be smoothed before reinstalling the bearing. Very rarely does the left shift drum bearing ever fall out, so a blind bearing puller must be used.

After all the bearings have been removed, set the case half aside for the time being. Then proceed to remove the bearings from the remaining case half.

Bearings that have spun in their bores are not that common on modern machinery, but it is always a good idea to examine the bearing bores for imperfections. In addition to spun bearings, these imperfections can also come from ham fisted mechanics who previously worked on the engine. A bearing which has spun will leave long parallel lines around the bore. The bearing itself may also have some galled metal on it.

Any imperfections in the bore, if not addressed, will lead to the bearing having less contact with the bearing bore. Even with an interference between crankcase and bearing, when the bearing has less contact with the bore it becomes more susceptible to moving and spinning.

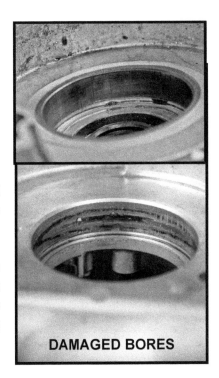

DAMAGED BORES

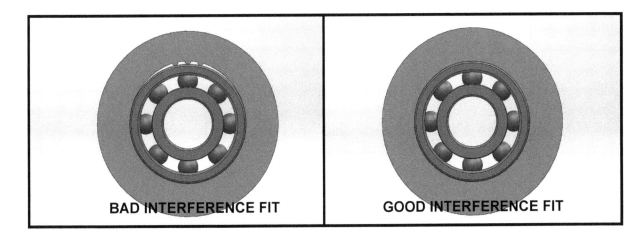

BAD INTERFERENCE FIT   **GOOD INTERFERENCE FIT**

HOT TIP: A wicking grade locking agent (Ex. Green Loctite) can be used to secure bearings in problematic bores. During installation be very careful to keep the locking agent out of the bearing itself. Also keep in mind when using a locking agent, bearing removal can become more difficult and cleaning up the old locking agent is a serious pain.

If small imperfections are identified, they can be corrected by carefully sanding them away. A Dremel tool can be very helpful for this sort of work. Large imperfections resulting from spun bearings may require sleeving of the bearing bore. Sleeving involves machining the crankcase bearing bore to a larger size and then pressing in a steel or plastic sleeve which houses the bearing.

Seal bores should also be inspected before the bearings are installed. While not as critical as bearing bores, seal bores must also be free of imperfections so that the seal can seat correctly. Any imperfections in seal bores can be corrected using the methods outlined for correcting bearing bore defects.

Lastly, inspect the shift shaft bore, kickstart bore, and any other auxiliary bores or features found on the crankcases. Make sure the bores are smooth and free of defects. If problems are found in the bore, be sure to inspect the mating parts for imperfections as well. On some engines a bushing is used in one or both of the shift shaft bores which can be replaced if damaged.

Cleaning Crankcase Oil Passages

With the first round of cleaning and preparation out of the way, the cases should look much more presentable. Two-stroke engines commonly utilize oil passages which have been machined into their crankcases to lubricate the main bearings. These passages typically extend from slightly below the cylinder base down past the bearings.

Cleaning these passages is of particular importance for engines which have self destructed and have strewn metallic particles throughout. If left unattended, the contaminates in these passages could be the first thing to lubricate the rebuilt engine.

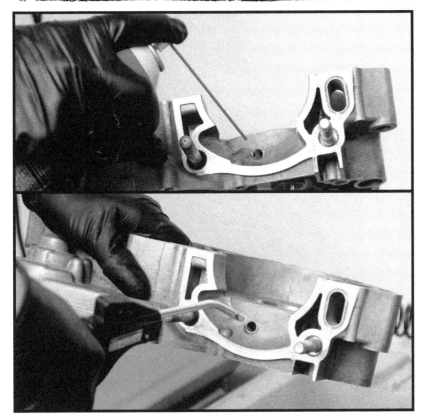

The best way to clean the oil passages is with a combination of an aerosol based cleaner and compressed air. Start by blowing out the passages with compressed air, then squirt cleaner through the passages. Repeat this process until the parts cleaner appears clean and there are no more signs of oil or debris.

Once the cases have been cleaned and inspected one final time, they can go back in the oven for 30 minutes to bring them back up to temperature. Grab whichever case half you plan on starting with along with the applicable bearings from the freezer.

TECHNICAL TAKEAWAY

Bearing Installation

When installing new bearings it is important to apply force in the correct locations. Neither ball bearings or roller bearings are designed to cope with a lot of lateral loading. Tapping on the inner race of a bearing, when the outer race is what is locating the bearing in the mating part, is incorrect. Application of force through the inner race to seat the bearing would cause the load to be passed through the inner race, to the balls, and finally to the outer race. If enough force is applied Brinelling can occur to the balls. Brinelling is a fancy term used to describe a process of wear. In the case of the ball bearings, small indentations can be left in the balls due to the force being transmitted through them. This is undesirable and can lead to bearing failure. A Brinelled bearing will feel notchy and won't spin smoothly.

The correct way to install the bearing is by applying all necessary forces to the race which is locating the bearing to the mating part. A combination of punch and hammer is the easiest and cheapest way to install a bearing. A step up would be using a set of bearing drivers which are available in various diameters. While not necessary, bearing drivers are nice to have for repetitive work.

Center the bearing in the bore and use the punch and hammer to tap evenly around the bearing bore. Even tapping is necessary to keep the bearing from getting cock-eyed in the bore and binding. As the bearing is tapped into place, a change in the tapping sound will occur once it seats against the bottom of the bore.

Carefully install the bearings into their bores. In order for the bearing to drop in trouble free, precise alignment is critical. Keep in mind the sequence and correct orientation of the bearings as they are installed. Many of the bearings should drop right into their bores without using any force due to the expansion of the cases and contraction of the bearings. For bearings utilizing retaining rings to keep them in place, pay close attention to the following advice.

TECHNICAL TAKEAWAY

Retaining Ring Installation

Retaining rings should be considered a disposable part since they can lose tension with repeated removal and installation, thus it is best to use new retaining rings when assembling an engine. Due to the way retaining rings are manufactured, one side of the retaining ring will be sharp while the other side will feel slightly rounded. It is best to face the sharp side of the retaining ring against the outer edge of the retaining ring groove. This way if any pressure is put on the retaining ring, the sharp side will bite into the groove.

Snap ring pliers are the only suitable tool for installing retaining rings. The retaining ring should be expanded or compressed just enough for it to fit into the bore or over the shaft. Excessive expansion or compression can distort the retaining ring causing it to have inadequate tension against the ring groove. A screwdriver or punch should always be used to confirm the entire retaining ring is seated in the ring groove. After the ring is fully seated, an attempt should be made to try and rotate the retaining ring inside the groove. A correctly installed retaining ring that has not lost tension will not rotate. Retaining rings which spin in their grooves should be discarded and replaced.

Any bearing retaining plates needed to secure the bearings should not be fully tightened at this time, instead the retaining plate bolts simply should be snugged. The reason they should not be fully tightened is because the expanded crankcases will have an affect on the torque of the fastener. Most of the time a locking agent is also required to secure these fasteners, which should be applied when the crankcases are at room temperature.

Once all the bearings have been installed, the case half can be set aside and the remaining case half's bearings can be installed. Before further work is done on the crankcases, they should be allowed to cool back down to room temperature.

Any bearing retaining plate fasteners can be temporarily removed, thread locking agent added, and then torqued to the appropriate specifications.

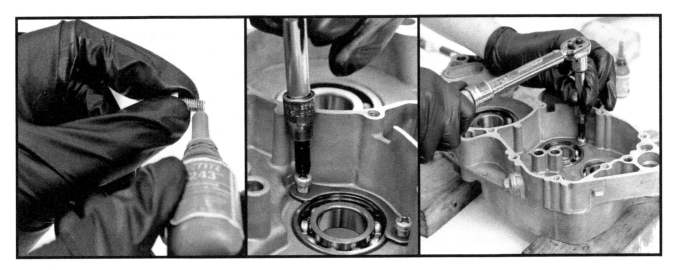

New seals will be installed into the crankcases next. A determination will have to be made as to whether or not installing the cranks seals makes sense at this time. I would advise to do so if the crank and crank bearings utilize a clearance fit.

If the crank and crank bearings feature an interference fit, holding off on installing the seals until the crank has been installed and the crankcases have been mated together may be advantageous. The first reason I suggest this is because by leaving the seals out, should shrink fitting the crank into the bearings go awry, the inner race of the bearing can still be utilized by a puller. The second reason I suggest this is because by leaving the seal out there is no chance it will be exposed to the heat source being used to warm the inner race of the bearing when the crank is reinstalled. The applicability of this advice depends largely on engine geometry.

For engines that feature crank seals that seal directly against the crankshaft, the previously mentioned advice is invaluable. If the crank seal was installed and the crank needed to be pulled through the bearing, the seal would not allow the puller to be

EXAMPLE OF A CRANK SEAL THAT SEALS DIRECTLY AGAINST THE SHAFT

seated against the inner race of the bearing. Since the inner diameter of the seal is usually the same diameter as the crank bearing, keeping heat off the seal when the inner race is warmed becomes more challenging as well.

For engines that utilize a seal that seals against a collar on the crankshaft, the seal typically has a large enough inner diameter that the inner race of the bearing will remain exposed when the seal is installed. In most cases, this will allow adequate room for a puller to be utilized if necessary. If this is the case, you'll just have to determine whether or not the seal is at risk of being inadvertently heated when the inner race of the bearing is warmed.

Prior to deciding what option is best, you may want to jump ahead to Chapter 14 to familiarize yourself with the methods outlined for crankshaft installation.

EXAMPLE OF A CRANK SEAL THAT SITS FLUSH WITH THE COLLAR

If any of this advice on when to install the crank seals is confusing or contradictory in your mind, I would encourage you to consult your service manual and review any outlined orders for seal installation.

TECHNICAL TAKEAWAY

Seal Installation

Seals are integral to an engine's ability to retain fluids. While they are simple in nature, a few things can go very wrong during installation. The methods used to install the seal and how square the seal is set in its bore are important factors to take into consideration during installation. Improper installation of the seal can lead to premature wear and failure.

Prior to installation, the new seal should be inspected. Check around the lip of the seal for nicks and tears. If the seal uses a spring, make sure the spring is situated correctly in the seal. Every once in awhile, a new seal may come with a lip turned inside out or a spring which isn't sitting properly. It is critical to catch these mistakes before installation.

Ideally, seals should be installed by pressing them into place. An arbor press is a helpful tool for this, however, not a lot of at-home mechanics have them, so I will provide a few other methods. Pushing the seal in by hand or tapping it in place with a hammer are also suitable methods, if done correctly.

Many of the seals which are used on engines have a thin metal outer shell coated in rubber. This metal shell can easily deform during installation if load is not distributed evenly. To load the seal evenly, using seal drivers is one option, another option is using sockets which are approximately the same outer diameter as the seal, and the final option is using flat metal plates.

COCK EYED SEAL

FLUSH SEAL

Refer to specific instructions provided in the service manual for depth requirements. Keep in mind that seals should never sit flush against the edge of a bearing for obvious reasons, so it is important to correctly set the depth of the seal upon installation. Dependent on application, the seal will be installed so that it sits flush with the edge, just past flush, or bottoms out on the bottom of the seal bore.

Start by using a plate or socket which is larger than the seal bore and gives the seal good support.

Press the seal into the bore until the object being used to press against the seal bottoms against the seal bore. This will ensure the seal is square to the bore, however, the seal may spring back a bit so additional pressure may be needed.

Use a socket of similar diameter to the outer diameter of the seal if the seal must be pressed down further. Take great care to make sure the seal remains square to the bore as it is pressed in. Use your fingers or the depth rod on a caliper to confirm the seal is flush with the top of the bore or slightly passed flush.

Ensuring the seal is square to the bore can't be stressed enough. If the seal is run cock-eyed in the bore, the lip of the seal will fail in short order. Be patient and take care during installation to ensure seal squareness.

Once the seal has been installed, it should be pre-lubricated with grease. This is necessary so the lip of the seal doesn't run without any lubrication and get ruined. A lithium based grease is ideal for pre-lubricating seals.

> **HOT TIP:** Avoid applying grease to the outer edges of seals to aid installation. Just as easily as the grease can help the seal go in, it can also easily allow the seal to come back out! Bore sealant is not necessary but is the only suitable lubricant which could be used during installation.

Once all the seals have been installed, any remaining auxiliary crankcase components can be cleaned and reinstalled. After any remaining parts have been installed, the crankcases are ready to go and can be set aside.

Crankshaft and Rod Inspection

There are a few different aspects to proper crankshaft and rod inspection. First, I like to carefully examine the old crankshaft assembly. This evaluation can lead to valuable information regarding the health of the engine before it was disassembled. If the engine failed, it may also provide answers as to what caused the failure. Inspection of the crankshaft is also necessary to determine if it can be rebuilt.

The new crankshaft assembly should also be inspected. This is important and necessary for a handful of different reasons. I believe that OEM manufacturers are highly skilled at assembling crankshafts, however, this belief lessens regarding aftermarket manufacturers and rebuilding services. If the crankshaft assembly came through the postal system, there is also a chance that it was poorly packaged and mishandled. To ensure all other parties did their jobs correctly, inspecting the new crankshaft assembly is vital.

Since most of the crankshaft assembly inspections will be the same for new and old crankshafts, I'm going to cover both inspections at the same time. Unless otherwise stated, it can be assumed that all inspection points are relevant for both new and old crankshaft assemblies.

Visual and Feel Inspections

A lot can be learned just by looking and feeling various parts of the crankshaft assembly. Start by inspecting the small end bore of the rod. Look for signs of wear which may come in the form of pitting, grooving, or discoloration. Feel inside the bore as well with your finger or a pick, noting any variations in smoothness, raised edges, or pits.

Pitting occurs when the microstructure (i.e. the bearing bore surface) fatigues. The exact causation of pitting is difficult to assess because many variables are acting on the rod at once.

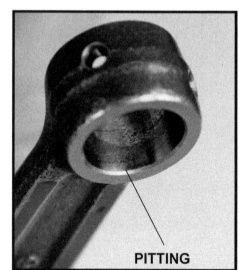

PITTING

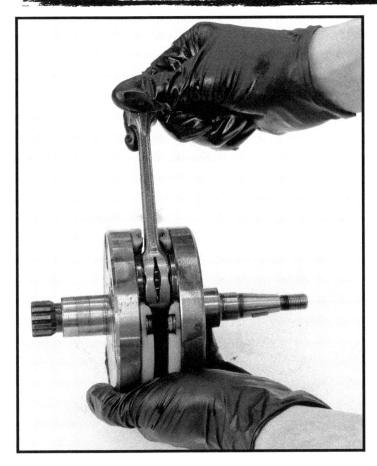

A combination of cyclic loading, elastic deformation, and debris passing between the needle bearings and small end bore, all contribute to the fatiguing of the small end bore surface and subsequent pitting. In any case, once the pitting has started, it will continue and it is best to replace the rod with a new one.

Striations or smearing the width of the needle rollers around the circumference of the small end bore or wrist pin is indicative of the rollers sliding under heavy loading. Inadequate lubrication is typically the cause of this phenomena.

Discoloration of the rod bore, needle rollers, or wrist pin also indicate inadequate lubrication. The components will take on a bluish hue with uniform distribution in the bore as a result of the bearing getting extremely hot. Usually discoloration is accompanied with additional wear such as striations or smearing and the bearing has seized.

HOT TIP: My comments regarding whether the rod is still in useable condition are not totally relevant to a full rebuild since the rod will be replaced. However, these assessments are important when performing top end work and deciding whether or not further disassembly is required.

Deep grooving found in the small end bore is rare, but it can happen due to large particles getting trapped between a needle roller and the small end bore. Once trapped, these particles leave impressions within the bore. If any grooving is observed, the rod should be replaced.

Rotate the connecting rod around the crankpin and feel for notchiness as the rod rotates. Any notchiness indicates the big end rod bearing is damaged. This can be caused by debris getting sandwiched between the bearing rollers and rod. If the crank assembly is equipped with big end thrust washers and they have worn abnormally, they can also contaminate the rod bearing.

Check for axial play between the crank pin, bearing, and rod by pushing and pulling on the rod. Normally, it won't be possible to feel any play and a dial test indicator will be needed to measure axial free play.

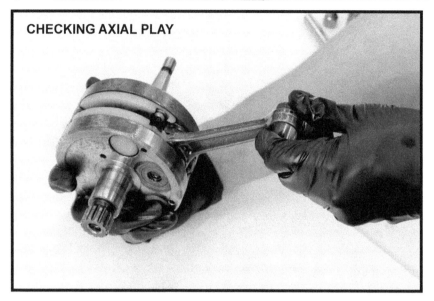

CHECKING AXIAL PLAY

Inspect the crankshaft bearing journals for wear. Use your fingernail to feel for any raised edges on the journals. Raised edges or deep scratches running in parallel lines all the way around the journal are good indicators that the journal spun inside the bearing. Lines or scratches running perpendicular to the journal may have come during the installation or removal of the bearing.

If crank journals, which run inside a bearing, have imperfections which can be felt with a fingernail, these imperfections should be addressed before returning the crankshaft to service. A combination of filing and sanding can remove most minor blemishes. Just as the fit between the bearing and crankcase is important, so is the fit between the bearing and crankshaft journal. Raised edges and other problems will reduce the contact area between the journal and bearing.

SCRATCHED CRANK

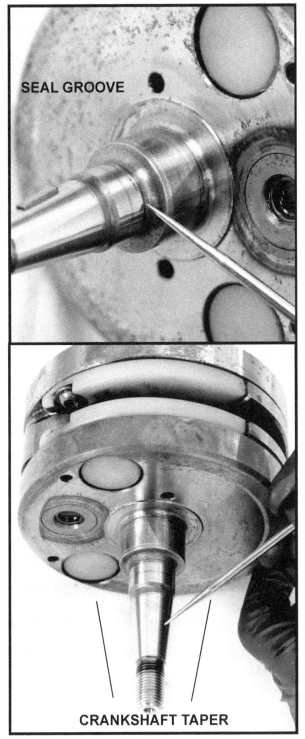

SEAL GROOVE

CRANKSHAFT TAPER

Pitting can also occur on the crankshaft bearing journals. The pitting occurs on the journals for the same reasons that it occurs inside the small end rod bore. Pitting is most often seen on crankshaft journals which run on roller bearings. Any crankshaft halves with journals that are pitted should be replaced. Roller bearings require near perfect surface finishes for correct operation and will quickly get damaged if run on pitted journals.

The crank seal surface should also be inspected and felt. Shaft seals can leave grooves in metal parts and it is important to make sure the seal surface is in good shape if the crankshaft is to be rebuilt. Running a fingernail across the area where the seal contacts the crankshaft will give a good indication of any problems. If a fingernail catches on the seal contact area, corrective action should be taken. On many engines the crank seal bore is a through hole. This means the seal could be positioned at a different depth in the bore so that the lip of the seal no longer runs in the old groove. More expensive fixes, which usually aren't necessary, include new crankshafts or refinishing the affected seal surface to a smaller diameter.

Another important area on the crankshaft to check is the tapered portion which mates with the flywheel. While the keyway locates the flywheel, the tapered fit in combination with the nut is what primarily holds the flywheel tight and in position. Tapered fits depend on near perfect surface finishes between the mating parts in order to function correctly. Any imperfections on the crankshaft or flywheel which reduces the contact areas or promotes unevenness between the two parts will make the flywheel more susceptible to coming loose.

Check the crankshaft taper, examining it for deep scratching or scoring. Any imperfections should be smoothed and blended so that the flywheel can seat correctly. Deep scratches running parallel to the direction of engine rotation found on the crankshaft taper are indicative that the flywheel came loose at some point, sheared the key, and spun on the crankshaft.

The contact area of any suspect taper fits can be checked quickly using Prussian Blue, Machinist's Dye, or a marker to color in the tapered portion of the crankshaft. The flywheel can then be pushed onto the crankshaft and rotated back and forth. Once removed, the marker will have displaced to the flywheel and the areas of contact between the two parts will be visible. The contact area between any flywheel and crankshaft exhibiting a poor fit can be improved by lapping the components together using a fine grit lapping compound.

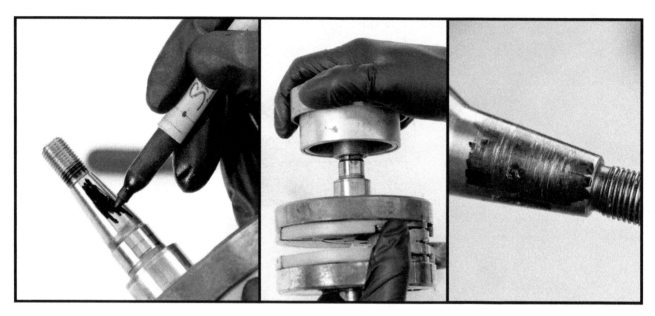

Checking Runout

In the engine building world, runout is a term used to describe how closely a shaft is aligned with its main axis. While shaft alignment is a factor in a runout measurement, it is not the only one. Runout also measures out-of-roundness of the shaft and any setup errors. This means that measurement of runout is not definitive. When runout is measured it could be due to any of the three reasons previously listed, but we can't pinpoint which it is. These three variables and how they affect runout are often misunderstood. This oversight can lead to improperly diagnosing crankshaft problems.

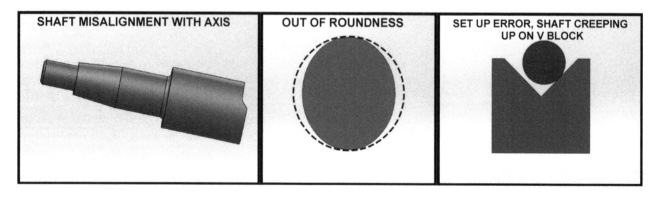

In practice, utmost care can be taken when setting up a runout measurement and since the crankshaft is precision ground, it can be assumed that any out-of-roundness of the crankshaft is negligible. This leaves shaft misalignment error which can come in two forms. The shaft could be offset (radial runout) from the main axis or at an angle (axial run-out) to the main axis.

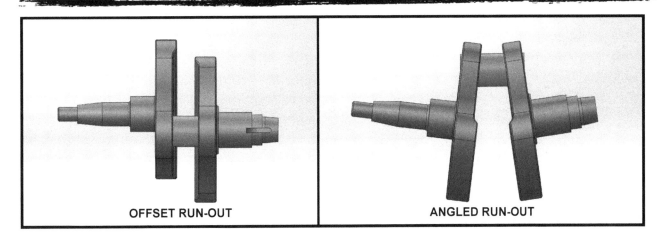

OFFSET RUN-OUT   ANGLED RUN-OUT

Runout measurements are taken on the crankshaft's outer features as it is rotated using dial test indicators or dial indicators. These features usually consist of a flat surface just before or after the flywheel taper and crank gear surfaces. The measurement is recorded at a specified distance from the ends of the crankshaft or from the bearing journal faces. Assuming a perfect setup and no out-of-roundness of the crankshaft, the measurement can be attributed to shaft misalignment.

> **HOT TIP:** The further the indicators are placed from the center of the crankshaft, the more variation in runout measurement readings there will be. For applications like race engines, where crankshaft runout should be next to nothing, measure runout as far out on the outer surfaces as possible.

The service manual will specify runout in one of two ways. A total runout comparison can be made, which is equal to the maximum difference between the two measurements, or each side can be compared separately.

Checking the runout of both new and old crankshafts can be beneficial. Determining the amount of runout an old crankshaft had can help determine why the engine was having problems prior to teardown. Crankshafts with excessive amounts of runout will cause engines to vibrate abnormally and put more load on the crank bearings. If the engine was a shaker or experienced a crank bearing failure, checking the runout of the old crankshaft will help determine what the problem was.

New crankshafts should also be checked to confirm the runout is within the acceptable range specified by the service manual. While it doesn't happen often, new or rebuilt crankshafts can arrive out of spec. This could be due to an assembly error at the factory, rough handling during shipping, or an inexperienced crankshaft rebuilder. Installing a crankshaft that is outside of factory specs and not true will lead to an engine that vibrates excessively and wears out prematurely.

The best and cheapest way to check runout is with a pair of v-blocks and two dial test indicators. Dial indicators could be used as a substitute, however, the accuracy and resolution won't be as good. Measurements are taken at set distances from the ends of the crankshaft and compared. Either a comparison of both sides is made by taking the maximum difference of the two measurements or each side is compared individually.

Another method of measuring runout that I want to discuss, but discourage the use of, entails centering the crankshaft at each end, usually with live centers, in a lathe or special fixture. There are a couple of problems with this method. First, the fixturing method of centering the crankshaft at its ends doesn't make sense because the important feature which requires correct alignment is the crankshaft bearing journals. In order for the ends to be suitable for fixturing, it would have to be assumed that the ends of the crankshaft are perfectly concentric to the journals. This may be the case when the crank comes from the factory new, but a lot of used crankshafts end up with minor imperfections at the ends, mainly from installation and removal procedures. These imperfections can lead to improper centering of the crank and false runout readings.

Second, a light amount of pressure must be applied to the crankshaft to hold it in place between the live centers. The pressure can cause the crankshaft to flex which may also lead to inaccurate runout measurements. Due to these sources of error when centering the crankshaft at its ends, v-blocks are preferred.

One final option noteworthy of discussion is to set each crankshaft journal on a pair of ball bearings. This is similar to the v-block method, but because the ball bearings rotate an additional source of error is introduced. Each ball bearing will have its own runout, which will contribute to the total runout measured. The quality of the bearing and its runout, which may or may not be negligible, should be considered when using this method.

Checking Run-out Procedure

To start, set a pair of v-blocks on a surface plate or flat surface. The flatter the surface the better, as setup error is less likely to come into play. Spread the v-blocks apart so the crank wheels fit between them and support the crankshaft journals. Use a straightedge to align the v-blocks so the "V's" are parallel. Lightly oil the crankshaft journals and v-blocks then lower the crankshaft onto the v-blocks.

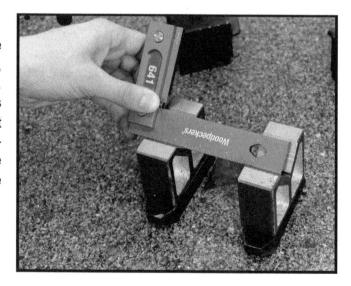

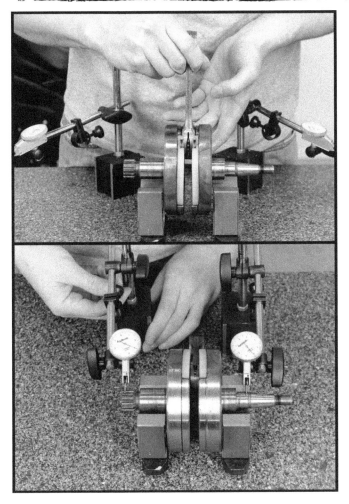

The service manual will specify where the measurements of runout should be taken from. Set the dial test indicators up at the specified points. If no points are specified, set the indicators up so that they measure runout on flat surfaces towards the outer ends of the crankshaft. Be sure to keep the contact point of the indicator away from any defects on the surfaces used for measurement which may affect the readings. Also remember to keep the dial test indicators parallel to the surface and slightly preload them. Make sure both the indicators and v-blocks are secure and won't move as the crank is rotated. If necessary, clamps or magnets can be used to steady the v-blocks and indicator stands.

Slowly rotate the crankshaft around and make sure both indicators are reading throughout the entire rotation of the crankshaft. Once the setup is working, rotate the crankshaft until the left or right indicator is at its highest or lowest point. Then zero both of the indicators. Rotate the crankshaft around a couple of times while observing the needles on the indicator. Note the greatest variation between the two indicators. For example, if the left indicator reads +0.001" (0.025mm) and the right indicator reads -0.002" (0.050mm) the runout on the left side would be 0.001" and the runout on the right would be 0.002" or the total runout would be 0.003"(0.075mm). After taking the measurements, rotate the crankshaft back to its zeroed position and double check to make sure both indicators still read "0" at this position.

TECHNICAL TAKEAWAY

Crankshaft Truing

Easy to talk about - difficult to master. Learning how to true a crankshaft is not out of reach for anyone to learn, however, it will require a lot of practice, time, and patience when first starting out. Crankshaft truing entails correcting any shaft alignment issues which are discovered when measuring runout and before installing the crankshaft. These issues are corrected by using a combination of hammers, clamps, wedges, and brute force to change the shaft alignment. A certain amount of feel is necessary to know how much force to apply to invoke a minor change. Crankshaft truing is definitely a procedure where everything must be done just right. Too much force when striking the crankshaft and one can pound the crank back and forth for hours without getting anywhere, too little force and the crank will never move.

There are three conditions of misalignment which can occur to a pressed together crankshaft.

  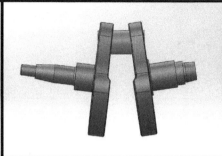

#1 The crank webs can be offset from one another.

#2 The crank webs can be pinched opposite the crankpin.

#3 The crank webs can be spread opposite the crankpin.

These conditions often occur simultaneously making correction more difficult. The good news is that only two of the three conditions can exist at any given time. Either the crankshaft can be offset and pinched or offset and spread but it can never be offset, pinched, and spread.

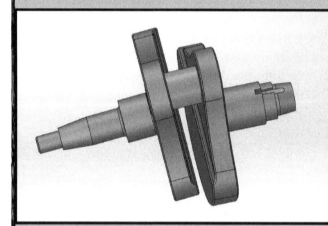 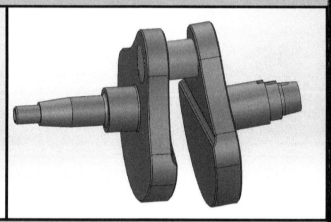

Exaggerated offset and pinched

Exaggerated offset and spread

The easiest way to true a crankshaft is to separate the conditions by correcting them one at a time. First, any offset present should be corrected. Then any pinched or spread conditions should be fixed.

Using Runout Measurements to Determine the Misalignment Conditions

Before any force can be applied, the problematic conditions must be identified. This is done by determining where runout exists along the crankshaft journals. To do this the same procedure previously outlined for checking runout is followed. In each of the three scenarios for misaligned crankshafts, runout measurement high and low points will occur at different positions around the crankshaft journals.

A crankshaft with purely offset journal misalignment will have its high and low runout readings approximately 90 degrees from crankpin. The indicators may measure runout on one or both crankshaft measurement features. If runout is measured on both features, one indicator will read high while the other indicator will read low. A mark should be made on the crankshaft web where the indicator reads the highest. Due to the way the crankshaft journals sit in the v-blocks, this is actually the lowest point on the web. To correct this, force should be applied on the opposite side of the mark. This is counterintuitive and confusing but the pictures below do a good job illustrating this scenario.

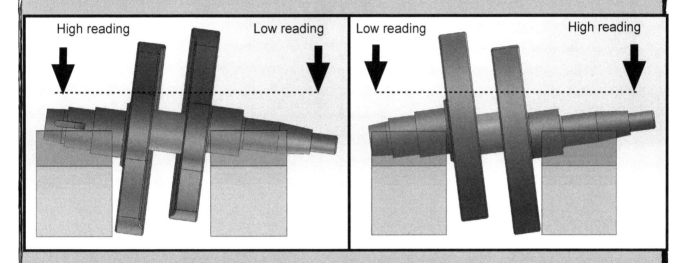

A crankshaft that is pinched opposite the crankpin will exhibit low runout readings on one or both sides when the crankpin is up and high readings when the crankpin is down. This is an easy scenario to understand. Marks should be made on the crankshaft webs where the indicators read highest. To correct the pinched condition, a wedge will need to be driven between the crankshaft webs at the point where the marks were made.

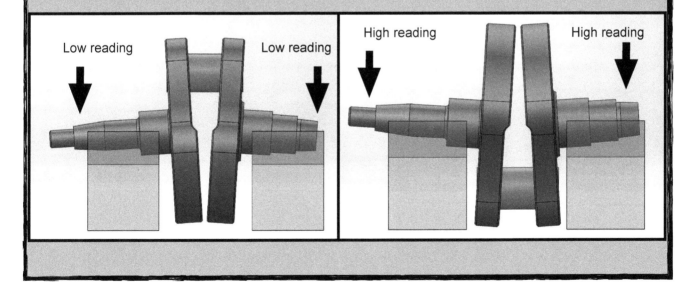

A crankshaft that is spread opposite the crankpin will exhibit high runout readings on one or both sides when the crankpin is up and low readings when the crankpin is down. Marks should be made on the crankshaft webs where the indicators read the lowest. To correct the spread condition, the crankshaft webs should be clamped at the point where the marks were made.

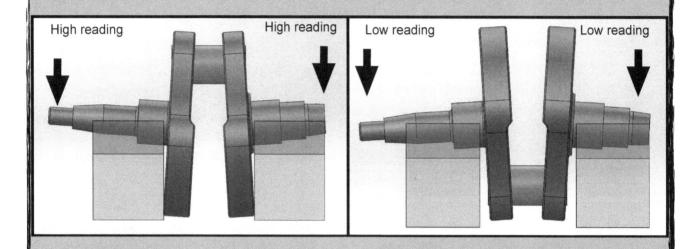

If the crankshaft webs have machined outer faces, measurements can also be taken from web face to web face to help confirm pinched or spread misalignment conditions. A pinched crankshaft will be widest from web face to web face at the crankpin. A spread crankshaft will be widest 180 degrees from the crankpin. Once a crankshaft is trued, the distance between the crankshaft web faces should be nearly equal at all points.

Procedure for Truing the Crankshaft

Now that it is understood how the indicators will read and the corrective action that must be taken for each of the three misalignment conditions, the process of truing the crank can begin. Any offset misalignment should be corrected first, followed by corrections of the pinched or spread conditions. As corrections are made and the alignment is honed in, it is typical to have to work back and forth between the various misalignment conditions. Being patient and making minor adjustments is much better than taking big wallops. It is best to move the crank webs around the crankpin as little as possible.

To start, measure the runout of the crankshaft and identify the misalignment conditions which are present. If the crankshaft has a lot of runout, it can be helpful to start by using dial indicators then switching to dial test indicators for fine tuning. Since any of the three misalignment conditions can be present, a brief overview of how to correct each one will be covered.

Correcting an Offset Misalignment Condition

Use chalk or a marker to draw a line across the crank web at the highest point indicated by the indicator. Remember that at this point even though the indicator reads "high" on the journal, the web is in fact low, so force must be applied to the crank web opposite of the mark made.

Secure the crankshaft against a workbench or table so that the crank web being struck hangs out over the edge. Only secure the crankshaft against soft surfaces, which won't leave marks on the webs. Hold the crankshaft and rod in place with one hand while using your other hand to strike the crankshaft with the hammer. Remember to strike softly until you start to understand how much force is required to move the crankshaft a certain amount. Surprisingly little force is necessary to make the crankshaft webs move around the crank pin. After striking, set the crankshaft back in the v-blocks and measure the runout.

Correcting a Pinched Misalignment Condition

Use chalk or a marker to draw lines across the crank webs at the point where the indicators are reading highest. This should be about 180 degrees from the crankpin. This is the point where a wedge should inserted between the crank webs so that the webs can be spread apart. A dense plastic log splitting wedge works well for splitting the webs apart. Other objects can be used as splitters, just make sure whatever is chosen won't damage or mar the crank webs.

Use a hammer to tap the wedge between the crank webs and spread the webs. Remove the wedge and then recheck the runout.

Correcting a Spread Misalignment Condition

Mark the crank webs where the indicators read lowest. This should be approximately 180 degrees from the crankpin. Use a vice with soft jaws or a C-clamp to pinch the crankshaft webs together. Remember to go easy at first until you begin to get a feel for how much force is required to affect the amount of runout.

Continue to tweak the crankshaft journal alignment using a combination of the three corrective methods until the crankshaft falls within spec. With patience and further adjustments, the crankshaft can be aligned so that it is almost perfectly true. For race engines, the target runout value being aimed for should be less than 0.0005" of total runout. This will result in a very smooth and reliable engine.

Measuring Rod Big End Radial Clearance

Measuring the radial clearance of the rod big end will quantify any movement previously felt by pushing or pulling on the rod. This is a good measurement to perform to help diagnose problems with the old crankshaft, but is less necessary when working with new crankshaft assemblies. The clearance should be measured in two directions. First, a measurement should be taken parallel to the small end of the rod with the crankpin positioned inline with the rod. This measurement has the highest chance of showing the largest displacement since the forces on the crankpin are highest around TDC. A second measurement should be taken with the small end of the rod perpendicular to the crank pin plane. Once the measurements have been taken, they can be compared to the standard values and service limits provided by the service manual.

ROD AND CRANKPIN PARALLEL TO V-BLOCKS   ROD PERPENDICULAR TO V-BLOCKS

To measure the rod big end radial clearance, position the crankshaft in a pair of v-blocks. Position the crankpin 90 degrees from the top. This will allow a dial test indicator to be positioned on the rod big end. Use blocks to support the small end of the rod so that the rod sits horizontally.

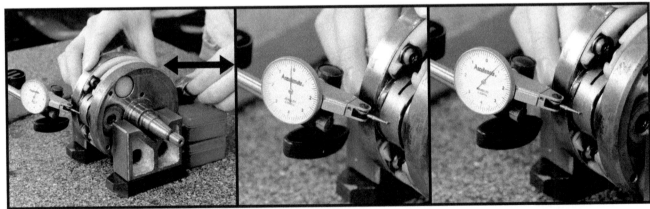

PUSH AND PULL HORIZONTAL   PULL MEASUREMENT   PUSH MEASUREMENT

Zero the dial test indicator. Then gently pull on the rod and note the recorded value. Next, push on the rod again noting the value. The difference of the two values is the measured clearance. Be very careful not to push too hard and move the crankshaft up the v-blocks.

Next, lift the rod so that the small end is vertical. Gently try to move the big end of the rod from side to side. Note the measured movement in each direction and find the difference to determine the total clearance.

PUSH AND PULL SIDE TO SIDE

Checking Rod Big End Side Clearance

It is a good idea to check rod big end side clearance on new and old crankshafts. This is especially true for crankshafts which have been rebuilt. Rod big end side clearance is a measurement taken between the side of the rod and the side of the crankshaft. The side clearance is very important because a certain amount is necessary to allow the rod to move freely back and forth along the crankshaft. It is always better to have more clearance than not enough clearance. Too little clearance will cause the rod to rub against the side of the crankshaft, or if equipped, a pair of thrust washers. This rubbing will create friction and result in excessive heat build up and wear of the parts. Neither is good when the crankshaft is spinning past 10,000 RPMs!

To measure the side clearance between the rod and crankshaft, a set of lash gauges are used. Pull the rod to either side of the crankpin and then insert appropriately sized lash gauges between the rod and crankshaft.

Lash gauges should be inserted between the crankshaft and rod along both sides of the crankpin. This method will ensure even spacing on both sides of the crankpin and yield the most accurate measurements. If lash gauges are only inserted on one side of the crankpin, the rod could rock, resulting in inaccurate measurements. Once the lash gauges just start to drag between rod and crankshaft, the clearance has been found. Compare the measured clearance to the specifications found in the service manual.

Checking Rod Small End Diameter

The rod small end diameter can be measured by using small hole or telescoping gauges. For new crankshaft assemblies, measuring the small end diameter will be necessary for calculating the clearance between the piston pin and rod small end bore.

On old rods, measuring the rod bore in the X and Y directions can be useful for diagnosing out of round problems with the rod bore. Since transfer gauges are being used to measure the bore, take three to five measurements to confirm repeatability. Then take the average of those measurements as the final bore diameter.

TRANSMISSION, SHIFT FORK, SHIFT DRUM, AND SHIFT FORK SHAFT
DISASSEMBLY / INSPECTION / REASSEMBLY

Transmission problems can be identified by carefully inspecting all of the components which make up the transmission assembly. If the bike was previously experiencing trouble shifting or jumping out of gear, this is where the problem lies. Making accurate assessments of the transmission assembly is critical, because it is a lot of work to open the engine up to get back to this point!

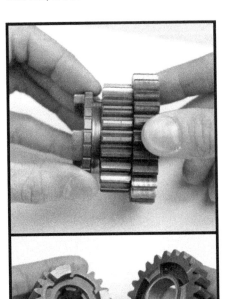

Almost all transmission related problems are caused by worn gear dogs or gear dog slots. The gear dogs are located on the sides of the transmission gears and are what engage with mating gears.

Missed shifts or half hearted shifts, where the gears don't fully engage with one another causing them to pop back out or grind, are the hardest on gear dogs. Normal use is also a contributing factor to gear dog wear, however, it takes much longer for gear dogs to wear out due to normal use.

Worn gear dogs will contribute to wear and damage of other components within the transmission assembly. The shift forks and shift drum can both suffer from worn gear dogs. Since the gear dogs have a top down effect on all the other transmission components, it makes the most sense to start the inspection by looking at the culprit of most problems.

The information and specifications provided by manufacturers for disassembly and inspection of the transmission assembly varies significantly. This means the number of quantifiable measurements which can be taken won't be the same for all manufacturers. Fortunately, most major problems associated with the transmission assembly are easily identified visually, so it is not a problem if every part can't be measured.

Initial Transmission Shaft Inspections

Before I get into the specifics of inspection and disassembly, I want to warn you that the amount of information provided by service manuals in regards to transmission shaft disassembly varies. If shaft disassembly is necessary, it is important to have a good understanding of how the parts fit together. This may come in the form of diagrams provided in the service manual, subassembly microfiches, or step-by-step photos you take as you disassemble the shafts.

Confirming if any problems exist which require the shafts to be disassembled is a good first step. This is easily done by working with previous knowledge of how the gearbox performed when the engine was together and observing the condition of the gear dogs and gear dog slots on all of the gears. A gearbox which functioned well prior to disassembly will show minimal signs of gear dog and slot wear. A gearbox which popped out of certain gears will show signs of worn or damaged gear dogs. These gear dogs and slots will be excessively rounded. The rounded dogs no longer engage securely into the slots, causing them to pop back out.

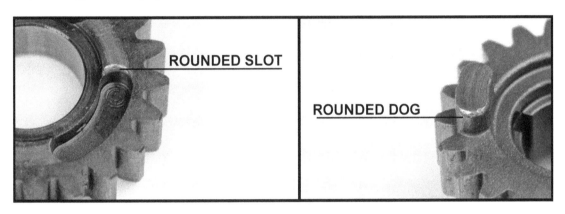

As the transmission shafts are inspected for damaged gear dogs, it is easy to correlate damaged gears to the overall problematic "gear" the transmission was in when it was dysfunctional. On the primary shaft (clutch shaft) the gear with the smallest diameter/number of teeth is first gear and the largest diameter/highest number of teeth gear is fifth or sixth gear depending on the number of gears in the transmission.

On the secondary shaft (output shaft) the gear with the largest diameter/highest number of teeth corresponds to first gear. The gear with the smallest diameter/fewest teeth is fifth or sixth gear.

After the gear dogs have been inspected, all gears should be inspected for chipped or missing teeth. Chipped or broken gear teeth are usually the result of a large and hard piece of debris passing between the gears.

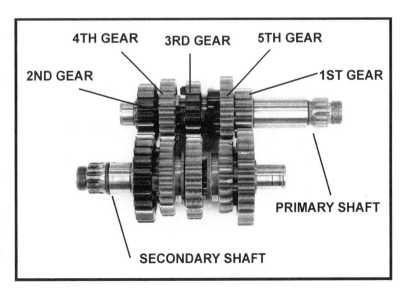

Don't forget to closely inspect the mating gear's teeth as well. If any gear teeth are damaged, there is a good chance another component within the transmission is severely damaged, as the debris must have come from somewhere.

Carefully inspect the condition of the shift fork grooves on the three gears which are guided by the shift forks. If at some point any of the gears popped out, it is possible the shift forks could have bent, which results in the shift fork rubbing on the side of the groove in the gear. The rubbing can create a lot of friction and heat, resulting in discoloration of the groove, marring, or scratches in the groove. In addition to visual inspection of the groove, some service manuals provided specifications for the width of the groove which can be measured using a caliper.

Once the shift fork grooves have been inspected, feel how well the gears engage as the shift forks slide back and forth. The gears should slide easily, but if they don't there could be a problem with one of the shafts or the splines on the gear.

Next, spin any gears which rotate freely on bushings. These gears should spin with ease. If they don't, debris may have passed between the gear and bushing. The debris may have gotten sandwiched into the soft bushing material or marred the gear or bushing surfaces leaving a raised edge. In either case, the debris will reduce the clearance between the gear and bushing making it spin poorly. If any free spinning gears don't spin well, the shafts should be disassembled and components inspected.

If the transmission didn't experience any shifting problems before the engine was taken apart, all the gear dogs and gears look to be in good shape, the shift fork grooves are in good condition, all gears slide and spin freely, and it is known the transmission oil was changed regularly resulting in little metallic debris passing through the gearbox, further disassembly of the shafts is not necessary. Simply clean any old oil off the gears and shafts, then set them aside until it is time to reinstall them. However, if any problems or damage is present, we can move on to disassembling the transmission shafts.

BROKEN GEAR DOG

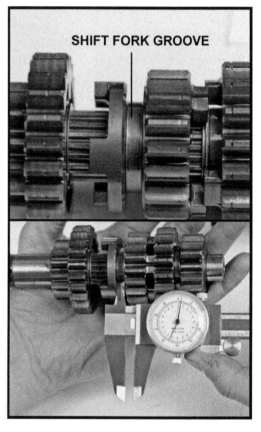

SHIFT FORK GROOVE

FREE SPINNING GEAR

Transmission Shaft Disassembly

Transmission shafts are all very similar to one another in regards to design and retainment of the gears. A series of thrust washers and retaining rings are used to locate gears on both shafts. All that is necessary for disassembly is a keen eye for detail and a good snap ring pliers.

Plan your disassembly carefully before removing any parts from the shafts. I want to provide a couple pointers which help when taking apart the shafts. First, it is a good idea to only disassemble one shaft at a time. Second, keep the orientation of the shaft constant during the disassembly and allot enough room to lay the parts out in the order they are taken off the shaft.

Start by orienting the shaft and removing any loose washers and gears. Set parts that can be taken off the left side of the shaft to the left, and parts native to the right side of the shaft to the right. Once laid out, it should be evident which side of the shaft the parts came from and the order in which they must be reinstalled.

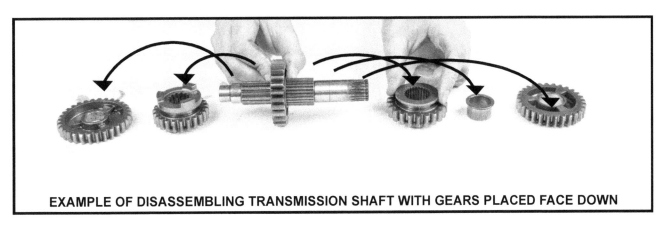

EXAMPLE OF DISASSEMBLING TRANSMISSION SHAFT WITH GEARS PLACED FACE DOWN

As parts are taken off the shaft, lay them flat with their outer face laying down, doing so will result in a systematic approach and eliminate the possibility of reassembling any components in the wrong orientation. When it comes time to reassemble, the face up side of all parts must be oriented inwards towards the center of the shaft. Pay special attention to the orientation of thrust washers, retaining rings, and bushings. Thrust washers regularly incorporate a chamfer or radius on the outer edge of one side of the washer. Unless otherwise specified by the service manual, this chamfered or radiused edge should always face towards the thrust side (towards the gear).

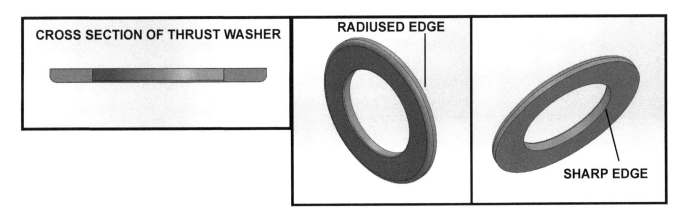

CROSS SECTION OF THRUST WASHER

RADIUSED EDGE

SHARP EDGE

RETAINING RING

OIL HOLE ON BUSHING

Positioning of the openings between retaining ring ends is also commonly specified. In most cases, the opening between the ends of a retaining ring should be aligned between two spline teeth.

Some bushings incorporate oil holes which may need to be oriented a certain way. Most modern designs have eliminated any direction or positional requirements of the bushing, but older engines may have bushing which must be oriented a specific way. Keep your eyes out for any bushings that require special orientation and pay attention to any information provided in the service manual.

GEAR DOG IN GOOD CONDITION

GEAR SLOT IN GOOD CONDITION

Final Transmission Shaft Inspection

Once the shaft has been disassembled, the parts can be further inspected and replaced as necessary. Any gears with rounded dogs should be replaced along with the mating gear that is slotted to lock with the dogs. It is imperative that both mating gears are replaced together because if only one gear is replaced problems will still exist. A fresh set of gear dogs trying to lock into a series of slots with rounded edges will still function just as poorly as two gears with rounded engagement features. Gears with damaged shift drum grooves should also be exchanged for new ones.

Gear bushings and their corresponding gears should be inspected for wear or damage. This is particularly important for any gear/bushing combos which didn't rotate smoothly or were sticky. The bushings are made of soft materials which are susceptible of becoming impregnated with debris. If any of the bushings are impregnated with large pieces of foreign debris, the bushing should be replaced.

As a result of the impregnated bushing, scoring or scratching of the gear mating surface can occur. Minor scores or scratches can be dressed by using a file to remove the raised edge then carefully blending the imperfection smooth. To check to see if the problems have been fixed, temporarily reinstall the bushing and gear on the shaft and try spinning the gear. The gear should spin freely with little resistance.

Any visible scratching or scoring of the shaft should be addressed by attempting to fix the problem or by replacing the shaft, depending on the severity of the problem. Most minor scratches can be filed and blended using a diamond file. Sanding and smoothing of the problematic area may also be necessary to ensure the mating part won't get caught on the imperfection. Gears operating over trouble areas on the shaft can quickly be fit, then moved or spun to confirm any problems have been corrected.

GALLED GEAR BUSHING

Once all the problematic parts associated with the gear shaft have been replaced or fixed, a final cleaning of all the parts can be performed before reassembly. Clean the parts one at a time so the order of the parts doesn't get mixed up. Be careful not to confuse the correct orientation of the part while cleaning or set the part back down wrongly positioned so that it is installed incorrectly.

Transmission Shaft Assembly

The only way the transmission shaft can go back together correctly is in the reverse order of how it was disassembled. Special attention must be paid to the orientations of the gears, washers, and retaining rings. As a reminder, new retaining rings should be used when assembling the transmission shafts.

At this point, introducing assembly lube and the merits it has throughout the build becomes relevant.

TECHNICAL TAKEAWAY
Using Assembly Lube

Assembly lube is a fantastic lubricant which should be used throughout the reassembly of an engine. Prelubrication is necessary to prevent wear to moving parts before oil circulates at startup. Assembly lubes have been designed and formulated for just this purpose and will provide the best protection against wear.

How do you know where to apply assembly lube? This is a good question! As a rule of thumb, assembly lube should be applied to any parts which make metal to metal contact and slide or rotate against one another. There is no downside to applying assembly lube, so it is better to be safe than sorry.

Along with my general recommendation, service manuals provide good insight into where to use assembly lube as well. Instead of calling out assembly lube application points, service manuals will specify the use of another lubricant called molybdenum disulfide grease. Most assembly lubes meet or exceed the lubricating specifications of molybdenum disulfide greases and can be used in their place.

As the transmission shaft is assembled, apply assembly lube to the thrust faces of washers, the shaft, and the bushings and gears to pre-lubricate them. While the transmission will be filled with oil at the end of assembly, applying assembly lube doesn't hurt and will be beneficial when the functionality of the transmission is tested just after the crankcases are assembled.

Here are some helpful reminders for reassembling the transmission shafts.

1. Pay close attention to the orientation of washers, bushings, gears, and retaining rings during reassembly.

2. When installing gears and bushings be careful sliding them past the sharp edges of the shaft as the shaft can scratch the bushing.

3. Remember to keep the chamfered edge of the washer oriented towards the thrust side (gear side) unless otherwise specified.

4. Make sure bushings are oriented correctly if there are any positional requirements such as aligning oil holes or oil grooves.

5. Due to manufacturing processes, retaining rings often feature a side with a radiused edge. The radiused edge should be positioned towards the thrust side (gear side) so that the sharp edge of the retaining ring can bite against the groove.

6. Remember to only spread the retaining ring open enough so that it can be slid onto the shaft. This will decrease the chances of stretching the retaining ring.

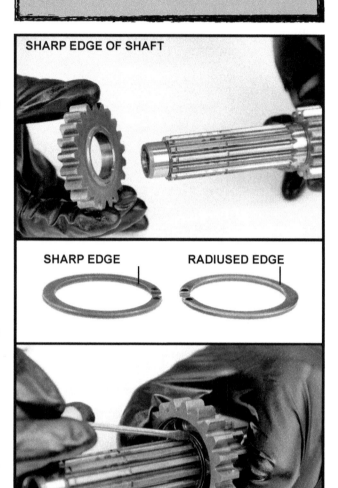

> **HOT TIP:** Avoid applying assembly lube to any parts which are not meant to rotate, such as retaining ring grooves. Consider sequences of application which keep the assembly lube from getting in undesirable spots.

SHARP EDGE OF SHAFT

SHARP EDGE   **RADIUSED EDGE**

CHECKING TO MAKE SURE THERE IS NO ROTATION

7. Once the retaining ring is seated in the groove, check to make sure it has not been stretched. Use your finger or a screwdriver to try and rotate the retaining ring around the groove. The retaining ring should remain tight to the groove and not rotate. If the retaining ring rotates, it has stretched and should be replaced with a new one.

8. Confirm any final orientation requirements of the gap between the retaining ring ends are met. Normally the gap should be situated between a pair of spline teeth.

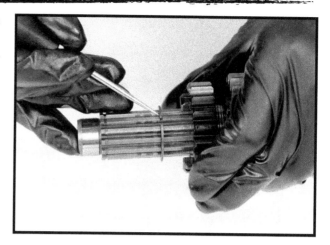

That covers the finer points of disassembling, inspecting, and assembling transmission shafts. Proceed to take apart the remaining transmission shaft following the previously outlined instructions. Once both shafts have been squared away, inspection of the remaining transmission assembly components can commence.

TECHNICAL TAKEAWAY

Transmission Shimming

Some manufacturers incorporate thrust washers of different thickness into the design of the transmission shaft assemblies. Different thickness washers are used to account for variation in component widths which occur during manufacturing. The use of different thickness washers effectively allows more variation in part dimensions at the manufacturing level. This allows for a wider range of parts to be passed off as good by the manufacturer. This makes sense as knocking out a couple different washer options is usually a cheaper alternative to controlling part tolerances more tightly. If an engine utilizes thrust washers of different thicknesses and some of the corresponding parts were replaced, checking the specified clearance and reshimming as necessary is a good idea.

CHECKING GEAR FREE PLAY

If the transmission shafts utilize thrust washers with different thickness options, the service manual should have further details on thrust washer options and how to take clearance measurements. Normally, taking clearance measurements is very easy and a set of lash gauges are used. The clearance will likely be specified between the face of a washer or gear and the edge of the transmission shaft.

Shift Drum Inspection

The shift drum grooves are the most important feature to inspect on the shift drum. In order for the shift fork pins to move smoothly through the shift drum grooves, the grooves must be free of imperfections. It takes a significant amount of force to damage the shift drum grooves, since the entire drum is made from a hardened steel alloy. Damage to the grooves can occur though as a result of gears popping out. When the shift fork pins are forced hard into the sides of the shift drum grooves, impressions can be left inside the grooves, the edges of the grooves can chip, or marring can occur. Any imperfections will result in shifting problems if not corrected. Minor blemishes can be carefully smoothed, however, it is best to replace the entire drum if major damage has occurred.

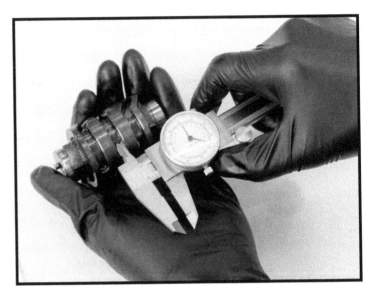

In addition to visually inspecting the shift drum grooves, some manuals will specify a maximum groove width. The shift drum groove width can be measured using the internal jaws of a caliper. Unless a significant amount of debris has passed through the engine or contaminated the transmission oil, it is quite rare to see shift drum grooves which have become too wide since the shift drum and shift forks are heavily lubricated.

Shift Fork Inspections

Problems arise with shift forks as a result of gears popping out and disengaging from one another. Since the shift drum dictates where the shift fork is positioned, a lot of stress is put on the shift fork when a gear jumps out of position. This loads the shift fork laterally and can cause the shift fork to bend.

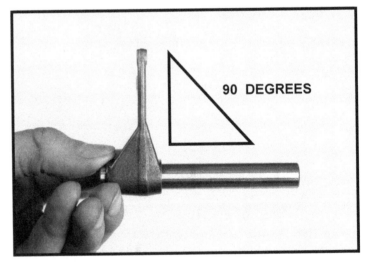

90 DEGREES

Inspect each shift fork for straightness by temporarily sliding them onto the shift fork shaft. Each shift fork should be 90 degrees to the shift fork shaft.

Other indicators of damaged shift forks can be found by looking at the ends of the forks. Any discoloration present on the shift fork will likely be accompanied by irregular wear marks. The discoloration occurs due to excessive heat build up caused by the side of the shift fork rubbing against the groove in its mating gear. The discoloration is a good sign that the shift fork is bent.

The irregular wear marks will present themselves at three points: on each end of the shift fork and towards the center of the shift fork. If wear is severe enough, the entire shift fork will feature a circular groove which connects the three previously mentioned points.

In addition to the visual inspections of the shift forks, the majority of manuals will specify shift fork widths. These widths can easily be measured to determine if the fork is within spec.

Inspect the bore of the shift fork and the dowel pins, which slide in the shift drum grooves, for any signs of trouble. It is rare that any problems occur in these areas, but it is worth a look nonetheless. If any of the shift forks are bent or damaged, they should be replaced. There are limited suitable corrective actions to remedy bent forks, so replacement is the best solution.

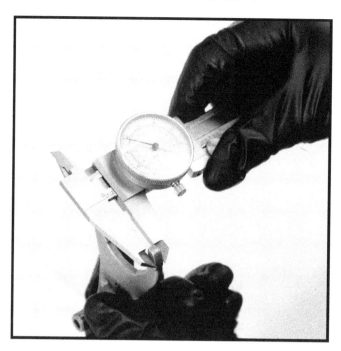

DISASSEMBLED RATCHETING MECHANISM

CORRECT PAWL DIRECTION

Shift Fork Shaft Inspections

The shift fork shafts should be felt for any grooves which can catch one's fingernail. The shafts should also be inspected for straightness. This can either be done visually or by rolling the shaft across a flat surface, such as a surface plate. In my experience, the shift fork shafts are a couple no-frills parts which seldom wear or get damaged. If the shafts are bent or grooved, replacement is the only option which will ensure a good functioning gearbox once the engine is built.

External Shift Mechanism Inspection

Not a whole lot can go wrong with the external shift mechanism components. Ensuring the components are clean and assembled correctly are the primary concerns. The ratcheting mechanism features spring loaded plungers, which apply pressure to a pair of pawls. The pawls can be directional so ensuring they are oriented correctly before final assembly is important.

Disassemble the ratcheting mechanism. Clean the individual parts then reassemble. Apply assembly lube to the components to pre-lubricate them.

Shift Shaft Inspection

Inspect the shift shaft surfaces where they mate with the crankcase bores for signs of wear, grooving, or marring. Any surface imperfections on the steel shaft can damage the softer mating bores in the crankcase. Use a file and sandpaper to remove any blemishes, making the surface as smooth as possible. Along with shaft imperfections, check to see if the shaft is straight.

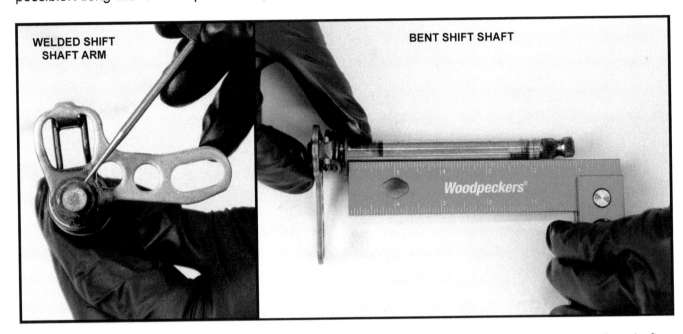

WELDED SHIFT SHAFT ARM

BENT SHIFT SHAFT

Some shift shafts feature a press fit arm instead of an arm which has been welded to the shaft. Occasionally the press fit between the shaft and arm loosens causing the arm to rotate out of position. When this happens the bike will not want to go into gear and the shift pedal may not return to its original position. This problem is more likely to be diagnosed when the bike was still running and being ridden, but worth mentioning. Shafts and arms that have come loose can be carefully welded.

CLUTCH INSPECTION

The inspection of the clutch system will be broken down into three subparts. Each part will address a specific component and consist of a combination of visual/feel inspections and measurement inspections. Start by cleaning the oil and debris from all the clutch components.

Basket Inspection

Inspect the driven gear which is secured to the basket. Look for damaged gear teeth and other imperfections. Grasp the gear and basket firmly, then try to twist the gear. The gear is secured to the basket either with rivets or fasteners. With use, the rivets or fasteners can loosen causing the gear to become loose. Most baskets use round rubber dampers to locate the gear to the basket, which are sandwiched behind the backing plate. The dampers can wear out and break, which will create excessive play between the gear and basket. Any looseness may have been accompanied by excessive gear noise or rattling sounds when the engine was previously running.

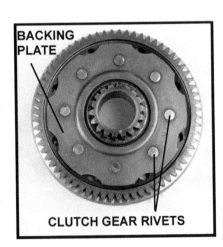

BACKING PLATE

CLUTCH GEAR RIVETS

NEEDLE BEARING SURFACE

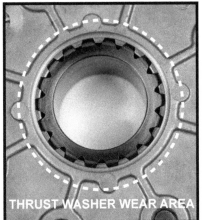
THRUST WASHER WEAR AREA

GROOVED BASKET FINGER

On baskets with riveted gears the corrective action which will need to be taken is to either replace the basket or drill the rivets out. The idle gear may need to be pressed off in order to remove the backing plate. Once this is done, holes can be tapped and bolts installed which will secure the gear in place. Any rubber dampers that have worn can be replaced with aftermarket options.

Inspect the needle bearing bore surface on the basket next. Run your fingernail across the bore feeling for signs of wear. The bearing surface should be smooth and free of imperfections. If the surface is grooved or worn the basket will need to be replaced.

Inspect the area inside the basket where the large thrust washer resides. Wear should be minimal in this area. If any grooving is present, the needle bearing and spacer the basket rides on may have worn causing the basket to wobble or the pressed in steel insert has backed out, ultimately causing the face of the basket to rub on the edges of the washer.

Check for bent clutch basket fingers on the basket. Then look for grooving on the basket fingers where the clutch discs come in contact with the fingers. Grooving is caused by the clutch discs slamming into the clutch basket fingers. Normally grooving will be more pronounced on the drive side fingers. Grooving is not abnormal and occurs through usage of the clutch.

If any grooving is present, use the end of a pick to evaluate how deep the grooves are. Any grooving that can catch the end of the pick is also likely to be able to catch the edge of the clutch discs. When this happens the clutch will have difficulty engaging and disengaging. If your bike had clutch disengagement/engagement problems prior to disassembly, basket grooving is the most probable cause.

A file can be used to smooth the grooves so the discs no longer catch, however deep grooving is an indication that the basket is near the end of its life. When filing clutch basket fingers, attempt to remove as little material as possible and remove material evenly from all the fingers.

Some manufacturers provide a specification for the clearance between the clutch disc tang and the basket fingers. This clearance can be measured by temporarily installing a clutch disc into the basket and using a set of lash gauges to check the clearance

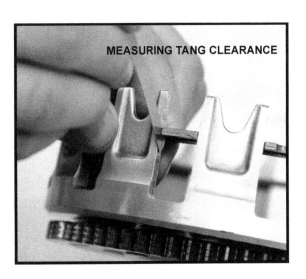
MEASURING TANG CLEARANCE

between the two parts. Both the clutch disc tangs and basket fingers will wear so if the clearance is outside the service limit it may be possible to prolong the life of the basket by installing new clutch discs. This is a short term fix however, and replacing both components at once is advisable.

Bearing/Spacer Inspection

Inspect the clutch hub needle bearing and spacer for signs of wear. The needle bearing will be replaced with a new bearing, but if the spacer is in good condition it will be reused. Check for grooving or concavity along the surface of the spacer where the bearing rotates. While the needle bearing won't be reused, it can be inspected as well to help confirm any problems associated with the clutch basket or spacer.

SPACER INSPECTION

LOOK FOR CLUTCH HUB GROOVING

Hub Inspection

There are two main areas on the clutch hub which will wear. First, grooving can occur on the splines which locate the clutch plates to the hub. The grooves are a result of normal clutch use and occur when the steel clutch plates rotate back and forth in the spline grooves. Any grooving which catches the end of a pick should be considered problematic. Careful filing to smooth the grooves or hub replacement are the two options available for remedying the issue. The clutch plates must be able to easily slide back and forth along the hub, otherwise clutch disengagement/engagement problems will occur.

The second area susceptible to wear on the clutch hub is at the back face of the hub. This is where the outer clutch disc contacts the hub. When the clutch is engaged, the clutch disc and hub will rotate in unison. However, when the clutch is partially engaged or disengaged, the clutch disc will rub against the face of the hub causing both the hub and disc to wear. Look for uneven wear patterns and indications of how deep the clutch disc has worn into the clutch hub. If the face of the clutch hub has worn excessively or unevenly, the hub should be replaced.

Pressure Plate Inspection

The interaction between the pressure plate and clutch disc is identical to the situation previously described between the clutch disc and clutch hub. Wear will occur on the face of the pressure plate which contacts the outside clutch disc. Determine the condition of the pressure plate by looking for signs of excessive or uneven wear on the face of the pressure plate.

Disc and Plate Inspection

Both the clutch discs and clutch plates are designed to be wear items which will need replacement from time to time. Thickness and straightness are the primary inspection criteria used to determine if either component requires replacement. If there are any problems with any of the discs or plates replacing them as a set is best.

INSPECT FOR CLUTCH HUB FACE WEAR

INSPECT PRESSURE PLATE

Clutch Disc and Clutch Plate Inspection

Clutch discs are made out of various compositions of fibrous materials which wear at different rates, while clutch plates are made from steel. Service manuals will specify a minimum thickness that the clutch discs and plates can be. This thickness can easily be measured by using a caliper. Take measurements at three to four locations around the clutch disc or plate to confirm either has not worn unevenly.

MEASURING CLUTCH DISC THICKNESS

Once all the disc and plate thicknesses have been measured, both should be inspected for warpage. This can be done by laying the disc or plate on a surface plate or other flat surface. A set of lash gauges are used to determine any warpage. The service manual should specify a maximum warpage value which is usually around 0.006" (0.15mm). Attempt to insert the 0.006" lash gauge underneath the clutch disc or plate at multiple points. If the feeler gauge slides beneath either of the parts, those parts are warped and should be replaced.

Clutch discs which have been overheated due to excessive clutch fanning by the rider, not only may warp, but also emit an unpleasant stinky burnt smell. If a noticeable smell is present, the discs have overheated and should be replaced. Likewise, clutch plates that have overheated will likely be warped and exhibit discoloration. The discoloration is a sign of excessive heat build up. Once the clutch plates have overheated, the material properties of the plate change, the hardness is reduced, and the plate becomes less wear resistant. This means discolored plates should be replaced.

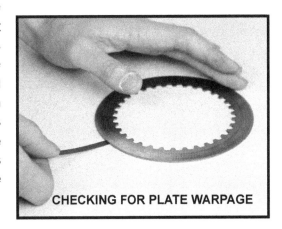

CHECKING FOR PLATE WARPAGE

Lastly, inspect the clutch disc tangs for wear, chipping, or damage. If any tangs are damaged the disc should be replaced.

Clutch Spring Inspection

Over time and due to normal clutch use, the clutch springs will shorten. Clutch spring minimum free length specifications are provided by manufactures and can easily be measured using a caliper.

Clutch springs that are shorter than the minimum spec provided by the manufacturer will not have sufficient spring pressure to keep the clutch from slipping under heavy loads. Any springs at or past their service limits require the replacement of all springs as a set. This way when the new springs are installed, even pressure is applied to the pressure plate.

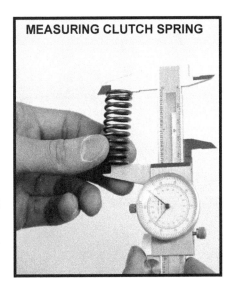

MEASURING CLUTCH SPRING

Primary Gear Inspection

Inspect the primary gear teeth for chips and imperfections. Any damage found on the teeth should result in replacement of the gear. Double check the condition of the mating clutch driven gear as well if damage was found on the primary gear teeth, but not originally on the clutch gear. Normally the gears will wear and exhibit signs of damage together.

The many primary gears now feature a seal surface which mates with the crankshaft seal. Carefully inspect the surfaces the crank seal runs on for grooving. If a fingernail can be caught in the groove created by the seal, the seal should either be positioned to a different depth or the gear replaced.

Balance Shaft Inspection

The balance shaft is a stout piece of metal which isn't likely to fatigue or fail. Damage to the shaft is more likely to occur to the bearing and seal surfaces on the shaft. Check the shaft for scoring, grooving, and pitting. Roller bearings require near perfect surface finishes for correct operation and long bearing life, so any imperfections where the roller bearing contacts the shaft may render the shaft defective.

Keep an eye out for any grooves created by the balance shaft seal. Either investigate repositioning the seal or replace the shaft to remedy grooving problems.

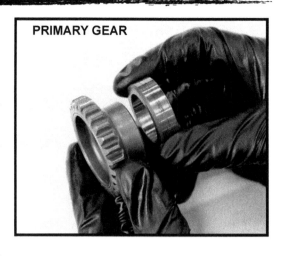

PRIMARY GEAR

CHECKING BALANCE SHAFT SURFACE FINISH

Kickstart Assembly Inspection

There are only a handful of things which can go wrong with the kickstarter assembly. The most common of these are rounded engagement gears and broken return springs. More severe problems such as bent shafts, damaged gear teeth, and worn out gear bushings are possible but infrequent.

Both worn engagement teeth between the ratchet and kickstart gear and broken return springs can be diagnosed without disassembling the kickstart assembly. Honestly, it would be quite surprising if a broken return spring was not previously discovered when the assembly was removed from the engine.

Any annoying starting problems arising from the kickstarter skipping teeth and making a ratcheting sound as the engine is kicked over will be found within the kickstart assembly. Check to see if disassembly of the kickstarter is necessary by inspecting the two interlocking gears on the assembly.

As the kickstarter shaft is rotated, the ratchet will engage with the kickstart gear once it clears the guide plate. This locks the assembly and transmits kicking power through the series of gears to the crankshaft which will turn the engine over. Through usage the ratchet teeth and kickstart gear teeth may round. The rounding of the gear teeth is what causes the kickstarter to disengage and skip when the engine is kicked over.

INSPECTING RACHET GEAR MESH

GUIDE   **RETURN SPRING**

Check the profile of the teeth by locking the gears together. Then try rotating the kickstart gear into the ratchet gear, simulating the movement of the assembly in operation, and note how easily the gears engage or skip. Due to the way the gears are manufactured, there may be gaps between the teeth. This is normal and the area of concern is on the leading edge of the gear. Any rounding of the leading edge will make the gear more susceptible to ratcheting and slipping. If the gear teeth are rounded, the assembly will need to come apart and the gears replaced.

The remaining features which should be looked over to determine if disassembly is necessary are the kickstart gear teeth, which mesh with the idle gear and the end of the kickstart shaft which mates with the crankcase. When the ratchet is pulled away from the kickstart gear, the gear should spin freely. The gear teeth should be free of damage along with the end of the shaft. If any scoring, scratches, or other imperfections are present on the end of the shaft these imperfections should either be carefully dressed or the shaft replaced. If no problems are found with the kickstart assembly and it was in good working condition before taking the engine apart, it is seldom worthwhile to further disassemble the assembly. Simply clean any remaining old oil from the assembly and apply fresh assembly lube to the moving parts.

ALIGNMENT MARKS

Assuming the kickstart assembly does need to come apart the procedure is simple. When disassembling lay the parts out in order similar to how the transmission shaft was disassembled. Start by removing the return spring and guide.

Remove the retaining ring from the end of the shaft using a snap ring pliers. Then remove the washer and spring. There should be an alignment mark or punch mark on the end of the shaft which corresponds to a mark on the ratchet. These marks are incorporated on all modern engines and ensure correct alignment of the ratchet on the shaft. Some old engines may not have these marks in which case a marker should be used to dot the shaft and ratchet so they can be aligned correctly when it comes time to reassemble.

Carefully remove and lay out all the remaining parts in the order they came off the shaft.

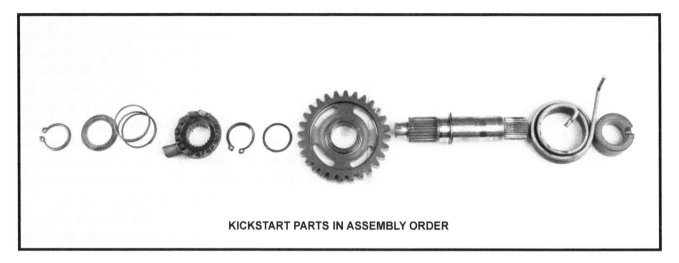

KICKSTART PARTS IN ASSEMBLY ORDER

Visually inspect the kickstart shaft for straightness, wear marks, and other imperfections. Inspect the inner diameter of the kickstart gear and bushing if equipped for signs of wear. Gears or bushings with impregnated metallic debris, scoring or scratches should be replaced or carefully mended depending on the severity of the imperfections.

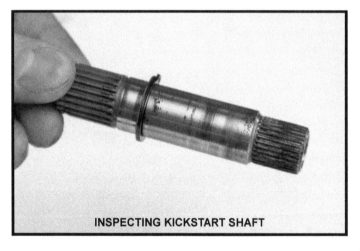

INSPECTING KICKSTART SHAFT

Once any further problems have been diagnosed, the assembly can go back together incorporating any necessary replacement parts. Apply assembly lube to all moving and sliding surfaces. Make sure to install all parts in the correct order, align the punch marks on the end of the shaft with the ratchet, and use a new retaining ring to secure the assembly. Don't forget to align the radiused edge of the retaining ring to the thrust side (gear side) and double check that the ring won't spin on the shaft with a screwdriver.

RIGHT COVER SUBASSEMBLY

Right Cover Disassembly

The right cover disassembly, inspection, and reassembly will be handled similar to the crankcase halves. First, start by removing the water pump cover.

Once the cover is removed, rotate the water pump shaft and feel for play in the bearing. Even though the bearing will be replaced, identifying any potential problems the engine had while it was together is insightful. If the bearing is worn and there is a lot of slop in the shaft, this would have accelerated seal wear. Common symptoms of a worn bearing and damaged seal when the engine was together and running include coolant leakage from the weep hole or coolant mixing with the transmission oil.

Follow the service manual for specific instructions on removing the water pump impeller from the shaft. In most cases the impeller will be threaded onto the shaft. A wrench will be necessary to secure the water pump shaft and a socket can be used to remove the impeller.

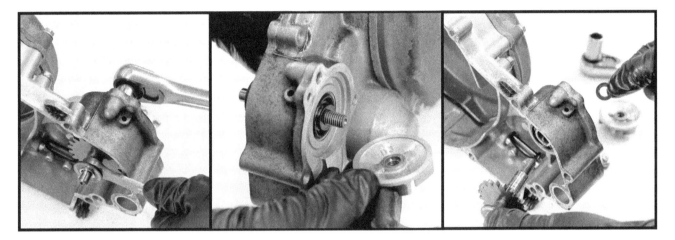

Lay the right cover on a soft surface and use a brass or plastic punch to tap the water pump shaft out of the cover.

PUNCH AGAINST BEARING

Once the shaft is out, use a seal puller to remove the water pump seal from its bore. Both the water pump seal and oil seal will need to be installed in specific orientations. Note the orientation of the seal before removal in case the service manual lacks clarity.

Use a punch to carefully drive the water pump bearing from its bore. Remember to tap evenly and avoid striking the side of the bore with the punch. Once the bearing has been removed the remaining oil seal can be tapped out using an appropriately sized socket or punch to drive the seal out. Don't forget to again note the orientation of the oil seal in case the service manual is not clear.

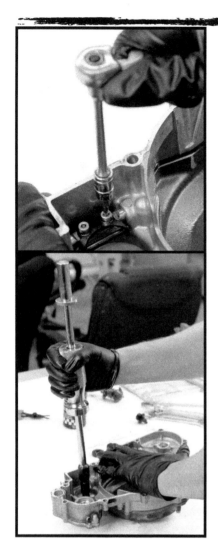

The power valve governor control arm typically resides in the cover. A small oil seal is used to seal the shaft of the control arm and the cover. To service the seal the governor fork must be removed. The governor bearing can be removed by using a bearing puller.

Once the control arm shaft seal has been removed proceed to remove the kickstart oil seal, and any other auxiliary components.

Use a gasket scraper to carefully remove any gasket material from the right cover and auxiliary covers. Once all gasket material has been removed, use parts cleaner to thoroughly clean all the parts.

Right Cover Inspection

Inspect the right cover for damage to the gasket surfaces, kickstart bore, seal bores, and bearing bores. If the cover previously leaked, check it for flatness by laying it on a surface plate. Refer to the crankcase section for further information on how to correct any problems with the cover. Also check the water pump and any other covers for damaged surfaces at this time. If any problems with the covers were corrected, don't forget to clean any resulting debris from them before beginning reassembly.

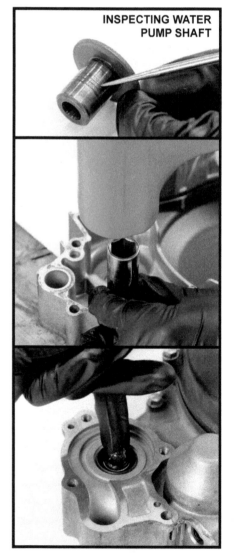

INSPECTING WATER PUMP SHAFT

Run your fingernail against the water pump shaft surface. Note any grooving in the water pump shaft caused by the seal lip or bearing. Replace the shaft if necessary. Shafts are relatively inexpensive and it is usually difficult to reposition the seals to adjust their depths and avoid running in the old grooves.

Right Cover Reassembly

Begin reassembly by installing new seals into the right cover. The seals will have directional requirements so pay close attention to the instructions provided in the service manual and any notes or photos taken when the seal was removed. Remember to apply even pressure to the seal face and set the seal squarely in the bore.

If the seal lips didn't come pre-greased, they should be greased with a lithium based grease. Carefully apply grease to all the seal lips so that they are lubricated.

Use a punch and hammer to drive a new water pump bearing into its bore. Don't forget that a slight gap must exist between the bearing faces and seal faces. Apply assembly lube to the bearing to lubricate it.

Proceed to reinstall the shaft and impeller, torque them, and assemble any other auxiliary components. Be sure to use new gaskets or o-rings to ensure leaks won't be an issue. Once all the parts have been installed, the cover can be set aside.

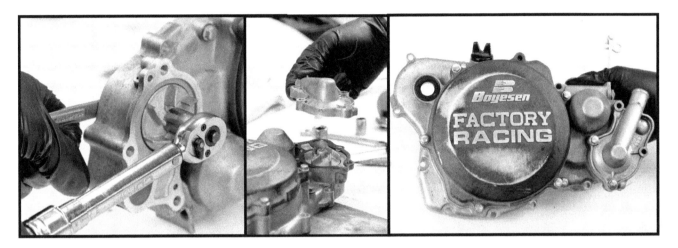

POWER VALVE GOVERNOR DISASSEMBLY/INSPECTION/REASSEMBLY

Mechanical power valve governors rarely wear to the point of requiring serious attention, however, they should be inspected nonetheless. Most governors actuate as a result of centrifugal force and consist of some combination of balls, retainers, washers, thrust bearings, spacers, shafts and gears.

The majority of governor assemblies can be disassembled by compressing a spring and removing a pin or retaining ring from the shaft. The components can then be removed from the shaft individually, cleaned, and inspected.

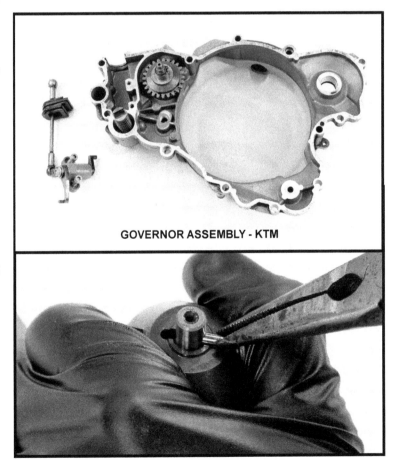

GOVERNOR ASSEMBLY - KTM

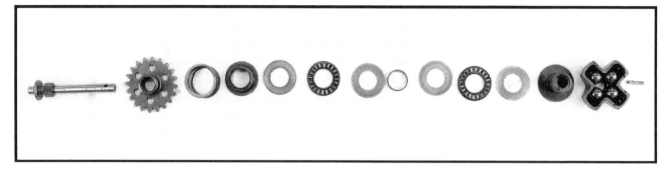

Refer to the service manual for specific inspection points. If the manual is vague or unclear confirm all sliding or rotating components are in good condition. Check for grooving on shafts and surfaces that contact thrust bearings. Ensure retainers that house any steel balls are not cupped or worn where the balls move in and out.

Carefully inspect any linkage assemblies that are housed in the engine cover and between the governor and cylinder assembly. Check for excessive free play in any pinned joints. Usually by design, some axial free play will be permissible, however, radial free play should be minimal. The radial free play can be assessed simply by pulling and pushing outward and inward on the pinned joint. Axial free play refers to the amount of movement present when parts are pushed and pulled up and down along the axis of the pin. To further assess the condition of the joint consider how the joint functions and which features are important to ensure precise operation of the assembly.

Use the service manual to confirm any special reassembly instructions. If none are provided, reassembly can be assumed to be the reverse of disassembly. Install any new bearings required and apply assembly lube to all sliding or rotating components. If a pin or retaining ring is used to secure the assembly be sure it is seated correctly.

STATOR AND FLYWHEEL INSPECTION

There isn't much that can go wrong mechanically between the stator and flywheel regardless of whether the stator plate is adjustable or non-adjustable. Procedures for inspecting both types are identical. Electrical problems are another story, which can be best troubleshot by carefully following along with procedures outlined in service manuals.

Start by cleaning the stator cover, stator, and flywheel. Check to make sure the stator and crankshaft position sensor are secured tightly to the plate or cover. If either of these parts happen to get loose while the engine is running, they can rub against the flywheel. The raised bosses on the outside of the flywheel and contact of the pickup sensor will show parallel wear lines due to the crankshaft sensor making contact.

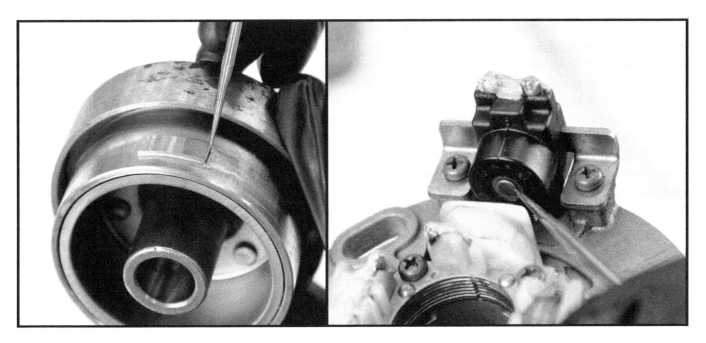

A loose stator which contacted the flywheel will result in both parts having signs of scratching and scoring. Chances of the stator or crankshaft sensor coming loose and contacting the flywheel are extremely rare on non-adjustable systems but are more common on adjustable units.

Depending on the gap between the raised bosses on the outside of the flywheel and the crankshaft sensor pickup, it is possible when crank bearings wear or crankshafts become misaligned that the runout at the end of the crank is severe enough to cause the flywheel to contact the crankshaft sensor. One last possibility of contact can occur on engines with stators housed in the cover when the stator cover dowel pins are not used to secure the cover to the crankcases.

If the flywheel taper was not previously inspected in conjunction with the crankshaft taper, inspect the taper for surface imperfections. Any imperfections should be corrected to insure a good fit between the flywheel and crankshaft. Refer to suggestions referenced in the crankshaft inspection section for further guidance on assessing and correcting fitment issues. Unless the stator or crankshaft sensor are damaged or defective, it is not necessary to remove them from the cover or stator plate. Proceed to remove any remaining gasket material on the gasket surface of the stator cover, then inspect the sealing surfaces for nicks, scratches, and other imperfections. Take any corrective actions necessary, clean the parts, and then set them aside.

TOP END

The time has come to start looking at the subassemblies which comprise the top end of the engine. After squaring away the covers and some of the simpler bottom end parts, working with the top end components will be a welcomed change! Top end components are by far the most difficult and time consuming components to inspect and prepare for final assembly. Not only should the old parts carefully be examined, and in some cases measured, but also the new top end parts should be looked over too. We'll start by examining the reed valve, power valve system, old cylinder, piston, and rings, then the new components will be fit and prepped for final installation. Once complete we'll have everything we need ready for final assembly of the engine!

Reed Valve Inspection

With the onset of composite reeds the penalty for ingesting broken reed petals is not as severe as it was when reeds were made from metal. In most cases if a broken reed is ingested into the engine the rider will not know it until it comes time to restart the engine. The reason I bring this up is because I believe it is no longer a necessity to replace the reed valves every time the engine is rebuilt. Instead, a methodical approach can be taken to inspecting the reeds and decisions can be made whether or not they should be replaced.

CHECK FOR CHIPS AND CRACKS

To start, inspect the reed petals for chips and cracks. If either are present replace both sets of petals.

Next, visually check to confirm that the petals are seated against the edge of the reed cage. Ideally, the petals will seal on the rear edge; however, it is permissible for a small gap to exist. Consult your service manual for specifics. If necessary, use a lash gauge to measure the gap between the petals and cage. Replace the reed petals if the gap between them and the cage falls outside the specified service limit.

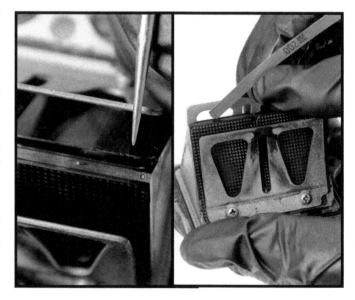

Next, if the reed cage you're working on has stopper plates, confirm that the stopper plates reside within the height specifications provided in the service manual.

If the stopper plates fall outside the height specifications they should either be bent so they fall within spec or replaced. If bending is required be sure to remove the plates from the cage prior to bending them.

Gently move the reed petals away from the cage and inspect the cage itself. Many cages now feature a rubber coating which helps dampen the seating event of the reed as it closes. If the rubber has worn away from the cage the reeds will wear out more quickly.

Any cages missing large quantities of dampening rubber should be replaced.

Lastly, be sure to remove any old gasket material from the reed cage and/or spacer plate.

Reed Valve Disassembly and Assembly

If further disassembly is required to replace the petals simply loosen the small screws securing the petals to the cage.

Be vigilant of any specific instructions detailing reed and stopper plate orientation when installing the new reeds. Many reeds have a slight bow to their cross section and should be installed as detailed in the accompanying photo. By orienting the bow as shown we are ensuring that the tip of the reed seals well against the cage.

Adhere to any thread locking callouts specified in the service manual when reinstalling the small screws. Also note the minimal torque required and be sure to tighten gradually to ensure the petals don't warp.

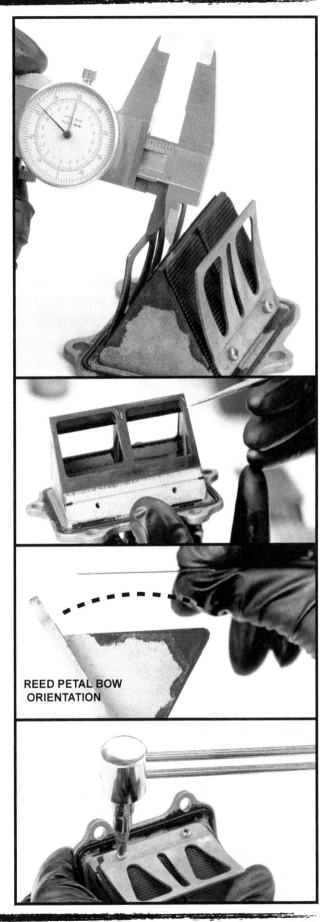

REED PETAL BOW ORIENTATION

Intake Manifold Inspection

Visually inspect the intake manifold for cracks. Any cracks protruding all the way through the manifold warrant immediate replacement.

If no cracks are present proceed to clean the manifold and prep it for reuse.

Power Valve Disassembly

Each manufacturer has their own unique power valve system which makes covering this section challenging! I don't intend to cover each unique system in detail but I do want to provide some examples and pointers for making servicing the power valve system less daunting.

One of the concerns I always hear is how do I take the assembly apart? The power valve system is no different than any other system covered in the service manual and all the information required to do the job successfully should be provided. If visual clarity lacks for a given step part microfiches are a great tool to cross reference. Typically part microfiche exploded views are designed to represent the way the parts must be assembled in order for everything to fit back together.

The next concern is usually how do I set or tune the system? The actual procedure for setting or tuning the system, if it is adjustable, is not always in the assembly section of the service manual. Many times power valve tuning is covered as a periodic maintenance task or under a different section so you may have to search for it.

Before we dive in, I want to provide a few universal suggestions. First, for me, when working on an unfamiliar system, it always helps to think about how the system was designed to work. I would advise that you do the same as it will keep you from taking things apart without thinking about their purpose. This usually leads to a better success rate when the parts are reinstalled. For example, consider how the spinning shaft with the balls in a cup overcomes the spring force to move the linkage assembly. Then consider how the linkage assembly actuates the valves.

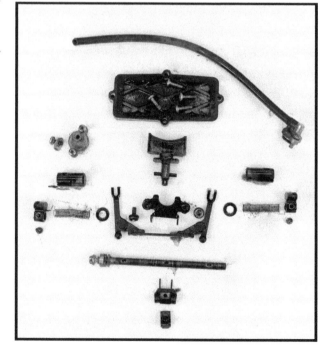

If the system you're working on features adjustment points, whether it be a threaded rod or a means to alter the governor engagement RPM find a way to document the current settings. This way if questions arise as to the positions of things during reassembly you will have two reference points, the notes you took and what the service manual suggest.

When removing components be sure to consider how you are going to keep track of them. I recommend laying the parts on a piece of paper in an orientation that is similar to how they were positioned in the engine. This way parts that belong on the left or right side of the cylinder cannot get mixed up. For added clarity you can also label the piece of paper.

Finally, if you respond better to visual images rather than text take copious amounts of photos as you take the assembly apart. This way you'll have proof of how things were and a lot more reference points when it is time to reassemble everything.

For specifics, adhere to the instructions outlined in your service manual to begin the disassembly process. Typically the power valve covers are the first parts that are removed.

Many power valve systems will feature retaining plates that must be removed before any shafts can be extracted.

Actuating components or the power valves themselves are often affixed to shafts with bolts. In order to remove the shaft these bolts must be removed first. Due to the environment the securing bolts operate in they can be hard to loosen. Take care when trying to free them so that they don't strip.

As you remove components be cognizant of springs and small components that may want to take off on you before you document their position and function.

On occasion, the power valves can be gummed up and difficult to remove. If this happens to you and the parts are magnetic try using a pen magnet to aid in removal. Alternatively, careful application of compressed air can also be helpful.

If the power valve system you're working on features a main blade there is usually a retaining plate that must be removed before it will come out. Be sure to note any special alignment markings on the blade to ensure that it will be installed in the correct orientation later. Many times special machined features will make it impossible to install the valve incorrectly.

Don't forget to remove any seals or o-rings as well, once all the other components have been removed.

At this point, you should have just about all the components of the power valve system removed from the cylinder. We'll move on to inspecting the power valve assembly next.

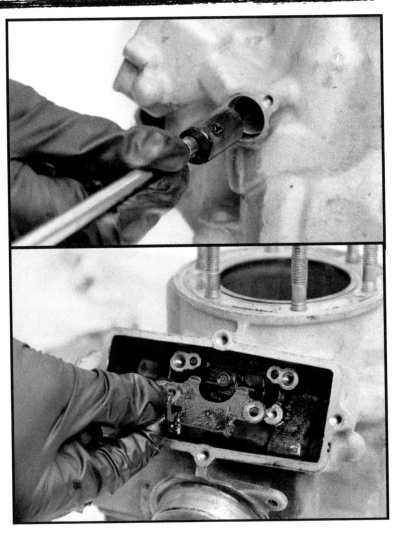

Power Valve Inspection

Prior to any inspection work the fun process of cleaning all the power valve parts must happen. Using a wire wheel to remove carbon from the parts may be tempting but keep in mind that many of the components are made from aluminum. Aluminum tends to be too soft to clean with a wire wheel and it will scratch. Steel wool and parts cleaner are a safer option although this method will take longer.

Proceed to clean all the power valve parts. At this time the cylinder should also be cleaned so that the surrounding power valve geometry can be inspected and subsequent inspections of the bore can be carried out later.

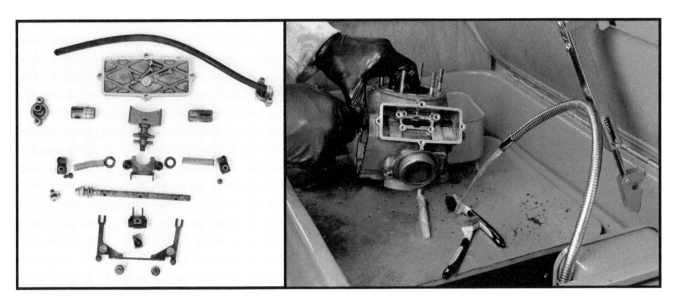

Wear points and inspection criteria will differ for each type of power valve system depending on design. Be sure to consult your service manual for specific inspection points and any necessary measurements that should be taken to ensure the parts are within spec.

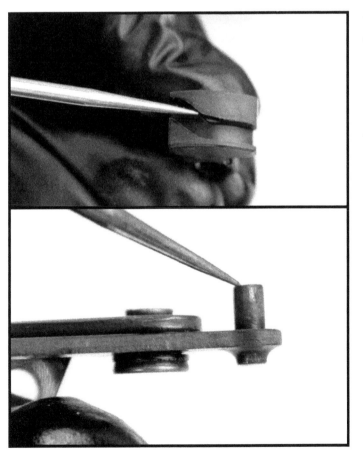

Wear points will be somewhat universal and will predominantly occur on components that slide or rotate against each other. Keep this in mind as you check the condition of your assembly. In the image to the left, the actuating part featured mates with a pin which has begun to round the corner of the slot. In this case, the worn part will cause the sub exhaust ports to open differently than intended.

Be sure to take a look at the corresponding pins of components intended to slide together. Worn slots can occasionally cause their mating pins to square or flatten. Luckily, this is not the case in the example shown to the left.

For power valve systems that feature blade style valves, inspect the condition of the edges of the blade. Worn leading edges of power valve blades often indicate the blade was in contact with the piston. This may already have been readily apparent if exhaust side of the piston was scuffed or if the leading edge of the blade lacked carbon deposits. In the image shown, I was merely too aggressive with my cleaning tactics.

Some components may feel excessively sloppy to you, however, they may still be okay. Take the linkage assembly shown to the right as an example.

Due to the way the assembly was manufactured it has a fair amount of axial free play, meaning the pivot points allow the parts to move up and down quite a bit. The key consideration is how the linkage actually functions. When it is installed it is well constrained so the axial free play doesn't have a big effect. In this case, the radial free play is what's of importance. The radial play qualifies how much movement is in the joint when the components are pulled apart and pushed together. Usually, in normally functioning assemblies, the radial free play of pinned joints should be small. I understand this is vague, but usually there are no measurable specs written around the free play to reference. Typically, the joint should feel tight radially and you should not be able to observe much if any movement.

Some components will show signs of surface finish defects which will be unappealing visually. However, these defects will have no effect on

CHECKING FOR LINKAGE RADIAL PLAY

SUB EXHAUST VALVE PITTING

performance. For example, the sub exhaust power valve shown to the right has pitting on its surface. The pitting is a result of the valve face being exposed to hot exhaust gas. However, from a functional standpoint the valve will continue to work just fine. Situations like this are common in power valve assemblies due to the environment they must operate in. Keep in mind how the part must function in order to determine what wear is merely cosmetic versus wear that hampers performance.

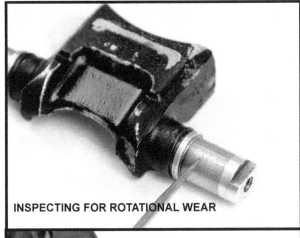

INSPECTING FOR ROTATIONAL WEAR

Shaft wear can be confusing at times as well because both functional and cosmetic wear can be prevalent depending on the type of power valve system the engine features. Be on the lookout for shaft wear that results from components that rotate against the shaft versus components that are merely stationary and rotate in unison with the shaft.

Also, many shafts mate with an o-ring or seal so be sure to ensure that there are no defects or deep grooving on the shaft where either of these types of seals mate. On the shaft shown second below to the left, stationary wear, which does not affect the performance of the system, has occurred due to washers that have consistently vibrated against the shaft.

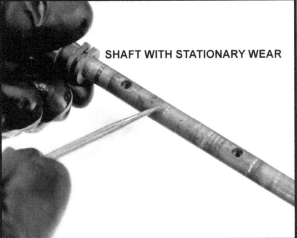

SHAFT WITH STATIONARY WEAR

Sealing surfaces should be inspected for signs of leakage. Leaks are usually easy to spot as black carbon deposits will reside on both sides of the seal.

O-rings and seals can also be examined for signs of leaks. In the example below, the o-ring shows signs of discoloration due exhaust gas leaking past it.

INSPECTING FOR LEAKAGE

O-RING INSPECTION

Once all the individual components have been inspected, the areas of the cylinder where the power valve assembly reside should be inspected next. Carefully inspect any slots or bores which house valve blades or drums. Temporarily install any blades and drums and ensure that they move freely in their respective bores.

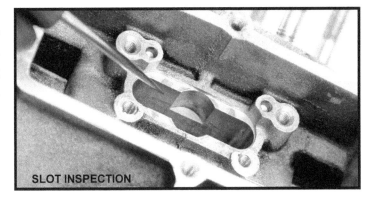

SLOT INSPECTION

LINKAGE INSPECTION

Lastly, don't forget to inspect any remaining linkage assemblies that connect the power valve assembly in the cylinder to the power valve governor housed in the engine cover.

Cylinder and Piston Assembly Inspection

Since the cylinder, piston, and rings all go hand in hand, it only makes sense to inspect these parts as a set. If the engine broke or power faded, we want to look for any subtle clues which may help pinpoint the cause of the problem. Obviously, if a piston melted or something else catastrophic happened, the signs will be evident.

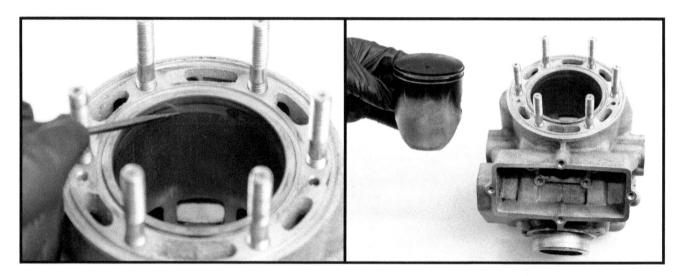

Ensure the cylinder bore is clean then inspect the bore. Look for scuff marks, scoring, and deep scratches. Any imperfections which can catch the end of a fingernail should be considered serious problems and considerations regarding replacement or replating of the cylinder will need to be made. A quick way to get an idea of how much the cylinder bore has worn is to feel the bore at the point where the top piston ring stops and changes direction. If a fingernail can be caught at this point, this is an early indicator that the bore is worn excessively. If any major imperfections exist, orient the piston so that it coincides with its original position when the engine was running. Then look for matching imperfections between the piston and cylinder.

Look over the alignment of the ring ends to see if they coincide with any troubled areas on the cylinder bore. Check to see if any of the rings are stuck. Examine the faces of the compression rings and note the amount they have worn. Ring face wear can be quantified by observing the width of the polished portion of the ring face. Since the ring face utilizes a barrel shape on most compression rings the contact strip will start out narrow as the engine breaks in and widen as the ring accumulates run time.

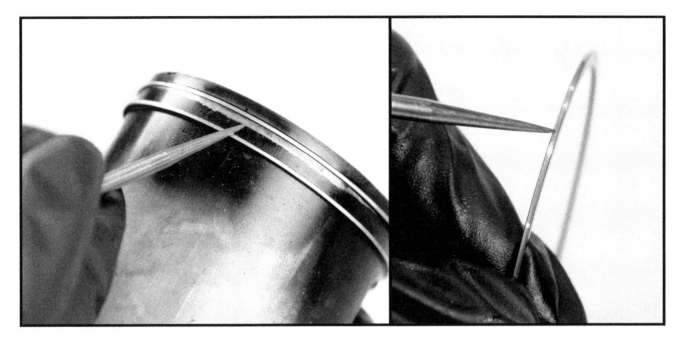

Once the rings have been checked, remove the compression ring(s). Compression rings are directional most of the time. Most manufacturers and aftermarket companies denote the top of compression rings with a dot or letter. A chamfered edge will coincide with the marking and is located on the top inner edge of the ring. The chamfer allows combustion gases to get back behind the ring and forces the ring against the cylinder bore. This improves the ring's sealing ability. Confirm the compression ring or rings were installed the correct way in the old piston.

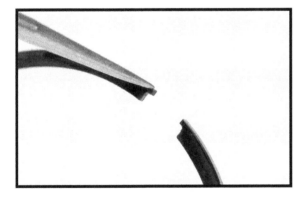

Next, note any sharp burrs on the ring ends which may have contributed to any scratch patterns found in the cylinder bore. Sometimes burrs will be present as a result of how the ring was manufactured or how the ring was filed by the previous builder.

If the engine overheated at any point in its previous life, scuffing can occur between the piston and cylinder bore. Once the cooling system can no longer dissipate heat at the rate which the engine is producing heat (through combustion and friction), the piston will get increasingly hotter. If the piston gets too hot it will expand in size to the point where it has difficulty fitting in the cylinder bore. In severe cases of overheating, the piston can seize in the cylinder bore or scuff the bore. When scuffing occurs aluminum from the piston is transferred to the cylinder bore.

Signs of detonation will be able to be seen by examining the piston crown. When detonation occurs, the piston crown will erode and pits will form in the piston crown. If severe enough a hole will melt all the way through the crown. Detonation can occur when the air/fuel mixture is lean, when ignition timing is incorrectly set, when a significant amount of carbon has deposited on the piston and cylinder head, and when there is a loss of coolant.

Inspect the wrist pin bore in the old piston. Look for signs of ovality in the bore. Due to the high inertia forces experienced by the piston, the bore can elongate from top to bottom. If the bore elongates severely enough, the fit between the wrist pin, needle bearing, and piston will become looser and the forces will be distributed over a smaller area.

Ideally, the piston and rings will only have polished the cylinder bore, primarily on the thrust faces of the bore (intake and exhaust sides). Before the cylinder is put back in service, the polished surfaces must be returned to a nice cross-hatch finish by deglazing the cylinder. Deglazing is important for a couple reasons. First, the cross-hatch finish helps the rings wear and seat into the bore. Second, the cross-hatch surface promotes oil retention on the bore aiding in lubrication of the piston and rings.

Depending on how worn the cylinder bore is, restoration of the cross-hatch finish can be achieved by honing, replating, or replacing the cylinder. Normally before a cylinder has worn out, a few piston replacements and hone operations can be performed before the cylinder bore falls outside of spec. Compared to replating or replacement, honing is by far the cheapest and fastest way to return a cylinder to usable condition. In order to determine which restorative option is best, the old cylinder bore should be measured and further inspected for warpage.

Cylinder Warpage Check

If applicable, start by cleaning any remaining gasket material from the cylinder head gasket surface. Before spending the time measuring the cylinder bore, the cylinder should be checked for warpage first to confirm a major flaw doesn't exist. Warpage of the cylinder can be check by laying a straightedge across the top and bottom of the cylinder and attempting to insert a lash gauge between the straight edge and cylinder surface. Warpage should be checked along each of the four sides of the cylinder and along the two diagonals when possible. Obviously, the cylinder skirt will make the diagonal checks across the bottom of the cylinder impossible.

Warpage limits will be outlined by the manufacturer and are normally 0.002" (0.05mm). If the lash gauge slides between the cylinder and straightedge, the cylinder is warped. A warped cylinder surface can be caused by overheating of the engine or improper tightening of the cylinder and/or cylinder head fasteners. Regardless of cause, the warped surfaces will have difficulty sealing and are more likely to leak.

Severely warped cylinders should be replaced, however cylinders exhibiting minor warpage, which would be anything less than 0.002" (0.05mm), can be brought back to a flatter state. A surface

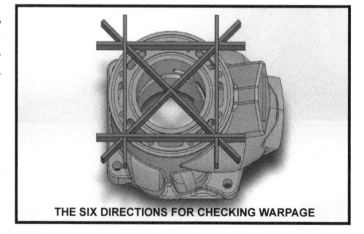

THE SIX DIRECTIONS FOR CHECKING WARPAGE

plate, machinist's dye, and sandpaper can be used to remove high spots on the top clamping surface. Start by applying machinist's dye to the warped surface. Then use 400 grit sandpaper laid flat on a surface plate to carefully sand down the high spots. Be mindful of how pressure is applied to the

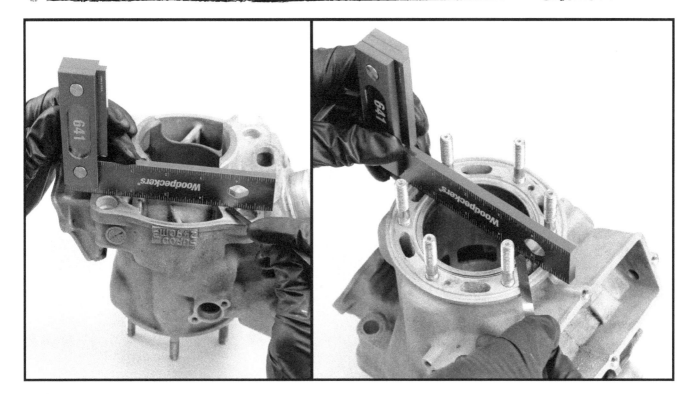

cylinder as you sand. The goal is to remove as little material as possible and keep the gasket surface as parallel to the cylinder base surface as you can. As the machinist's dye is sanded away, the high spots will become evident and it will become apparent when the gasket surface has become perfectly flat again. Be sure to keep in mind that any alterations to the top of the cylinder will increase the compression ratio and reduce the squish clearance.

TECHNICAL TAKEAWAY
Using Muriatic Acid to Remove Aluminum From the Cylinder Bore

If the cylinder bore has been scuffed the imbedded aluminum should be removed from the bore prior to measuring and deglazing. The aluminum stuck to the plated cylinder bore is best removed chemically. This way when the cylinder bore is deglazed it will not require excessive honing nor will the chances of it becoming oversized, out-of-round, or tapered increase.

Muriatic acid should carefully be used to remove imbedded aluminum from the cylinder bore. The muriatic acid will attack and break down the aluminum while leaving the plating or iron liner undamaged. I want to stress that care must be taken when working with the acid because the acid will not differentiate between imbedded aluminum inside the bore and aluminum behind the plating!

Muriatic acid can be a harmful chemical if the proper precautions are not taken. Ensuring the skin and eyes are protected is essential as well as working in a well ventilated area. For a full run down of precautionary measures please refer to your product's material safety data sheet (MSDS) or label.

Application Instructions

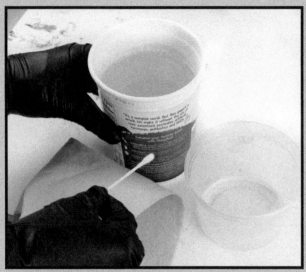

1. Make preparations for application by having a small jar of muriatic acid at the ready, Q-tips for applying it, water for flushing, and a rag for wiping the acid off.

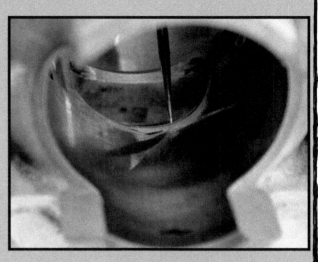

2. Position the cylinder so that the area of interest lies horizontally at the lowest point in the cylinder. This will ensure the acid pools in the correct spot and lessen the chances of acid getting behind the plating or sleeve.

3. Apply enough acid so that it forms a shallow pool over the scuffed area. As the acid reacts to the aluminum it will smoke and bubble.

4. Allow the reaction to go on for approximately 10 minutes. Then carefully wipe the acid away with a rag or paper towel. Inspect the treated area and if necessary apply more acid and repeat the process. Continue this rinse and repeat process until all the problematic areas have been remedied.

Once the acid has been wiped away it will be easy to tell whether or not all the aluminum has been removed. After all the problematic areas have been treated flush the cylinder bore with water to ensure no acid remains.

Cylinder Bore Measurement

Once it has been determined that the cylinder isn't warped, the old cylinder should be measured to confirm the cylinder bore diameter, taper, and out-of-roundness are not out of spec. If the cylinder bore is out of spec before honing, any efforts to hone the cylinder would be futile and a waste of time. Drill operated hones are great for restoring cross-hatch finishes, but are not the appropriate type of hone for correcting taper, out-of-roundness, or making big changes to cylinder bore diameter.

If you are new to honing cylinders, measuring the cylinder bore before honing is also beneficial for another reason. Honing the cylinder will alter the bore dimensions slightly. By measuring the cylinder before and after, you will learn how the hone speed, duration, and grit affect bore diameter. Once you start to develop a technique for honing, you will be able to work more quickly and gain confidence.

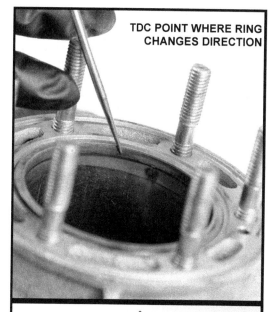

TDC POINT WHERE RING CHANGES DIRECTION

The majority of cylinder bore wear and dimensional changes occur on the thrust faces of the bore, which corresponds to the intake and exhaust sides of the bore. The cylinder bore will wear at points in the bore which correspond closely to TDC and BDC. Wear near TDC and BDC occurs due to the directional change of the rings. The oil film between the rings and cylinder wall temporarily breaks down as the rings change direction and lubrication is momentarily lost. At and near TDC combustion pressure heavily loads the piston rings forcing them against the cylinder bore, which also contributes significantly to bore wear. Ring loading gradually reduces as the volume above the piston increases as the piston travels downward. This is the primary reason why cylinder bores must be checked for taper.

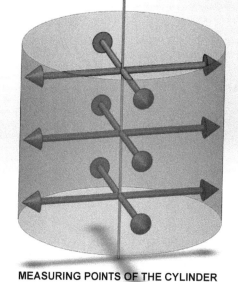

MEASURING POINTS OF THE CYLINDER

Due to the predictable way cylinder bores wear, the procedure for measuring cylinders of two-stroke dirt bike engines has become close to being universal across brands. The procedure entails taking measurements at three different heights inside the cylinder bore and in two directions.

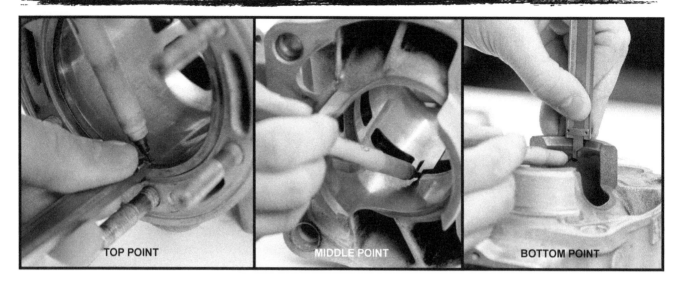

TOP POINT | MIDDLE POINT | BOTTOM POINT

Service manuals will provide specific details regarding the heights of the inspection points which correspond to the points in the bore that are susceptible to the most wear. Some manufacturers may leave choosing the measurement heights open, in which case measurements should be taken at or near TDC, BDC, and in the middle of the stroke. Start by using the depth rod end of a caliper and fine tipped marker to mark out the specified measurement points in the cylinder bore. Be sure to mark both sides of the bore so the marks are easy to reference.

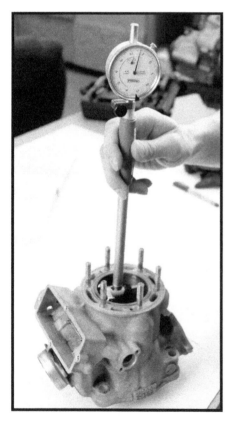

Prepare to use a dial bore gauge to measure the cylinder by calibrating the gauge to the cylinder diameter outlined in the service manual. For detailed instruction on how to use the dial bore gauge refer to Chapter 8, Precision Measuring.

Insert the dial bore gauge into the cylinder and measure the cylinder at each of the six measurement points. Record the measured values in your notebook. To help confirm repeatability I like to go back through and measure each point at least once more to confirm I didn't make an error when I took the first measurement. If after two measurements I achieve the same value I'm satisfied, however if I measure a different value I'll take one final measurement. For final confirmation that the measurements have been taken accurately, be sure to check the calibration of the bore gauge after measuring.

To determine the diameter of the cylinder at each of the measurement points, the calibrated diameter the bore gauge was set to should be added to the measured value at all six measurement points. An assessment can then be made to determine if the cylinder bore is still within the service limits.

Cylinder Diameter = Calibrated Bore Gauge Diameter +/- Measured Bore Gauge Value

Assessing taper and out-of-roundness is easier in the sense that the measurements can be compared directly to one another. However, understanding what taper and out-of-roundness mean and knowing which measurement points to use for comparison may be less straight forward if you are new to the cylinder measuring scene.

Taper is a way to assess how much the diameter of the cylinder has changed in one direction of measurement from the top to bottom of the cylinder. When comparing taper values, the measured values taken on the thrust faces are compared to one another. Then the measured values perpendicular to the thrust faces are compared.

Out-of-Roundness assesses variations in diameter (roundness) at each of the three measurement heights. When assessing out-of-roundness, the thrust face measured value is compared to the measured value taken perpendicular to the thrust face.

For the cylinder to still be considered useable, the cylinder must conform to the specifications provided in the manual for all three criteria: cylinder diameter, taper, and out-of-roundness.

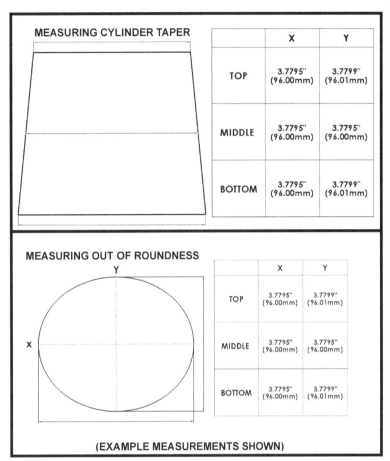

MEASURING CYLINDER TAPER

	X	Y
TOP	3.7795" (96.00mm)	3.7799" (96.01mm)
MIDDLE	3.7795" (96.00mm)	3.7795" (96.00mm)
BOTTOM	3.7795" (96.00mm)	3.7799" (96.01mm)

MEASURING OUT OF ROUNDNESS

	X	Y
TOP	3.7795" (96.00mm)	3.7799" (96.01mm)
MIDDLE	3.7795" (96.00mm)	3.7795" (96.00mm)
BOTTOM	3.7795" (96.00mm)	3.7799" (96.01mm)

(EXAMPLE MEASUREMENTS SHOWN)

If the cylinder doesn't meet all three requirements the cylinder should be replated or replaced. For cylinders which are still within spec, preparations before honing will be covered next followed by the honing process.

HOT TIP: For cylinders that require replating all the hardware must be removed first. Cylinder head studs can be tough to get out especially if they have been installed for awhile. I have found the best way to remove them is with a pair of jam nuts and heat. Lightly heat the top of the cylinder around the base of the stud to help free it up.

When reinstalling studs consider applying anti-seize to the threads to help ensure they are easy to remove in the future.

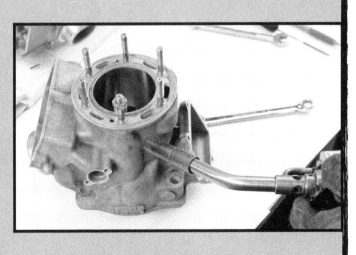

TECHNICAL TAKEAWAY

Cylinder Honing

Before getting into the specifics of how to hone a cylinder I want to debunk a couple myths related to the term "honing". By definition, honing is an abrasive process which alters the surface finish of a bore. In the engine building world this can mean a couple different things.

First, a honing process can be carried out to remove material from a cylinder's bore and alter the surface finish of the bore. This process is most applicable when describing how the bores of new cylinders are finished to their final size. The hones used to perform this work are rigid in design and are mounted in expensive machinery specifically designed for this task. The rigid hone ensures the final diameter, taper, and out-of-roundness are all precisely controlled.

The second type of honing process involves hones which are only designed for altering the surface finish of the bore. A more suitable way to think of this honing process may be to consider it a "deglazing process". The hones used for deglazing and altering the surface finish of the bore are flexible and can be turned in an electric drill. Due to their flexible design, these hones will not correct any major taper or out-of-roundness conditions present in the cylinder bore. They will simply create the desired cross-hatch finish necessary for the rings to seat correctly against the cylinder bore while removing little to no material.

In some instances it may be possible to correct taper and out-of-roundness issues present in a cylinder bore without first replating by using a rigid hone. As stated before, performing this type of work requires special machinery and expertise. This scenario also depends if the plating is thick enough to support the removal of additional material and if pistons are offered in slightly larger sizes.

The majority of the time cylinders will simply require refinishing (deglazing) of the cylinder bore between rebuilds to bring the necessary cross-hatch pattern of the cylinder bore back to good condition. This type of honing process can be performed by anyone mechanically inclined and is within the budget of the at-home mechanic. There are three types of deglazing hones available: the ball hone, the brush hone, and the spring loaded stone hone. My preference and recommendation for anyone learning how to deglaze the bore of a two-stroke cylinder is to use a brush hone. I believe brush hones are more forgiving than stone hones, remove less material, and don't run the risk of damaging port edges which can occur with ball and stone hones. For these reasons I'll cover in detail how to correctly operate a brush hone.

The grit and material of the hone will depend on the material used to line the cylinder bore (Nikasil, cast iron, etc.) as well as surface finish requirements of the piston rings for correct operation. Fortunately, both cylinder liner materials and ring surface finish requirements have been reduced to a few options so choosing the correct hone is not difficult. If you are unsure of the type of hone to use, refer to any of the major hone manufacturer's websites for assistance.

Cylinder Honing Instructions

Cylinder honing is much easier than most are led to believe. The process consists of preparation work, honing, and cleanup. As long as care is taken throughout the honing process, the right grit and type of hone are selected, and the proper instructions are followed it is very difficult to ruin the bore of the cylinder.

To get started, the top of the cylinder should be protected by covering it in duct tape. The tape will keep the hone from damaging the gasket mating surface and help keep the top edge of the bore from becoming radiused as the hone passes in and out of the cylinder.

Once taped, use a razor blade to cut a hole through the tape so that access to the cylinder bore is regained.

Couple the hone to an electric drill and set the drill to its lowest speed setting.

HOT TIP: If you won't be honing deep cylinders or having to contend with tall studs, most hone shafts can be cut to length. Reducing the shaft length will increase control over the hone.

Apply honing oil to the cylinder bore and hone so that both the bore and hone brushes are completely covered. It is better to be over lubricated than under. Just keep in mind that once the drill starts turning, some of the oil on the hone will fly off. I don't recommend honing a cylinder next to your favorite poster or near engine parts which have been cleaned and prepped for reassembly.

The cylinder should be positioned so that the hone can pass in and out of the bore vertically. By honing straight up and down the likelihood of loading one side of the hone and subsequently removing more material from one area than another is reduced. The cylinder can be set in a vice without clamping so the bore isn't distorted. Just remember to hold on to it!

A 30 to 45 degree cross-hatch angle (from the horizontal plane) is what should be aimed for. The diameter of the hone affects the speed which the hone should be turned. Smaller diameter hones require faster speeds, while larger diameter hones require slower speeds. In combination with the overall speed the hone is spinning at, the rate at which the hone moves up and down in the cylinder will affect the angle of the cross-hatch. Due to these variables, applying a universal rule to follow for all hones so that the correct cross-hatch is achieved is impossible.

 A rule of thumb to follow for most dirt bike engine applications is to turn the hone at around 500 RPM, stroking the hone from the top of the cylinder to the bottom of the cylinder in a second or less. This should put the cross-hatch angle in the ballpark. Keep in mind the faster the hone spins, the more quickly it must be moved in the bore. If 500RPM feels too fast, reduce the speed and slow your stroke down. The best way to perfect the cross-hatch angle is to make a couple passes, inspect the pattern left in the bore, and make adjustments to the subsequent passes. Keep in mind the hone must be spinning at speed before entering the cylinder bore.

It should take the hone around one second to pass down through the bore. It should spend little to no time at the bottom of the bore before changing direction.

Again, it should take the hone around one second to come up. Once at the top, the hone should quickly change direction. This back and forth procedure is repeated until the hone is removed.

When the hone is removed it should be kept spinning as it is removed from the bore.

The number of strokes required to restore the cross-hatch of the cylinder's bore will be dependent on the condition of the bore and grit of the hone. After stroking the hone a couple of times, clean the bore with a clean rag. Then inspect the condition of the bore. After the first couple of strokes the cross-hatch finish should replace the polished finish throughout the majority of the bore. A few additional strokes should take care of any remaining blemishes.

The goal is to make as few passes as necessary with the hone to restore the bore. Once all the polishing has been removed, vertical wear lines eliminated, and 45 degree cross-hatch restored the hone process is complete. As a guideline it usually takes around 3-5 passes to restore the bore of a Nikasil plated cylinder.

Once the honing process has been completed a thorough cleaning of the bore is necessary to remove honing grit stuck in the cross-hatch. Start by using warm soapy water and a brush to clean the cylinder. Take your time cleaning the cylinder. The cleaning process is by far the most important part, because if the cylinder is installed dirty with excess honing grit, the rings will prematurely wear out.

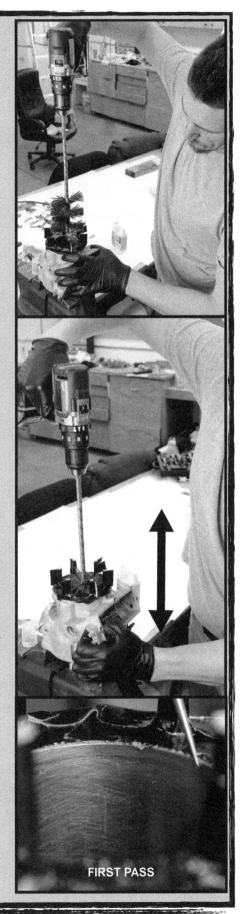

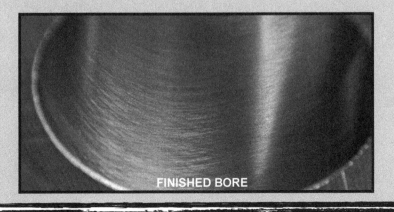

FINISHED BORE

FIRST PASS

After the majority of the honing grit has been removed switch to automatic transmission fluid and a lint free rag for one final cleaning.

As a test to check cleanliness, rub a cotton swab against the cylinder bore. If the swab picks up any debris and changes color your cleaning duties are not over. The swab should be able to be rubbed against the bore and remain perfectly clean.

Final Cylinder Measurement

After cylinder honing has been performed the cylinder should once again be measured. Measuring the cylinder again will make it possible to determine the piston to cylinder clearance and confirm how much, if any, material the hone removed. Normally, the difference between the first and second measurements of the cylinder will only vary by a few ten thousandths of an inch.

Proceed to repeat the procedure for measuring the cylinder bore. Record all measurements and note any changes to the diameter, taper, and out-of-roundness of the cylinder.

Replated Cylinders and New Cylinders

I want to briefly touch on a few details associated with replated and new cylinders. First, both varieties must be cleaned prior to assembling. Normally the cylinders will arrive looking clean, but looks can be deceiving. I have no doubt that the factories and replating services clean the cylinders as part of their processes but I highly recommend cleaning the bores one final time prior to use. Shown to the right is a new Yamaha cylinder that I extracted quite a bit of honing grit out of.

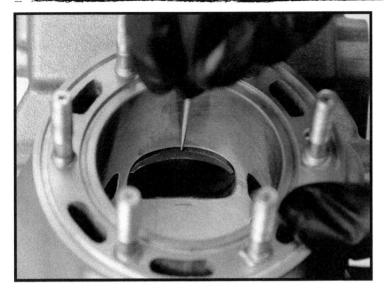

The second item I want to bring to your attention is port dressing. Port dressing is a term used to describe the process of deburring/breaking the edge at the intersection of the cylinder plating and the ports in the cylinder. During the plating process plating usually builds up excessively at the edge of the port and must be removed after honing. Proper removal is critical to ensure acceptable piston ring life.

Manufacturers and plating services will break the edge in different ways and to different magnitudes which ends up being a whole other topic. The important thing is to ensure that any new or replated cylinder you use shows visible signs that the port edges have been dressed. A dressed port edge will be easy to spot because it will feature a different surface finish than the cross-hatch created from honing. Many port dressing operations are done manually so some irregularity in the geometry will usually be present. If there is no visible edge break on the port edges I would be highly suspicious and contact the service that plated the cylinder or sold the cylinder and confirm with them if a step was missed. Typically a chamfer or radius in the .020 - .040" (0.5 - 1mm) range is used.

Lastly, it is possible that some of the power valve components, such as blades or drums, will not fit correctly on cylinders that have been replated. This is because the plating can occasionally build up in the slots or bores where the power valve parts reside. Prior to final assembly be sure to check the function of the power valve blade and/or drums to ensure they move freely in their respective locations within the cylinder.

If plating has built up in a power valve slot or bore it will need to be carefully removed. To do this appropriately sized burs for die grinders or Dremel tools can be used. If one is not careful irreversible damage to the slot or bore can result, so when performing this work proceed cautiously or leave it to a seasoned professional. Burs for the job can be difficult to track down in stores but are readily available online from places like McMaster-Carr. When purchasing burs be sure to pick up a few variants, such as rounded and square edged, designed for removing hard materials.

If grinding was necessary to remove plating that was limiting the movement of the power valve blade or drums be sure to clean the cylinder after all the work has been completed. Use compressed air to blow out any tough to clean passages.

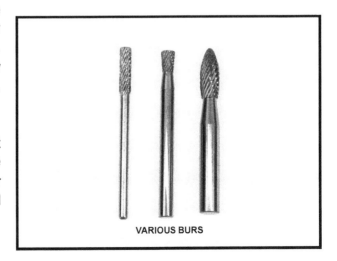

VARIOUS BURS

New Piston Inspection and Measurement

The new piston should be looked over and inspected for visual imperfections. Check to make sure there aren't any burrs on the piston which didn't get removed at the end of the machining process. This can happen from time to time, especially if the manufacturer entrusts the deburring process to manual labor.

In addition to the overall inspection of the new piston, there are three features that should be measured. Most importantly, the piston diameter needs to be measured in order to calculate the piston to cylinder clearance and confirm it is within spec. The clearance between the piston ring and ring groove should also be checked. For those with meticulous tendencies like myself, the wrist pin bore can be measured to calculate the clearance between the wrist pin and piston.

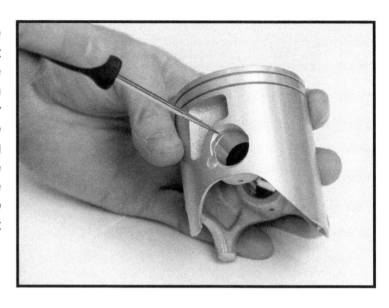

Measuring Piston Diameter

Pistons are tapered from top to bottom, which makes it very important to measure the piston in the correct place. The taper is incorporated into the piston design to account for variations in piston temperature. A piston at room temperature will be smaller in diameter at the very top of the piston and larger in diameter at the bottom. When the engine is running, heat from the combustion process is continuously being fed into the top of the piston, transferred to the rings, and then passed out to the cylinder into the cooling system. Since the top of the piston is significantly warmer than the bottom, the top will expand more than the bottom. The variation in piston temperature from the top to the bottom of the piston is why the piston must be tapered.

Manufacturer's will specify where to measure the piston diameter. Normally, a depth from the bottom of the piston skirt is specified in the service manual. Use the depth rod of a caliper and marker to mark out the appropriate measurement points on both sides of the piston.

Use a micrometer to measure the diameter of the piston at the correct point. Since a point along a tapered path is being measured with flat faced micrometers, a problem presents itself.

If the micrometer measuring faces are centered on the measurement point the micrometer will read a larger value than what is correct due to the taper. Align the edge of the micrometer's measuring faces with the alignment point and position the other end of the measuring faces so that they are down towards the top of the piston. This method allows the most accurate method of piston measurement. The piston diameter can be difficult to measure accurately, so take a few measurements and take the average of the measured values as the piston diameter. Record the piston diameter in your build notebook.

Measuring Piston Pin Bore Diameter

The piston pin bore diameter can be measured using small hole gauges or telescoping gauges, depending on the size of the bore. By measuring the piston pin bore diameter, the clearance between the piston pin and pin bore can be calculated. This will ensure no errors were made when the piston was manufactured. This may be beyond what is required for the casual weekend warrior, however I believe recording as much information regarding the build at the time of assembly is important. This is especially true if the engine is being raced and taken apart frequently. Having measurement and clearance values to refer back to during subsequent tear downs and builds can be helpful when assessing the condition of parts.

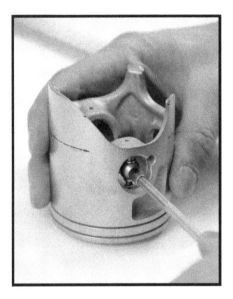

Since the measurement tools being used to measure the bore diameter are transfer gauges, I like to take around five measurements to ensure my measurements are consistent. Then I'll use the average of the results as my final value. Follow the procedure outlined in Chapter 8 Precision Measuring, for further details regarding measuring using small hole or telescoping gauges.

Measuring Wrist Pin Diameter

Measuring the wrist pin diameter will be necessary in order to calculate the clearance between the pin and piston pin bore. Use a 0-1" micrometer to measure the diameter of the piston pin.

Calculating Piston to Cylinder Clearance

Now that all the important features of the piston have been checked out, the clearance between the cylinder and piston can be calculated. This clearance is especially important because if it ends up being too tight the piston will be susceptible to seizing in the cylinder bore. If the clearance is too loose then the piston will rock back and forth in the bore, causing both the piston and cylinder bore to wear more quickly. Excessive clearances will increase the chances of the piston skirt cracking and causing a catastrophic failure. A piston which fits loosely in the cylinder bore will also cause the engine to make more noise. This noise is sometimes referred to as "piston slap", as a metallic slapping noise is often heard in engines running with loose pistons.

In theory, the clearance required between the cylinder bore and piston will primarily be dependent on the type of material the piston was made from and the amount of heat being soaked up by the piston. Since different aluminum alloys are used in different piston manufacturing processes, such as castings and forgings, the rates at which the pistons will expand may differ. In addition, if the engine being built will be producing more heat than normal during the combustion process, the clearances between the cylinder bore and piston will need to be higher since the piston will expand more. Two examples of a high heat applications, where more clearance may be required, include when the engine is setup to run with nitrous or a turbo charger.

Fortunately, most applications don't require a lot of special attention to achieve the correct clearances. The manufacturers will specify a range of clearances which the cylinder/piston combination should fall into. Normally as long as the cylinder bore is in spec and the piston is new, clearance requirements should be easily met. Clearance problems are likely to come up when working with cylinder bores which are near their bore diameter service limit. When this happens, either the cylinder bore will need to be replated or a larger piston fit. Depending on the engine in question, some aftermarket piston manufacturers offer slightly oversized pistons which can be used to help prolong the life of cylinder bores before they need to be replated.

For custom applications which require larger cylinder to piston clearances, two options are available. First, the cylinder bore can be honed to a larger size by a competent machine shop, assuming the plating is thick enough to do so. If not, the cylinder would need to be replated then machined to final size. The second option is to have a custom piston made. This is expensive because custom pistons usually require a minimum order.

Determining the piston to cylinder clearance is a simple mathematical calculation. However, it can be confusing because different manufacturers will specify different ways to perform the calculation. Between all the manufacturers there are at least three ways to calculate piston to cylinder clearance. Each way uses a different measured value from the cylinder bore. Manufacturers may suggest the smallest cylinder bore diameter be used, the largest bore diameter, or an average be used which is taken from all six measured bore diameters. Then to arrive at the clearance value, the piston diameter is subtracted from the cylinder bore diameter.

Piston to Cylinder Clearance = Cylinder Bore Diameter - Piston Diameter

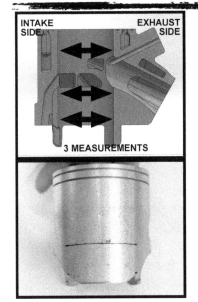

INTAKE SIDE | EXHAUST SIDE

3 MEASUREMENTS

In addition to following the manufacturer's recommendations, applying a little common sense to the situation can go a long way. Pistons are designed to be the widest towards the bottom of their skirt and smallest in diameter at the top when at room temperature. As the piston heats up the top of the piston will expand and, if designed correctly, the piston will be close to the same diameter from top to bottom once at operating temperature. The fact of the matter is the widest part of the piston must pass through the cylinder at its narrowest point with adequate clearance. For this reason, I believe using the smallest measured cylinder bore diameter makes the most sense for a two-stroke engine.

Calculating Piston Pin Bore to Piston Pin Clearance

Next up, a very easy calculation. Determining the clearance between the piston pin bore and piston pin is important. Just because the piston pin bore and piston pin measurements fell within the service limits doesn't always mean the clearances between the two parts will be correct. If one part is on the large spec end while the other is on the small spec end, too much or too little clearance between the parts can become a problem. If the parts are too tight, lubrication will be a problem and the increased tightness will cause excessive frictional heat buildup. If the parts are too loose, the piston will effectively bounce up and down on the piston pin as it reciprocates. The bouncing will lead to premature wear of the parts and put more stress on the piston pin bore and piston skirt. The clearance between the piston pin bore can be found by subtracting the piston pin diameter from the piston pin bore diameter.

Piston Pin Bore to Piston Pin Clearance = Piston Pin Bore Inner Diameter - Piston Pin Diameter

Piston Ring to Ring Groove Clearance Check

Before signing the piston off as good and committing any finger power towards forcing a temperamental circlip into the piston pin bore, the piston ring to groove clearance should be checked. Checking the clearance between the piston rings and their corresponding grooves in the piston is important since the compression ring must have a certain amount of free play between it and the ring groove. Installing the piston ring onto the piston is not necessary for this check. Simply note the clearance specification outlined by the manufacturer. Then position the ring in its groove and insert an appropriately sized lash gauge between the two parts.

Rotate the ring around the piston and take measurements at a few different points to confirm the groove width is consistent. When working with new parts it is unlikely the clearance will be out of spec, however this check is good for peace of mind and confirming no errors were made when cutting the ring groove into the piston. It also rules out any packaging errors when grouping the ring set with the piston. While the chances of receiving incorrectly machined or packaged parts isn't high, it does happen from time to time. If you don't take the time to check your parts you will be none the wiser to having installed someone else's mistake until it is too late and your new parts have been reduced to a pile of scrap. As the saying goes, "better to be safe than sorry".

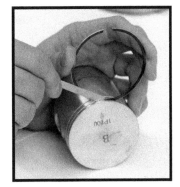

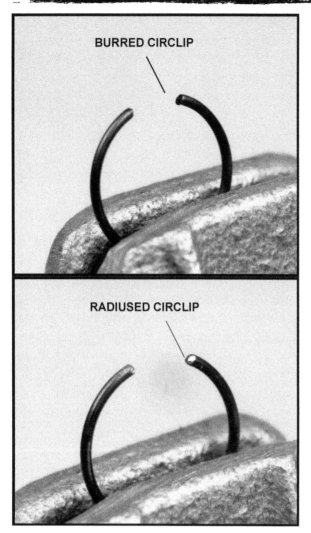

BURRED CIRCLIP

RADIUSED CIRCLIP

Piston Circlip Preparation

How great would it be if the piston circlips weren't such a royal pain to install? What if there was a way to make circlip installation less time consuming and painful? Well, there is. When circlips are manufactured they are left with sharp burrs around their ends. Albeit small, these burrs do a number on piston pin bores by scratching up the bores if the installer isn't careful. They also make circlips much more difficult to push into position when trying to coax them into their grooves.

The remedy to the burr problem is to carefully file a radius into each end of the circlip. By rounding, the end the circlip becomes much easier to install into the piston. Use a small diamond file to radius the ends of each circlip. Don't forget to wipe each circlip free of filing debris once finished.

Piston Circlip Open End Orientation

At this point the piston should have proven itself to be a suitable candidate for making power in your engine. Before setting ring end gap and installing the piston rings, it is easiest to install one of the circlips. This way the rings won't get displaced while the circlip is being wrestled into position.

Correct piston circlip open end orientation is dependent on two factors. First, the forces which act on the circlip. These forces are universal in all reciprocating engines and never change which reduces the number of correct open end positions of the circlip down to two choices. Second, the orientation of the machined dimple which is a necessary feature incorporated into the piston to help facilitate removal of the circlip.

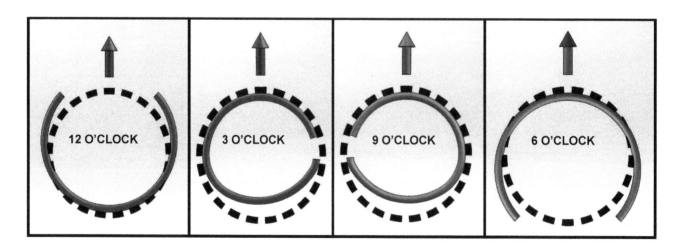

12 O'CLOCK   3 O'CLOCK   9 O'CLOCK   6 O'CLOCK

Inertia forces from the piston assembly reciprocating up and down are the primary forces acting on the circlip. These forces occur in an upwards direction parallel to the path of travel of the piston. Inertia forces peak around TDC. Considering this force, it is easy to illustrate how the circlip will respond to the inertia using the diagrams with commonly prescribed circlip open end positions as seen on the previous page.

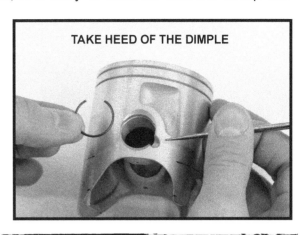

TAKE HEED OF THE DIMPLE

It is easy to see now that the only suitable open end positions of the circlip are at the 12 and 6 o'clock positions. At these positions the circlip will try to expand further into its groove. While at positions 3 and 9 o'clock, the lower half of the circlip will be trying to work its way out of its groove.

Now that your choices have been narrowed down to two open end positions, the only other deciding factor is where the manufacturer of the piston decided to put the dimple. When installing circlips it is best to keep the open ends out of the dimple. It is easiest to install the open ends of the circlip facing up when the piston design permits.

HOT TIP: Never reuse a piston circlip. When being removed the circlips are often damaged and won't retain the same amount of stiffness as when they were new. As inexpensive as circlips are, it is foolish not to replace them each time they are installed. The ensuing damage that can result from a "circlip gone wild party" is no joke and can make for some very expensive repairs.

Installing Piston Circlips

Choose which side of the engine you are most comfortable working from when it comes time to install the remaining circlip. Based on this decision, you will want to install the opposite end circlip at this time.

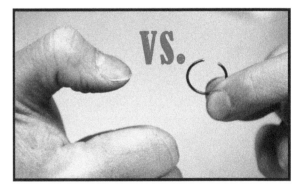

VS.

To correctly install the circlip no tools should be used. Installation basically comes down to an all out thumb war between you and the circlip. Tools such as needle nose pliers should be avoided as they can mar and damage the circlip.

Start by installing the wrist pin into the piston. The end of the wrist pin will be used to control how far the circlip can protrude into the piston pin bore. Remember, even with the radiused ends the circlip is somewhat sharp and can still scratch the piston pin bore. This should be avoided because any scratching of the piston pin bore will make the fit between the piston pin bore and wrist pin tighter, increasing friction, reducing the contact area of the wrist pin in the scratched area, and making the pin harder to install.

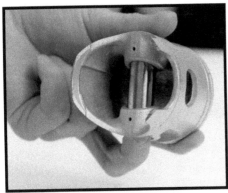

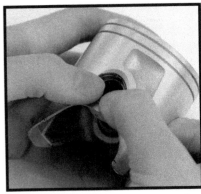

Use your non-dominant hand to hold the piston and control the depth of the wrist pin.

Insert the open end of the circlip into the piston pin bore first.

Use both thumbs to push the circlip down into the piston pin bore groove.

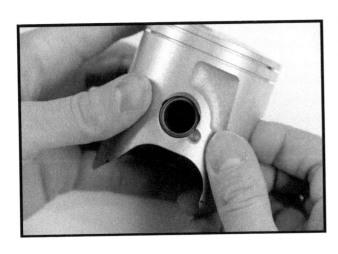

Once the circlip has been pushed far enough it will remain in the groove on its own but won't seat in the groove unless you have gotten lucky.

Use your thumbs to push the circlip down the rest of the way. If feeble fingered, or you have oversized hands like myself, use a flat blade screwdriver to carefully push the circlip down into the groove until it seats. Remember to keep pressure on the back side of the piston pin to help control the depth of the circlip and feed it into its groove.

An audible click sound should be heard once the circlip seats. Once this happens use the flat blade screwdriver to push down on the circlip all around it to confirm it is fully seated.

Carefully push against one of the open ends of the circlip to confirm it cannot rotate.

A circlip that can easily rotate it its groove has inadequate spring tension and is a recipe for disaster. Replace any circlips which can be easily rotated with new ones.

Ring End Gap Theory

Now that the primary features of the cylinder and piston have been checked out, the piston rings can be squared away. Ensuring that the piston rings are free of burrs and their end gaps are correct are essential to ensuring the cylinder bore remains in good shape for a long time to come.

Checking, and if necessary altering the ring end gap, is by far one of the most important steps in building an engine. Just like the piston, the rings will expand as they are heated inside the cylinder bore. The gap between the rings is what is used to compensate for ring expansion. The more the rings are heated, the more the rings expand, and the smaller the gap between the ring ends gets. If the gap between the ring ends is not large enough to account for all the expansion of the rings, the rings will have nowhere to expand. This will result in the rings binding inside the cylinder bore, which will ruin the cylinder, piston, and rings in short order.

On the flip side, the gap between the rings can also be larger than necessary. A large gap can affect performance by reducing the engine's ability to retain compressed air and combustion gases. While performance may be minimally affected by utilizing a ring with too much gap between the ends, it won't damage the cylinder and this scenario is much preferred over a ring gap that is too tight.

Since multiple compression rings are often used, the gap specification of each ring is also important. You may be wondering why the gap of the top piston ring is always less than the gaps of the second piston ring.

The reason rings and their gaps are designed this way is to account for the flow of combustion gases through the rings. A very small amount of combustion gases will always escape through the ring ends. Due to combustion pressure, under normal circumstances the top ring is forced against the bottom of the piston ring groove as the piston travels down in its stroke. If the top ring's gap is larger than the second ring, pressure can build up between the piston rings. The pressure between the rings will cause the top ring to unseat from the bottom of the piston ring groove and be forced to the top of the groove. When this happens the seal between the top ring and cylinder will be lost causing both combustion pressure to escape and ring lubrication to be compromised. This will affect performance in a big way and is very undesirable.

Checking and Setting Ring End Gap

Checking the ring end gap is easily done by setting the piston ring in the cylinder bore. Lash gauges are inserted between the ring ends to determine the end gap. If the end gap is too small a diamond file can be used to remove material from the end of the ring.

Start by setting the gap of the top piston ring. Insert the ring into the cylinder bore approximately 0.5" (12mm) down from the top of the cylinder. Use the depth rod end of a caliper to square the ring to the bore so that ring depth is even all the way around the bore. This will ensure an accurate measurement can be taken.

Once the ring has been positioned, insert lash gauges between the ring ends until the width of the gap is determined. The lash gauge should just fit snuggly between the ring ends. If the lash gauge fits too tightly, the ring may start to twist and yield an inaccurate measurement.

Either the service manual or ring manufacturer will provide suitable clearances for the ring. When using aftermarket rings, follow the aftermarket manufacturer's recommendations for end gap if provided, otherwise use the OEM specs. If the ring gap is measured and is determined to be too tight, a diamond file can be used to file the end of the ring.

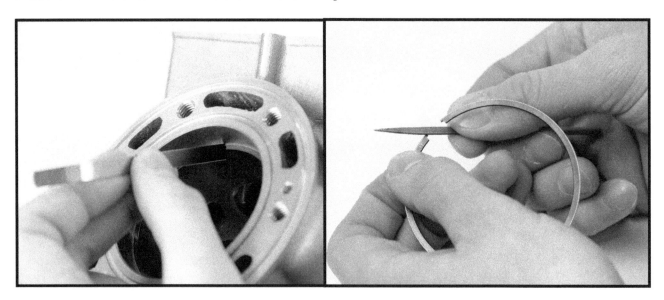

HOT TIP: If you ever find yourself working with chrome plated rings only file in one direction inward towards the center of the ring. This way the chances of plating chipping away is minimized.

Be careful to file squarely and consistently so that the gap between the rings remains parallel and consistent in width. Only file material away from one side to eliminate the risk of creating two out of square ends. Remove material slowly and check the gap often because it doesn't take a lot of filing to drastically alter the end gap. Once the top ring end gap has been set, proceed to check, and if necessary, alter the end gap of the second compression ring (if equipped).

Deburring Piston Rings

Regardless of whether or not the piston rings were filed, each ring end is likely to have a tiny burr on the end of it. This burr is created when the ring is manufactured or filed. Almost everyone I know overlooks this burr, however by removing it the cylinder bore is less likely to get scratched from coming into contact with the burr. This will in turn help prolong the life of the cylinder bore. In addition, any burrs on the top or bottom of the ring may alter the clearance between the ring and groove.

Dressing the ring ends to remove any burrs is simple and takes a minuscule amount of time. Simply use a diamond file to dress each edge of the ring by putting a slight chamfer on the ring end edges.

Once all gap setting and ring chamfering has been performed don't forget to degrease and wipe the ring clean.

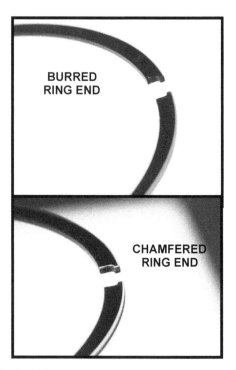

BURRED RING END

CHAMFERED RING END

Installing the Piston Rings

Whether you choose to install the rings now or wait until the piston is installed onto the engine comes down to personal preference. Prior to installation all rings should be clean and free of debris.

If two compression rings are used the second compression ring should be installed first. Otherwise proceed to lube up the top compression ring. Note any dots or lettering indicating the top of the compression ring. As mentioned earlier a chamfer is often present on the inner top edge of the compression ring which can be used to help determine the ring's orientation.

As long as care is taken to spread the top compression ring, a ring expander tool isn't necessary to fit the ring over the piston. Simply align the ring end with the ring peg and work the ring over the piston in even steps.

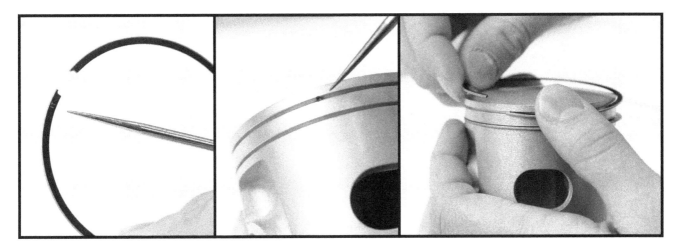

Once the rings have been installed attention can be turned to reassembling the power valve system.

Power Valve Assembly

At this point the power valve system can be reinstalled. The specific reinstallation procedure will be dependent on the type of system you're working on so be sure to consult your service manual for detailed guidance. In general, reassembly is simply the reverse of disassembly. I'll detail examples and point out important details to keep an eye on.

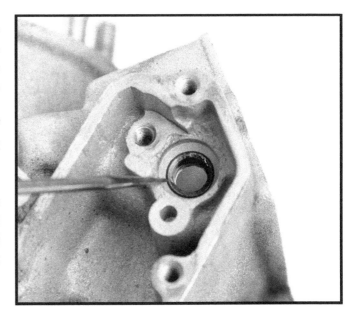

Most of the time new seals or o-rings will be the first items to be installed. Pay attention to seal orientation and ensure all seals are installed squarely in their respective bores. Don't forget to grease the lips of any seals once installed.

Almost all power valve blades will be directional. Pay special attention to any features used to correctly orient the blade. Be sure to apply a light amount of assembly lube to all blades and drums prior to installation as well.

HOT TIP: During disassembly you may have found some of the hardware difficult to remove. During reassembly don't hesitate to utilize anti-seize on fasteners as it will help make them easier to remove next time.

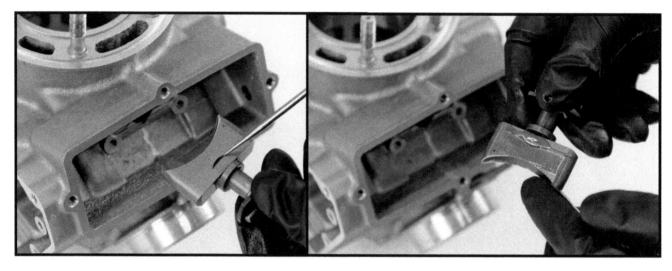

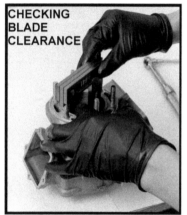

CHECKING BLADE CLEARANCE

On power valve systems utilizing blade style valves it is imperative to check that the blade does not protrude into the cylinder bore. There is not a lot of risk of this on cylinder/blade pairs that originated together, however, I have seen problems arise on cylinders that have been exchanged through plating exchange programs and on aftermarket cylinders. To confirm clearance between the blade edge and cylinder bore lay a straightedge down in the bore and note the clearance. Some manuals may provide a minimum clearance to adhere to.

When installing drums or similar components pay attention to their orientation to ensure that subsequent mating components can easily be paired with them. Be sure to apply small amounts of assembly lube on pinned joints of any linkage assemblies utilized. Likewise, use assembly lube on slotted components too.

Take care when sliding shafts past seals or o-rings.

Be sure to note any special orientations required to properly install components. Many gears that require alignment will feature small punch marks that must be aligned a specific way.

Once all the components have been installed, in most cases it should be possible to test the function of the assembly. I highly recommend doing this to ensure the valves are opening and closing as they should. Simply apply the correct motion to the assembly to ensure that it operates as it should. In some cases a wrench can be utilized to gain mechanical advantage to ease operation.

After the power valve system has been tested, complete the assembly by installing any remaining covers or plugs. Once these items have been buttoned up the cylinder is ready to go and work can progress to the cylinder head.

THE CYLINDER HEAD

For most two-strokes, the cylinder head is about as simple as it gets. In this section we'll focus on the spark plug, removing carbon, and ensuring the head can be returned to service.

Spark Plug Removal and Inspection

Start by removing the spark plug. Very rarely is a used spark plug, especially one that has been cycled through many different throttle positions, much help in accurately pinpointing lean/rich conditions at any particular point in the fuel map or jetting of the carburetor. It can however be used to get a general idea of how the engine was running and aid in diagnosing problems which occurred prior to disassembly.

GROUND ELECTRODE   CENTER ELECTRODE

INSULATOR

A spark plug that came out of an engine that was running normally will be tan to chocolate brown in color. There will be very few carbon deposits on the plug and the electrode will show very little signs of erosion. An oil fouled spark plug is gloss black and oily when removed. This indicates that an excessive amount of pre-mix oil was being burned. This could be due to an overly rich oil mixture in the fuel or improper carburetor jetting.

Similar to an oil fouled plug is a carbon fouled plug. A carbon fouled plug will exhibit signs of excessive carbon build up all around the plug. The plug will be matte black in color and is indicative that the engine has been running rich.

An engine that was detonating will feature a spark plug which has started to erode. The ground strap, center electrode, insulator, and base of the plug may all show signs of erosion. If severe enough, the insulator can crack and break away. Specks of aluminum deposits may also be present on the spark plug.

An engine which has been running lean for an extended period of time will feature a spark plug with signs of overheating. The plug will have very little color and have more of a grayish hue than tan or brown. The center electrode and ground strap may have started to erode due to the excessive heat.

Keep in mind these descriptions of plug conditions are very generalized and there are many factors contributing to how a plug looks. The main takeaway here is that if the plug has symptoms of detonation or overheating, these problems are not likely to go away on their own once the engine is reassembled. Alterations to the engine's fueling and possibly ignition timing should be pursued to eliminate these two conditions once the engine has been rebuilt.

HOT TIP: If you believe the fueling of the engine is okay, but are seeing signs of an overheated plug check the intake manifold for leaks or loose clamps. When additional air enters the intake through a leak in the intake system (between the throttle body/carburetor and cylinder head) the engine will also run lean.

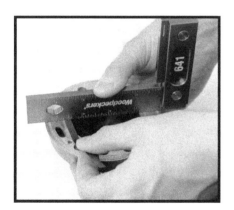

Once the spark plug has been removed inspect the combustion chamber for abnormalities. Any indentations present indicate either foreign debris entered the cylinder or part of the piston freed itself, either due to melting or breakage. By this point previous inspections of the piston and cylinder likely have alerted you to the possibility of cylinder head carnage.

After the combustion chamber has been inspected for damage proceed to remove any carbon that is present on it. Steel wool and parts cleaner usually work well to free up stuck deposits.

Cylinder Head Warpage Check

The inspection process for checking a warped cylinder head is the same as that for checking for warpage on the cylinder. Clean away any remaining gasket material on the cylinder head mating surfaces, then lay a straightedge across the head in six directions (sides and diagonals).

Use an appropriately sized lash gauge to make sure the cylinder head is not warped and conforms to the manufacturer's specifications for warpage. As previously mentioned slightly warped heads can be corrected, whereas severely warped heads will require replacement. Refer to the Cylinder Warpage section in this chapter for further information on correcting warped conditions.

Once it has been confirmed that the cylinder head is ready to go back in service the head can be set aside. We'll wait to install a new spark plug until we're ready to button up the engine.

Concluding Remarks

By this point nearly every single part within the engine should have been inspected and prepped for reassembly. Keep in mind there may be a few parts left that you didn't work directly with which could use a cleaning to remove old oil that has stuck to its inside. Once any stragglers have been dealt with, the reassembly of the engine can commence. By doing all the grunt work, inspections, and assemblies of the subassemblies at once, reassembly will progress much faster and be a lot more rhythmic than if you had serviced each part as you went through the build.

We are on the home stretch now! All the tedious cleaning, inspections, and reassemblies of the subassemblies are finished. All we have left are the major assemblies which are set to go back together. If you are building a stock motor, this section will be a breeze. If you are preparing a performance engine, there may be a few additional tasks that you will need or want to do to ensure your engine will make as much power as possible and run without trouble. These tasks may include checking and correcting port timing, setting squish, and checking the compression ratio. Each of these tasks will be outlined in Race Engine Technique sections and you will have plenty of guidance on what to do and when.

The assembly order will roughly be the reverse of the disassembly sequence. Along with this book, your service manual will give you a good path to follow and ensure everything you took out is reinstalled. All the parts should also have been laid out in their respective groups so as long as you are observant and pay attention to what you are doing it should be pretty hard to leave anything behind.

The major difference between stock and performance builds is that the stator and right covers will be left off on the performance build until the top end is buttoned up. Leaving the covers off is necessary because the engine will need to be rotated by hand to set port timing and perform other tasks. If you are building a stock engine, you may choose to do the same out of convenience.

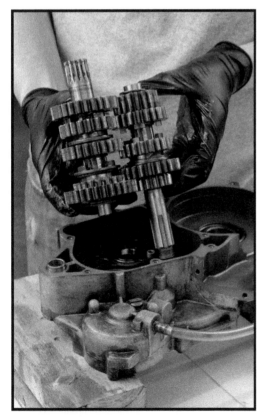

Crankcase Assembly

The first order of business will be reassembling the crankcases and installing the components that comprise the gearbox. Depending on the engine design, this will either be done sequentially or the entire gearbox will be installed at once.

Sequential Gearbox Installation

Start by applying assembly lube to all the crankcase bearings in both halves. Then block up whichever crankcase half all the internals will be installed in. Normally, this is the right case half. The two transmission shafts will be installed first. For successful installation, the shafts will have to be installed simultaneously. Carefully lower the primary and secondary shafts into their respective bearing bores.

Once the shafts have been installed the shift drum or shift forks will be installed next depending on the particular engine. Be sure to coat the shift drum grooves with assembly lube before installing the shift drum into its mating bearing bore.

HOT TIP: Depending on the engine design, in some instances it will be necessary to install the shift forks before the shift drum. The service manual should provide clarity on which component must be installed first.

It is easiest to install the shift forks into their respective slots before installing the shafts. Refer to any notes you took regarding where each shift fork goes or reference the service manual to ensure each shift forks goes in the correct location. Normally there is a cast marking which can be referenced to the service manual. This marking will specify where the shift fork must go in case you get confused. Lift up or down on the receiving transmission gears as necessary to align the forks in the gears and the pinned ends of the shift forks into the shift drum. Lube up the shift fork shafts and slide them into place.

Entire Gearbox Installation

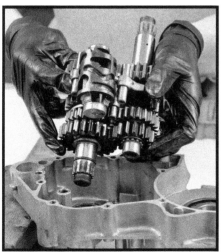

Installing the entire gearbox at once requires some planning and preparation. Start by checking the service manual to see if there are any pointers or visual aids that may help.

Next, mate the two gear shafts in one hand. Then set the shift drum on top of the shafts.

Complete the assembly by slotting the shift forks into the gear shafts and shift drum.

Secure all the components with both hands, then carefully lower the assembly into the crankcase. In some cases, it is easiest to bring the shafts in over the top side of the case half. Once installed, insure all the components are in their correct positions and that no washers have moved out of place.

Gearbox Testing

If you are at all uncertain as to whether or not the gearbox has been installed correctly, now is a good time to test it before the crankshaft, liquid gasket maker, or any other parts are added. To test the functionality of the gearbox prior to completely assembling the crankcases, start by installing the crankcase dowel pins. Then carefully lower the remaining crankcase half down onto its mate. Use a pair of crankcase bolts to secure the cases together.

Install the small dowel pin into the shift drum if it has been removed.

Then use a screwdriver to retain the spring loaded gear position lever so that the shift drum cam can be installed. In right case half gearbox installations, the shift drum cam can be permanently installed so, if specified, use any necessary locking agents and torque the bolt to spec. Before tightening completely, try to rotate the cam independently of the shift drum. Occasionally the dowel pin will misalign in the cam and the two parts will not seat correctly.

Once the shift drum cam bolt has been installed the gearbox can be tested. The neutral position on the shift drum cam is always easily identifiable because the cutout for the roller is always shallower than the rest of the slots. This is the main reason why neutral can be difficult to find from time to time.

Use a socket or screwdriver to drive the shift drum and proceed to engage all the gears. Start by engaging first gear, then work up to fifth or sixth. Since there is no oil in the gearbox and the shafts are not rotating, the gears will be much harder to engage than when the engine is running. To facilitate engagement, rotate the primary and secondary shafts back and forth, which helps the gear dogs that are trying to engage find their mating slots. Don't force anything. By patiently manually rotating the shafts back and forth, all the gears should engage. If they don't, there is a very good chance that one of the shift forks was installed in the wrong location. Luckily if this is the case, it isn't a big deal at this point to open up the crankcases and correct the problem!

NEUTRAL POSITION

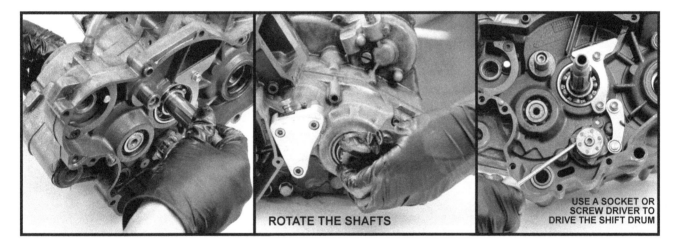

ROTATE THE SHAFTS

USE A SOCKET OR SCREW DRIVER TO DRIVE THE SHIFT DRUM

Once the gearbox has been tested and all the gears are working, the crankcases can be separated again. Make sure no transmission washers came off the shafts and inadvertently stuck to the crankcase as it was removed.

At this point it is time to bolt the crankcases together for good. If your engine features a crankshaft that utilizes a clearance fit between it and the crank bearings, things will be very easy. On the other hand, if the engine utilizes a crankshaft with an interference fit between it and the crank bearings, there will be a couple additional steps to work through. I want to discuss the additional steps involved with preparing for crankshaft installation into interference fit bearings at this time so that you can properly prepare.

Installation Options For Interference Fit Crankshafts

There are a couple different ways to install crankshafts into crank bearings which utilize an interference fit. The crank can be shrunk into the bearing by cooling the crank and warming the inner race of the bearing or the crank can be pulled through the bearing using a special puller tool. My preference is to use the heating and cooling method as I find it easiest, however a puller can be just as effective.

The interference fit between the crankshaft journal and bearing is much less than the fit between the bearings and crankcases, so the temperature difference between the parts doesn't need to be as drastic. The crankshaft can be put in a freezer for an hour to cool. The inner race of the crank bearings can be warmed by lightly and evenly heating them with a torch at the time of installation.

In order for the heating and cooling method to work, it must be well planned and executed. Making sure all the parts are accounted for in the crankcases and that everything fits together beforehand is an excellent idea. Once the assembly of the two halves commences, it is important to work quickly so that the crankshaft doesn't warm too much and get stuck halfway through the bearing. If the crankshaft does happen to get stuck in the bearing, it isn't the end of the world because a puller can be used to pull the crank the rest of the way through. Of course, it is nice when this scenario can be avoided altogether.

Final Crankcase Assembly Preparations

Temporarily remove the two crankcase dowel pins. Then apply anti-seize to the dowel pin bores in both crankcase halves. The anti-seize will help prevent the dowel pins from corroding and make separating the crankcases easier the next time around. You may be tempted to coat the dowel pins directly, but you will find that the anti-seize will scrape off and pool up on top of your nice clean gasket surface. Save yourself a clean up and coat the bores instead.

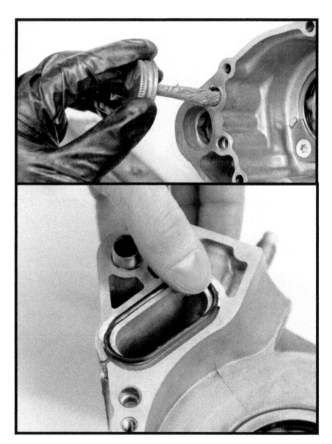

Next, confirm any remaining crankcase parts such as the coolant passage o-ring have been installed.

It is nearly time to install or make the crankcase gasket. Check out the following Technical Takeaway on working with cardboard gaskets and liquid gasket makers.

TECHNICAL TAKEAWAY

Non-Stick Cardboard Gaskets

To help prevent cardboard gaskets from sticking to the surfaces they mate to, apply silicon grease to the gasket before installing the gasket. Rub a thin coating of grease into both sides of the gasket. The gasket will darken once the grease has been rubbed in, confirming full coverage. The silicon grease will help prevent the gaskets from baking on and make the gaskets much easier to remove the next time the engine is disassembled. Applying grease to the gaskets isn't mandatory, but if you will be servicing the engine later down the road it is a good idea.

HOT TIP: Gaskets can be retained in place by applying a couple extra dabs of grease to them in a few locations if they try to wander. This can be especially helpful when working with gaskets being installed in the vertical plane.

Liquid Gasket Maker

Liquid gasket maker is commonly used to seal crankcase halves together. There are several different varieties of gasket makers which are formulated to work well in oily environments. Nearly all the top manufacturers have their own flavors and many other companies have great products as well. All of these gasket makers do the same thing, however they can vary in consistency (from runny to thick), base chemicals, and drying time. Personal preference largely dictates what you will find most pleasant to work with. Personally I like ThreeBond, Yamabond, and Permatex's MotoSeal.

Application instructions will vary, but for a good seal between parts there are a few commonalities that always hold true. The gasket surfaces must be free of old material, the surfaces should be clean of oil, and a little bit of gasket maker goes a long way. Before applying the gasket material check one last time for any raised edges, leftover material, and any other factors that can present a problem.

Since the gearbox shafts, dowel pins, and other parts are already installed into one of the crankcases it is usually easiest to apply the gasket maker to the remaining crankcase. Use your finger or a brush to spread a thin coating of gasket maker evenly over the crankcase mating surfaces. It takes very little gasket maker to seal the crankcases and overusing it will only increase the likelihood of large excess chunks of gasket maker coming free and roaming around inside the engine. Use just enough gasket maker to coat the surfaces, there is no need to build up a wall.

Installation of Clearance Fit Crankshafts

Installing crankshafts which slide right through the crank bearings is definitely the easier of the two installation varieties. Start by applying assembly lube to the crankshaft bearing journals and rod bearing. Rotate the rod a few times to help ensure the bearing is well lubricated.

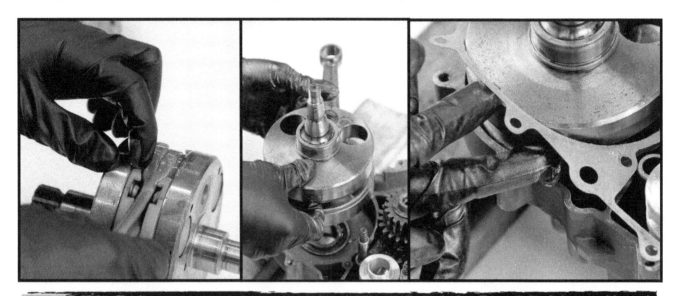

HOT TIP: Wrap electrical tape between the journal and primary gear splines to ensure a smooth surface for the seal to transition over as the crankshaft is installed. Alternatively, if the seal has not been installed yet the tape will aid in seal installation later. Be careful to keep the tape near the outer edge of the crank journal surface so the tape can easily be removed once the crank is installed. Also, use the tape sparingly so the seal can easily pass over it.

Carefully lower the crankshaft down into the crankcase. Position the end of the rod so it is aligned with the cylinder base area of the crankcases. The main focus here should be to lower the crankshaft straight through the bearing bore and past the crank seal, if installed at this point. Since some of the edges on the crankshaft are sharp, the more concentric the crankshaft is to the crank seal as it passes through, the better the chances are that the seal will not get damaged during installation.

When properly seated the edge of the crankshaft bearing journal will rest against the face of the crank bearing. Once the crankshaft is situated the crankcase gasket can either be installed or made. Take one final look around to ensure nothing has been forgotten, all the rotating or sliding components within the crankcases have been lubricated with assembly lube, and the dowel pins are installed.

Slowly lower the remaining case half down while trying to keep the case as parallel as possible to the mating half. Alignment of the crankshaft, gear shafts, shift drum, shift fork shafts, and dowel pins are all critical in order for the crankcases to seat correctly. If the crankcase half gets cock-eyed as it is lowered correct fitment of the shafts into their respective bores will be problematic and the dowel pins will bind. Once the crankcase halves have been joined remove any electrical tape used to install the seals, then rotate the crankshaft and gearbox shafts to confirm nothing is binding or amiss.

Installation of Interference Fit Crankshafts

Time is of the essence when shrinking the crankshaft into the crank bearings. To be efficient as possible start by checking over the crankcases making sure all the parts have been installed, the gasket surfaces are ready to go, and the dowel pins are in place.

Install the crankcase gasket or use gasket maker to make the gasket at this time. Remove the crankshaft from the freezer and apply assembly lube to the rod bearing and crankshaft journals. Try to hold the crankshaft by the webs so that heat isn't transferred directly into the journals.

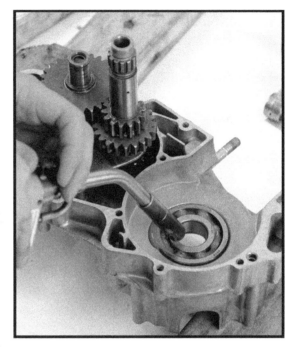

Use a small torch to heat the inner race of the crank bearing. I advised previously that it is advantageous to install the crank seals after the crank has been installed, but if the seals have already been installed due to the design of the engine, be very careful where the flame and heat are being directed. The inner race of the bearing only needs to be heated to around 150 - 200°F (65 - 93°C). A droplet or two of water can be applied to the bearing race to check the temperature. If the water sizzles upon contact, the inner race of the bearing is over 212°F (100°C) and plenty hot!

Once the bearing has been warmed, carefully lower the crankshaft down into the bearing. Try to keep the crankshaft as concentric to the bearing and seal as possible so that it does not bind in the bearing or damage the seal as it passes through. Be sure to keep the end of the rod positioned so that it aligns with the cylinder base area of the crankcases. The edge of the crankshaft journal should seat against the bearing face.

Warm the inner race of the bearing in the remaining crankcase half. Once warmed carefully lower the case half down over the crankshaft, transmission shafts, shift drum shaft, shift fork shafts, and finally dowel pins. Be sure to keep the cases as parallel as possible during assembly so that none of the shafts or dowel pins bind. After the crankcases have fully seated against each other, rotate the crankshaft and gearbox shafts to confirm they are spinning freely.

Pulling the Crankshaft Through the Crank Bearings Using a Puller Tool

Should difficulties be encountered during the assembly of the crankcase halves where the crankshaft gets stuck part way in the crank bearing, a puller tool should be used to pull the crankshaft through the remaining part of the bearing. Remember pounding on the crankshaft should be avoided because forces which may affect the trueness of the crankshaft should not be applied. Pulling the crankshaft through the bearings will be the easiest way to ensure the crank remains straight, if shrinking the crankshaft through the bearing proves problematic or is not an option.

The puller tool may be something that is bought for the occasion or nothing more than a combination of hardware found lying around the workshop. In its simplest form, the puller tool is comprised of a sleeve which sits against the inner race of the bearing, a large washer, and a nut or bolt which is installed on the end of the crankshaft that tightens against the washer and sleeve to pull the crankshaft through. Once the mechanical actions which are required to pull the crankshaft through the bearing are understood, any number of DIY remedies can be conceived to solve the problem.

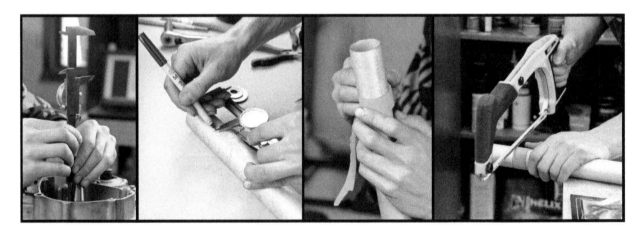

In the pictured examples a tube was used which extends to the threaded end of the crankshaft. A large flat washer covers the top of the tube and a nut is tightened down on the crankshaft to pull it through. As the crankshaft is pulled through and the nut runs out of threads, the nut can be removed and more washers added. This is the basic way a puller can be made, but more elaborate methods can easily be found by performing an internet search on the subject.

For Kawasaki engines which utilize retaining rings to secure the gear to the crankshaft fabrication of pullers can be more challenging. DIY methods could be conjured up but unfortunately I have not found any that I want to endorse at this time. My suggestion is to utilize the shrink fit method or buy the speciality tool for the job.

It is my recommendation to always try to pull against the inner race of the bearing first. However, there may be times when this isn't possible and the crankcases will have to be pulled against instead. One instance where the crankcase will have to be pulled against is when the seal has already been installed in the crankcase and the inner diameter of the seal is identical to the inner diameter of the crank bearing. In this case, it won't be possible to pull against the inner race of the bearing and the puller will have to be set up to pull against the crankcases.

Finishing Up the Crankcases

Since you are well organized, returning the crankcase bolts to their correct locations shouldn't be a problem, right? This is the ideal situation, but it is understandable if mixups occur and if there is uncertainty of where bolts must go. There are a couple ways to determine the locations of where the bolts go. First, you can install the bolt and see how much thread engagement the bolt has before it is tightened in its corresponding hole. Second, you can refer to information provided by the service manual or part microfiches.

Prior to tightening down a bolt, the head of the bolt will extend a certain distance away from the clamping face of the part. It will be easily apparent just by looking at this distance if the bolt is too short or too long for its current location. As a rule of thumb, the minimum distance the head of the bolt should extend away from the surface is equal to 1.5 times the diameter of the bolt. So for a 6mm bolt, the minimum thread engagement/distance the face of the bolt should be from the clamping surface is 9mm.

Service manuals or part microfiches found online are another great resource when trying to determine where bolts go. Many manufacturers provide bolt length information in their microfiches and the length of specific bolts can be referenced by looking up specific subassemblies.

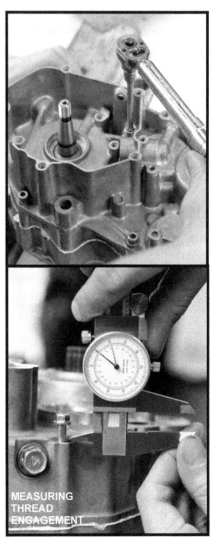

MEASURING THREAD ENGAGEMENT

Once the crankcases are together, proceed to install all the crankcase bolts, follow any specific tightening sequences, and torque them to spec. If no tightening sequence is provided, use a criss-cross pattern to evenly apply pressure to the cases. Don't forget to install any sealing washers, brackets, or tabs along with the bolts. The clutch actuation arm may also need to be installed at this time if it is retained by a bracket. Proceed to install the drive sprocket spacer onto the output shaft and any other auxiliary components. Secure the rod so that it doesn't rock back and forth from front to back by using rubber bands or wrapping clean rags around it.

Crank Seal Installation

Now that the crankcases have been buttoned up the crank seals can be installed. Take any necessary precautions, such as wrapping the ends of the crank with electrical tape. Position the engine so that the crankshaft lies vertically. Next, lube the lip of the seal and slide it into place. Use a punch or flat plate and a hammer to carefully and evenly tap the seal into place. Once installed, flip the engine over and install the remaining seal. Carefully remove any electrical tape once finished.

External Shift Mechanism Installation

The shift drum cam may have been installed when the transmission functionality was tested, however if this step was not performed the shift drum cam and bolt should be installed at this time. Once the shift drum cam has been installed, the ratcheting mechanism should be installed next.

Use assembly lube to lubricate the ratcheting mechanism. Then squeeze the pawls together and carefully lower the assembly into the shift drum cam. If you are having trouble squeezing the pawls closed enough to fit inside the shift drum cam, try using a pick or flat blade screwdriver to assist. Once the assembly is in place, install the guide plate bolts and torque them to spec.

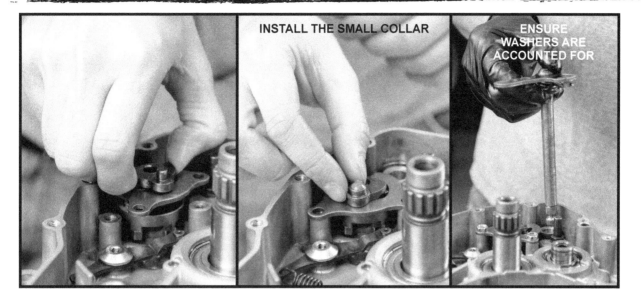

INSTALL THE SMALL COLLAR

ENSURE WASHERS ARE ACCOUNTED FOR

The shift shaft will be installed next. Install the small collar onto the end of the shifter drum arm. Make sure the washer is installed on the shaft if a washer is used, then lube up the shaft.

Slide the shaft into place and rotate it back and forth as it passes through the seal on the left crankcase half. Align the slot in the arm with the collar on shifter drum. The shaft is retained by the right crankcase cover, so until the cover is installed, the shaft can come out of position if the end of the shaft is disturbed. This can easily happen when moving the engine around and a final check of shaft alignment will occur just before installing the cover.

Kickstart Shaft Installation

Apply assembly lube to the kickstart shaft or crankcase bore, then align the ratchet arm so that it clears the guide plate on the crankcase. Make sure the notch in the plastic collar which fits around the kickstart spring is aligned with the spring and that the plastic collar is fully seated. Once seated, grab the free end of the spring and rotate it clockwise until the end of the spring aligns with the hole in the crankcase and insert it.

Idle Gear Installation

Design dependent, the idle gear will either float or be retained in place by a retaining ring. The idle gear may also be offset to one side or another, so it is important that the gear and any spacers are installed correctly. Correct installation of the gear can sometimes be deceiving because the resulting offset will misalign the engagement of the kickstart and idle gear. Refer to any notes taken during teardown, the service manual, or microfiches to ensure the idle gear is installed correctly. Don't forget the assembly lube. If a retaining ring is used, confirm the ring seats properly with a screwdriver.

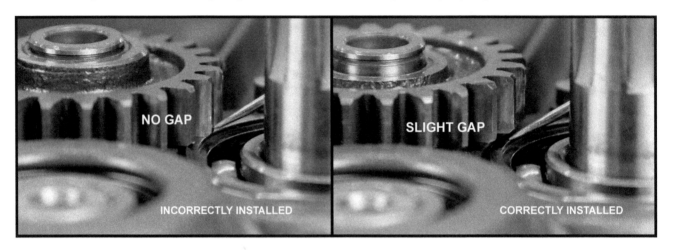

Balance Shaft Installation

For engines utilizing a balance shaft that resides in both crankcase halves make sure the bearings are lubricated, then carefully slide the shaft past the seal and through the bearings, adhering to any specific shaft orientations required for successful installation.

Balance Shaft Gear Installation

Before the clutch is installed, the primary gear and any balance shaft gears should be installed. If a balance shaft is utilized, the gears will feature a missing spline tooth or similar feature that makes it impossible to install the gears incorrectly on their respective shafts. Limiting the ways the gears can be installed helps prevent alignment errors between the crankshaft and balance shaft. It will still be possible to mistime the balance shaft with the crankshaft if the gears are not meshed correctly. If the timing of the crankshaft and balance shaft assemblies is off, expect the engine to vibrate excessively.

The balance shaft gear and crank balance gear will feature alignment marks which will ensure the gears are oriented correctly and the balancer assembly is timed right in relation to the crankshaft. Usually a pair of punch marks are used to aid in alignment of the gears.

Regardless of timing features, the counterweights on the balance shaft should always be opposite of the crankpin when the piston is at TDC. The counterweights are used to cancel out some of the reciprocating forces exerted by the piston assembly. Once the gears have been oriented correctly, it should be easily visible that when the crankpin is near its TDC position the counterweights are down.

Primary Gear Installation

After any balance shaft gears have been installed, install the primary drive gear. Use a coin to secure the balance shaft gears in place, then torque the balance shaft fastener to spec. Since the primary drive gear nut or bolt is torqued much higher than the balance shaft fastener, wait to tighten the primary drive gear until the clutch has been installed.

Clutch Actuation Arm Installation

Before installing the clutch we'll need to install the clutch actuation arm. Apply grease to the shaft, then rotate the shaft back and forth while sliding it past the seal. Install any necessary washers and bolts used to retain it. Once installed make sure the arm rotates freely.

Clutch Assembly Installation

Now that everything behind the clutch has been installed and the actuation arm is in place, the clutch assembly can be installed. Start by applying assembly lube to the primary shaft, a new needle bearing, and the sleeve, then install these parts and the clutch basket.

Install the large washer which sits between the clutch basket and hub after lubing it. Align the clutch hub splines with the splines on the primary shaft then slide the clutch hub into place.

Install the washer, and if equipped, a new lock washer, followed by the clutch hub nut, then finger tighten the nut. Use clutch hub pliers to hold the clutch hub in position so that the nut can be torqued. Once the pliers are in place, proceed to torque the nut to spec. After the nut has been tightened, bend over any lock washer tabs that may be used. A pliers, punch, and hammer work well to flatten the tabs against the flats on the nut.

Next prepare to install the clutch pack. Use new transmission oil to lubricate each of the clutch discs and plates before or during installation. The clutch plates will have a sharp side and a radiused side. This may be something you noticed during disassembly. Whether all the sharp sides face outwards or inwards doesn't make a difference, but the sharp sides should all be installed in the same direction. The sharp edge can easily be felt with your finger as you install the plates, so getting the orientation of all the plates to be the same won't be difficult.

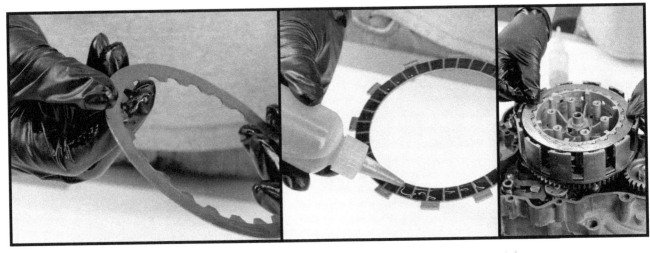

Before the pressure plate can be installed, the clutch pushrod assembly will need to be positioned in the primary shaft. Apply assembly lube to the pushrod, bearing holder/lifter, new thrust bearing, and washer. Lower the previously mentioned parts down into the primary shaft and don't forget the small ball if the engine you are working on uses one. Once the pushrod assembly has been lowered into place, rotate the clutch actuation arm and put pressure on the bearing holder/lifter. When the clutch actuation arm is oriented to its normal operating position, the flat spot on the arm will engage with the pushrod.

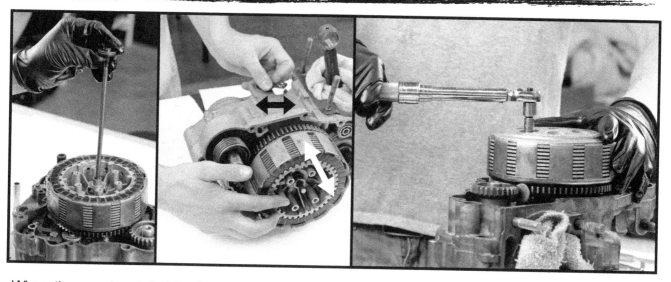

When the arm is rotated back and forth, the pushrod assembly should also move in and out of the shaft. Once the functionality of the clutch actuation arm and pushrod assembly have been checked, the clutch pressure plate can be installed. On some engines the pressure plate may need to be oriented a certain way in order for it to fit correctly. When a specific orientation is required, there will usually be a pair of alignment marks, one on the pressure plate and one on the clutch hub.

Install the clutch springs, washers, and bolts next. Tighten the clutch spring bolts down in two or three even steps so even pressure is applied to the plates. Once tight, place a coin between the clutch gear and primary drive gear, then torque the bolts to spec.

The last item that cannot be forgotten after the clutch has been installed is fully tightening the primary drive gear bolt. Use a coin to lock the primary drive and clutch gears in place, then torque the primary drive nut or bolt to spec. At this point the right side of the engine should be completely finished and all that remains is to install the right cover.

Right Cover Installation

For those preparing stock engines who are not planning on checking port timing or doing any other performance work, the right cover can be installed next. Start by installing the dowel pins which align the cover into the crankcase. If the pins showed signs of rusting or were difficult to remove, apply anti-seize to the pin bores on the crankcase and cover to help prevent them from sticking the next time the cover is removed.

Apply silicon grease to a new gasket, then install the gasket onto the crankcase. A few thick dabs of grease can be used to help keep the gasket in place. Double check to make sure all the necessary parts have been installed into the right crankcase and right cover. Apply assembly lube to all the gears and make sure all the seals in the right cover have been greased. Confirm that the shift shaft is seated against the crankcase and that the collar which slots in the shift shaft arm is situated correctly.

If the engine features a water pump shaft which slots into the balance shaft or crankshaft, the positioning of the slots is extremely important for correct installation of the cover. Position the balance shaft and water pump shaft slots horizontally prior to installing the cover.

Confirm that any power valve governors situated in the cover correctly engage with their mating linkage.

Once everything has been checked over one final time and any alignments corrected, the cover can be installed. The kickstart shaft will engage with the cover first, followed by the water pump shaft or gear,

SITUATED CORRECTLY ON COLLAR

CONFIRM POWER VALVE LINKAGE ENGAGEMENT

power valve governor, and finally the dowel pins. In order for the cover to go on without a hitch, the cover must be kept as square to these components as possible so misalignment and binding are avoided. To facilitate full seating of the cover, the crankshaft may have to be rotated back and forth

slightly so that the water pump shaft slot or gear and power valve governor gear meshes with its mating component on the crankcase side.

A successful installation should require little to no force if done right. If the right cover doesn't fully seat it is possible that the shift shaft is out of position, power valve governor gear, or the water pump shaft slot or gear has not meshed correctly. When this happens carefully remove the cover and recheck the alignment of the components. Once the cover is on rotate the crankshaft to ensure all components are rotating freely as they should. Then, proceed to install the bolts so that the right cover can be secured in place. Follow any specific tightening sequences or use a criss-cross pattern to tighten the bolts to spec.

Stator Installation - Behind Flywheel

Refer to the service manual for specific instructions on aligning the stator plate. If none are given, reinstall the stator plate so that the alignment marks on it correspond to the marks you made on the crankcase. Final ignition timing will either be set statically, which can be done with the engine on the bench, or dynamically, which requires running the engine at a set RPM. The service manual will outline which method is applicable for your engine.

If you don't intend on setting or resetting the ignition timing whether statically or dynamically torque the stator plate screws to spec at this time.

If dynamic timing is required confirm you've aligned the stator plate in accordance with the service manual and torque the screws to spec.

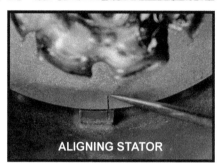

ALIGNING STATOR

> **HOT TIP:** While it takes a little time, checking the ignition timing is always something I recommend when rebuilding an engine. Adjustable stator plates can occasionally shift from their set position, a previous owner could have set the timing incorrectly, and variations in gasket thickness can slightly alter timing.

If static timing is required snug the screws but don't fully tighten them. Final adjustments to the plate's position will be made once the piston, cylinder, and flywheel are installed.

KEY AT TDC

Flywheel Installation

Make sure the key is installed into the crankshaft and that all the parts housed behind the flywheel have been installed.

It is easiest to install the flywheel when the key is positioned vertically, so rotate the crankshaft if necessary to achieve this orientation. Position yourself so that you are at eye level with the crankshaft and key. This positioning will give you the best view of the key and keyway in the flywheel for installation. Bring the flywheel into position, then align the keyway with the key. Slowly work the flywheel onto the shaft until it cannot be pushed on any further. When situated correctly, the crankshaft and flywheel should rotate in unison.

Once the flywheel is in place, install the washer and nut onto the flywheel. Hold the flywheel by hand and snug up the nut so that the flywheel doesn't accidentally come off when securing the flywheel holder or strap wrench around the flywheel.

If you're planning on checking port timing leave the nut snug so that the degree wheel can be installed. Likewise, if the stator plate screws cannot be accessed without removing the flywheel don't fully tighten the nut at this time.

Use a flywheel holding tool or strap wrench to secure the flywheel in place, then torque the flywheel nut to spec. Some manufacturers may have specific tightening sequences to follow when tightening the flywheel nut. For example, on some engines, the nut is initially torqued, a flywheel puller is installed and tightened to a specific torque to determine if the flywheel is installed correctly, then if the flywheel does not pop off there is confirmation that the flywheel is installed properly and can be torqued to its final value.

Piston Installation

Now that the sides of the engine have been assembled we can start to work our way up. Apply anti-seize to the dowel pin bores then Install the cylinder dowel pins into the crankcase. If you desire, apply silicon grease to the new base gasket to prevent it from sticking in the future. Then install the new gasket onto the crankcases.

Pull the rod up so that the piston will be near TDC when installed, this will yield the most room to maneuver your hands when installing the piston and circlip. It is imperative to have a clean rag in place covering the cylinder base so that if any circlip installation attempts are botched the circlip doesn't end up down in the crankcases!

Start by applying assembly lube to the wrist pin bores while trying to keep the lube out of the circlip groove. Reference your service manual and confirm the orientation of the piston is correct in relation to the cylinder and engine. Typically an arrow is imprinted into the piston crown to denote the exhaust side. Correctly orient the piston, align the wrist pin bore with the rod bore, then push the wrist pin into place.

Keep pressure on the back of the wrist pin with one of your fingers from your non-dominant hand. Then push the open end of the circlip into its groove with your thumbs. Once the circlip is partly installed, use a screwdriver or punch to push it the rest of the way in. Be extremely careful not to scratch or mar the piston pin bore during the installation of the circlip. Confirm the circlip is fully seated by trying to rotate it in its groove. As a reminder, the circlip should be next to impossible to rotate. Any circlips which rotate easily should be replaced because they have been squeezed too much.

Cylinder Installation

Confirm one final time that the compression ring ends are oriented in alignment with the ring pegs in the piston. Next, use engine oil to lightly oil the cylinder bore.

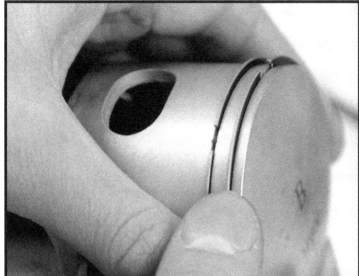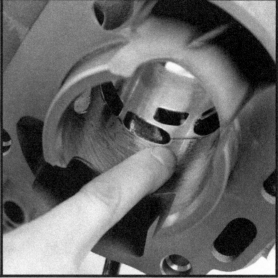

Use one hand to compress the compression rings while using the other to slowly lower the cylinder down onto the piston. Keep the cylinder as square to the piston as possible to reduce the likelihood of a botched installation. A large part of cylinder installation is based on feel, so pay close attention to how the cylinder is sliding past the rings. Normally the top compression rings will present no problems, however if the rings ends are not correctly aligned with their mating pegs installation will be problematic.

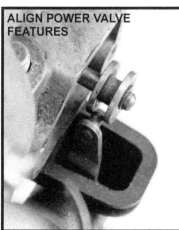

ALIGN POWER VALVE FEATURES

Once the cylinder has captured all the piston rings continue sliding it down towards the crankcase. At this point align any power valve actuation mechanisms (if applicable) before fully seating the cylinder to the crankcase.

Feel for how easily the piston slides in the cylinder. The piston should move relatively easily and there shouldn't be any feel of binding or sounds of scraping. If there are, the cylinder should be removed and the rings checked for damage.
Install the cylinder nuts and washers onto their respective studs. Adhere to any specific tightening sequences outlined in the service

TORQUING WITH CYLINDER BASE WRENCH

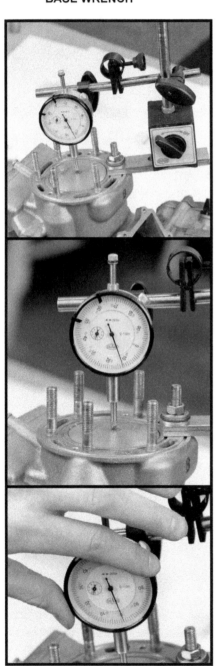

manual, otherwise use incremental steps and a criss-cross tightening pattern. Note any special torquing instructions or calculations when working with the cylinder base wrench.

Setting Ignition Timing

Many manufacturers specify a procedure for setting ignition timing statically. Typically this consists of finding TDC with a dial indicator, rotating the piston to a specified height, and checking the alignment of the marks on the stator plate with the marks on the flywheel.

This procedure can usually be done with the head on or off but I find it much easier in the latter configuration. Since each procedure is slightly different, depending on the brand of engine you're working on, I'm going to advise paying close attention to your service manual. However, I do want to share with you a practical setup you can use to get started and go through an example.

With the head off you have many options for positioning the dial indicator and you don't need one that threads into the spark plug hole. I recommend bolting a steel plate to the cylinder head. Assuming you have a magnetic base, you now have a good mounting point for setting up the indicator.

Position the indicator in the center of the piston. Make sure it is perpendicular from the face of the piston.

Next, TDC must be found in order to set the stator plate position correctly. Rotate the engine in its normal direction of rotation. TDC occurs precisely at the point where the dial indicator needle changes direction. Internally, this is where the piston motion changes from upwards to downwards. Once this point has been found, set the dial indicator to read "zero".

Ignition timing is always specified BTDC so it is imperative that the stator plate is aligned with the piston in the correct position. Rotate the flywheel approximately a quarter revolution in the direction opposite of engine rotation. This will position the piston so that it is coming up on TDC.

At this point your service manual will indicate what the target height is that the piston should be set to. Slowly rotate the flywheel in the direction of engine rotation and creep up on the target. Once the target position is reached align the mark on the stator plate with the mark on the flywheel. Then torque the stator plate screws to spec.

On the KTM engine setting timing is slightly more challenging. While a similar process to that detailed previously is used the stator plate and flywheel must be rotated in unison. To do this, a pin is inserted through a hole in the flywheel into a slot in the stator plate. Once TDC is found the stator plate is rotated in unison with the flywheel to the designated piston height BTDC. The flywheel is carefully removed and the stator plate screws torqued to spec.

If you encounter an engine that specifies a timing procedure such as this I highly recommend double checking timing to ensure the stator plate did not move when the flywheel was pulled back off.

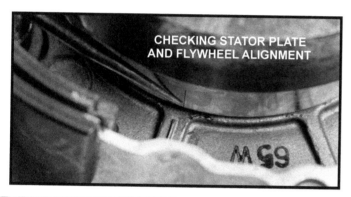

CHECKING STATOR PLATE AND FLYWHEEL ALIGNMENT

RACE ENGINE TECHNIQUE
Checking and Setting Port Timing

Checking and setting port timing is one of the most critical steps in building a high performance two-stroke engine since the port heights have a huge influence on how much power the engine produces and how well the engine runs. Due to stack ups in manufacturing tolerances the port timing of the transfer and exhaust ports can deviate slightly from the timings the engine was designed for.

Port timing specifications were often published in the service manuals of older machines, however, nowadays they are printed less frequently. If port timing values are not listed in the service manual a quick Google search often turns up the information.

Timing events will either be referenced as a duration or a point after TDC specified in degrees. The duration is simply the total crank angle that the ports are open for. The duration can be used to find the opening and closing angles. To do this simply use the following formula:

Ex open point = (360 - ex duration)/2

Trans open point = (360 - trans duration)/2

Here's a quick example:

Specified exhaust duration = 186

Ex open point = (360 - 186)/2 = 87 degrees ATDC

Adjustments to the engine's port timing can be made in one of three ways. First, by using a thicker or thinner base gasket than stock. Second, by machining the cylinder base. Finally, by adjusting the port heights themselves with the help of a die grinder. Since every engine is different there is no one size fits all solution. I would advise to think carefully about what must be adjusted in order for the timings to end up in their desired positions and to consider the simplest options first. Usually much can be accomplished simply by adjusting the thickness of the base gasket.

In the following procedure I'm going to focus on simple timing adjustments that can be achieved by altering base gasket thickness. A detailed discussion on modifying port heights using a die grinder or machining the cylinder base is outside the scope of this book. If you're building an engine that features significantly modified port timings chances are you'll be working with an experienced tuner who will perform this work for you, or at least you probably should be.

Given that the relationship between the transfer and exhaust port heights are fixed within the cylinder, without modification, there is a good chance that the relationship between the port heights will not be perfect. With this being the case there are two scenarios that can be accommodated by adjusting the base gasket thickness. The cylinder can be adjusted so that the exhaust ports open at the correct time, or the cylinder can be adjusted so that the transfer ports open at the right time. While it cannot be denied that both the transfer and exhaust ports play an enormous role in how the engine delivers power my preference is for setting the exhaust port timing correctly and letting the transfer timing deviate if the relationship between the ports is not perfect. In my experience engine performance has been altered more dramatically due to deviations in exhaust timing than transfer timing so it is more beneficial from a performance standpoint to correct the exhaust timing.

Port timing can be checked two ways. First, using a degree wheel and directly measuring the angular opening points. Second, by measuring the displacement of the piston and calculating the angular opening points. Either way is suitable and over time you may favor one over the other.

Measuring The Port Timing Directly

To start the process of checking the timing, a degree wheel and pointer will need to be installed on the engine. There are many ways of attaching these items and each engine will provide its own challenges. Here I've left the flywheel on and repurposed the flywheel puller tool to clamp the degree wheel in place. The pointer can be made from welding rod, a coat hanger, or anything else you can find. I used one of the cylinder studs to secure the pointer, then bent it into position.

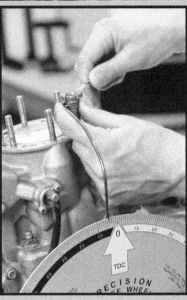

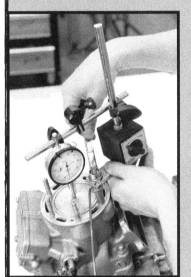

Before the port timing can be checked, TDC must be found. A dial indicator should be affixed to the cylinder head and positioned so that the pointer is centered on the piston. Ensure that the indicator is perpendicular to the piston face. The piston dwells a few degrees at TDC so more accuracy than zeroing the degree wheel to the piston's highest position is necessary.

TDC can be found by measuring equal distances on the piston's up and down stroke and then confirming that the degree wheel timing is equal on both sides at the measured distances. I like to target a distance of 0.050" (1.27mm) when finding TDC. This value is arbitrary and you can choose whatever distance you like as long as you ensure you're at least 0.020" (0.5mm) from TDC.

HOT TIP: If dial indicators are not available TDC can also be found by using a piston stop. A plate mounted across the cylinder head with a bolt and lock nut protruding down into the center of the cylinder bore can serve as a stop. Alternatively, piston stoppers can easily be made by removing the center section of a spark plug and then tapping a suitably sized threaded hole in the remaining part of the plug so a bolt and lock nut can be installed. The stopper can then be easily threaded into the spark plug hole. For this to be applicable the head would of course have to be temporarily installed.

Whichever method of finding TDC you decide to use, start by moving the crankshaft to the approximate TDC position. Then without rotating the crankshaft move the degree wheel so that TDC on the wheel coincides with the pointer. Next, set up your piston stops or measure piston travel on both sides of TDC. In this example I'm using a dial indicator affixed to a plate on the top of the cylinder. I've decided to take measurements at 0.050" (1.27mm) of piston travel before and after TDC. At each measurement point the number of degrees indicated on the degree wheel before and after TDC should be the same if I have found true TDC.

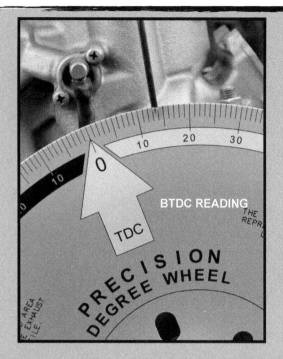

BTDC READING

TDC

PRECISION DEGREE WHEEL

ATDC READING

TDC

If the degree wheel values don't read the same before and after TDC, determine which way the wheel must be rotated so that the values become equal. Then carefully rotate the degree wheel without rotating the crankshaft to alter the degree wheel's position. Once altered, recheck and confirm that true TDC has been found. This can be a tedious process but is extremely important for checking port timing accurately. Repeat the procedure for checking TDC 3 - 5 times to ensure repeatability and accuracy.

After true TDC has been found, be extremely careful not to inadvertently move the degree wheel or pointer. Do not rotate the crankshaft using the nut or bolt securing the degree wheel to the crankshaft. Instead, use the primary drive gear nut or bolt to rotate the engine over.

Now that TDC has been established the dial indicator or piston stop can be removed so the cylinder bore is more accessible.

Next we're going to find the port opening event. Referencing the specified timings will help determine when to start sneaking up on the port opening. The port opening point is defined as the crank position where the top edge of the port becomes exposed by the top edge of the piston. Typically on engines with one main exhaust port and sub-ports the main port will open first. On engines with two main exhaust ports separated by a bridge both should open at the same time. When checking transfer ports, depending on design, they can all open at once or feature staggered timing.

The port opening can be gauged carefully by eye or with a lash gauge. I tend to use both visual cues as well as the lash gauge to determine the port opening event. I like to use the thinnest and narrowest lash gauge I can find. Due to the elliptical shape of the port edge using a wide lash gauge would require the port to open more before it can pass through.

HOT TIP: Illuminating the exhaust ports from the port exit and the transfer ports from the crankcase with a light can be very helpful when checking port timing.

HOT TIP: The diameter of the piston crown will not yield a tight fit to the cylinder bore so it may be necessary to rock the piston forward or aft when checking the port timing. Positioning the crown against the intake or exhaust side of the cylinder can make it easier to determine when the port in question has opened.

All that is left to do is carefully position the crank so that the lash gauge can be inserted or you can visibly see the opening. Slowly rotate the crank to the position you believe the port has opened. Then confirm by eye or with the lash gauge that the port has opened. If the lash gauge does not slide into the port rotate the crank slightly more. Once the port opening point has been found record the crank angle indicated by the degree wheel. Repeat this process for checking the transfer port timing. Due to a number of factors this process will have some ambiguity and you will need to settle on the best way to qualify your measurements based on your application. While striving for exact measurements is important, ensuring the process is repeatable is arguably more valuable. I often take three measurements of the opening event and then average them together to arrive at my final value.

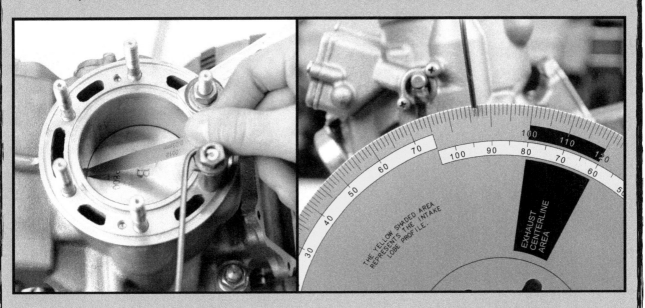

Port	Open ATDC (degrees)	Total Duration (degrees)
Main Exhaust	86.25	187.50
Sub Exhaust	86.25	187.50
Main Power Valve	101.00	158.00
A Transfer	122.00	116.00
B Transfer	122.00	116.00
C Transfer	122.00	116.00

In this example the YZ250 engine currently has the main exhaust port opening at 86.25, sub-ports at 86.25, A transfers at 122, and B and C transfers at 122 degrees ATDC.

Once the timings of the exhaust and transfer ports have been identified any necessary adjustments to the base gasket must be determined. The easiest way to do this is by measuring the necessary timing change and subsequently gasket height change with a dial indicator.

Reinstall the dial indicator. Then with the crank set at the port opening event, position the tip of the dial indicator on the center of the piston. Next set the indicator so it reads zero.

For the YZ250 my measured exhaust timing was 86.25 degrees ATDC. As an example, we'll investigate what needs to be done in order for the port to open at 85 degrees ATDC. To do so, I'll rotate the crankshaft to 85 degrees ATDC and measure the distance the dial indicator travels from its original position at 86.25 degrees ATDC.

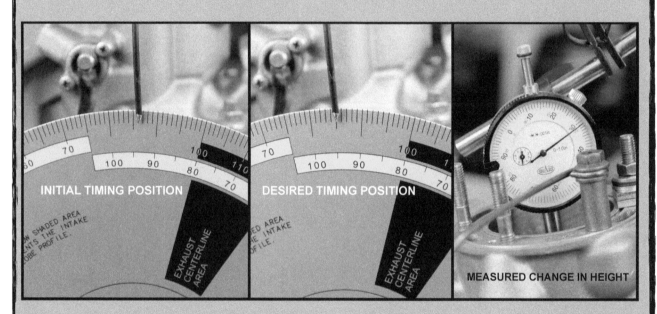

INITIAL TIMING POSITION

DESIRED TIMING POSITION

MEASURED CHANGE IN HEIGHT

The dial indicator measured .031" (0.787mm) of movement which corresponds to the height I would have to add to the base gasket to achieve the desired timing of 85 degrees ATDC. Conversely, if I wanted to delay the port opening event to a value greater than 86.25 degrees I would need to set the desired timing and measure the amount of material that would have to be removed from the gasket or cylinder base.

The measured distance indicated by the dial indicator is the change in height that must be made to the cylinder to achieve the desired port timing. Depending on whether the timing occurred sooner or later than specified, the height change required may either be positive or negative.

Depending on what is required gaskets can be stacked, custom gaskets can be ordered, or the cylinder base can be machined so that the timing arrives at the desired value.

Calculating the Port Opening Point

If the rod length, stroke, and deck height are known the port duration and angle at which the ports open can be calculated using equations or online calculators. Rod lengths normally aren't detailed in the service manual but can often be found in the catalogs of aftermarket rod manufacturers. The deck height refers to the distance from the top of the cylinder to the top of the piston crown. The deck height is an easily measurable value. Depending on the engine the deck height may be entered as a positive or negative value. If the piston resides below the top of the cylinder at TDC a positive value for the deck height will be used. If the piston resides above the top of the cylinder at TDC then a negative value for the deck height will be used. If you study the equation for variable "T" you will see that a negative deck height (C) will be additive to the distance the port resides from the cylinder (E), which is what we want.

The equation for calculating the port duration is as follows.

$$D = (180 - Cos^{-1}(\tfrac{T^2 + R^2 - L^2}{2 \, x \, R \, x \, T})) \, x \, 2$$

Where:
$T = R + L + C - E$
$R = stroke/2$
$L = con\ rod\ length$
$C = deck\ height$
$E = distance\ from\ top\ of\ port\ to\ top\ of\ cylinder$

If you want to enter the equation into a spreadsheet the formula should look something like this:

=(180-(degrees(acos((T^2+R^2-L^2)/(2*R*T)))))*2

Once the port open duration is known it may be necessary to find port opening angle which can be done using the formulas below. This may or may not be necessary depending on what timing specs are provided for the engine.

Ex open point = (360 - ex duration)/2

Trans open point = (360 - trans duration)/2

I'll resolve a worked example shortly after all the measurements from the KTM engine are collected.

To start, the height of the piston at TDC in relation to the cylinder deck height must be known. Reference previous instructions to position the piston at TDC. Next use a caliper to measure from the top edge of the cylinder up or down to the top edge of the piston. This measurement will be our deck height (variable C).

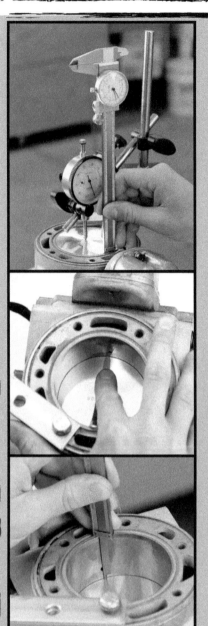

The deck height can be a positive or negative value depending on whether the edge of the piston protrudes above or below the top of the cylinder. Piston edges that reside below the top of the cylinder are entered as positive deck heights while piston edges that protrude above the top of the cylinder must be entered as a negative values. If you look closely at the equation it will become apparent as to why this seemingly counterintuitive assignment of plus and minus signs is required. In the example shown the top edge of the piston protrudes slightly above the top of the cylinder so a negative deck height will be recorded.

Next, rotate the piston down until the exhaust port opens. Insert a lash gauge into the port to help qualify the port opening point. Measure down from the top of the cylinder with a caliper. Subtract the thickness of the lash gauge from this measurement.

Once the deck height and port open height are known the port open angle can be calculated. Plug the numbers into the equation or program to output the port open angle. Here's an example calculation of determining the exhaust duration using the KTM engine.

R = 38.5mm
L = 135mm
C = -.30mm
E = 40.70mm

T must be resolved first:

T = R + L + C - E
T = 38.5 + 135 + (-0.30) - 40.70 = 132.5

Now the process of calculating D can begin:

$$D = (180 - Cos^{-1}(\frac{T^2 + R^2 - L^2}{2 \, x \, R \, x \, T})) \, x \, 2$$

$$= (180 - Cos^{-1}(\frac{132.5^2 + 38.5^2 - 135^2}{2 \, x \, 38.5 \, x \, 132.5})) \, x \, 2$$

$$= (180 - Cos^{-1}(.07973)) \, x \, 2$$

$$= (180 - 85.43) \, x \, 2$$

$$= 189.14 \; degrees$$

So the main exhaust port on the KTM engine has a duration of 189.14. The calculation can be repeated for the remaining ports. Life can be made easy by creating a spreadsheet that outputs the measured port heights into port durations.

KTM 380			
Port	Open Height (mm)	Total Duration (degrees)	Calculated Open Angle (Degrees ATDC)
Main Exhaust	40.70	189.14	85.43
Sub Exhaust	40.70	189.14	85.43
Main Power Valve	50.86	158.27	100.87
A Transfer	61.64	119.95	120.02
B Transfer	61.64	119.95	120.02
C Transfer	62.94	114.62	122.69

If the port timings are off from the target value all that has to be done is to manipulate the port height value (E). Once the port height has been altered to arrive at the desired port timing the difference in the current height and the required height can be calculated to determine what changes must be made to the base gasket or cylinder base.

For example if I wanted the exhaust duration to be 190 degrees the port height from the top of the cylinder would need to be 40.40mm. The current port height is 40.70mm, so the difference in height would be 0.30mm. If I wanted to set the port timing to this position I would need a 0.30mm thicker gasket so that the cylinder sits higher and exhaust port opens sooner.

That wraps up how to calculate port timing. Whether you decide to measure the port timing directly or calculate it, either method will work, just be sure to work slowly and thoroughly so that you achieve accurate results.

RACE ENGINE TECHNIQUE

Checking Squish Clearance

Squish clearance is simply the clearance between the cylinder head and piston. It is frequently checked when custom cylinder heads are installed or when port timing has been adjusted. Setting squish correctly on a modified engine will ensure that the piston never comes in contact with the cylinder head and will improve performance.

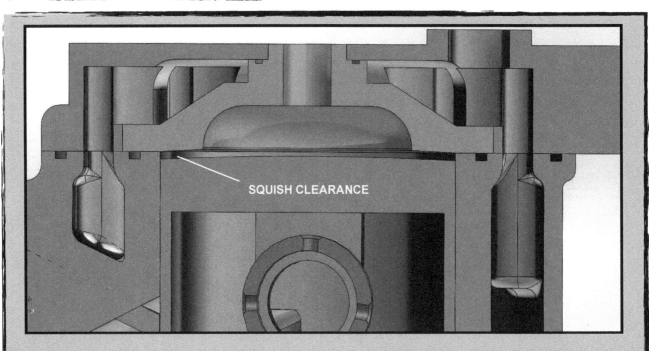

SQUISH CLEARANCE

Squish clearance values are not specified in the service manual and modifying the clearance is not typically a modification you'll perform on your own. Professional engine builders who offer a cylinder head modification service will often request your squish clearance measurements before carrying out machining work on the cylinder head. Any desired alterations to port timing will need to be carried out first since base gasket adjustments will directly influence squish clearance.

Once the squish clearance measurements have been taken they can be sent with the cylinder head to the service making the modifications. The machinist will use these measurements to correctly machine the head to the desired clearance, and if necessary, compression ratio.

Squish clearance is measured by inserting a piece of solder on the piston crown, installing the cylinder head, and rotating the engine over. The piston flattens the solder against the head which yields a measurable strip.

The thickness of solder required will depend on a few variables which include the size of the engine, the manufacturer's original clearance, and if any adjustments have been made to the height of the cylinder. It's wise to have solder on hand that ranges from 0.040" (1.0mm) to .125" (3.2mm). The solder used should be a type of hollow core solder. This will make it easier to rotate the engine over and put less load on components.

HOT TIP: If you're unsure of what thickness solder you need, modeling clay can be used to narrow the selection. Simply roll out a thin strip of clay, lay it on top of the piston crown, install the head, hold it in place, then rotate the engine over. The flattened clay should be measurable and yield the required solder thickness.

To get started checking the squish clearance ensure that the port timing is set as desired and that the cylinder nuts are torqued to spec. Cut a piece of solder that is approximately 1.5 times the the length of the bore diameter. Carefully file both ends of the solder strip flat.

Form a camelback in the middle of the solder strip. Then spread the strip so that it's length is slightly wider than the cylinder bore. Allowing the solder to act as a spring, which effectively preloads the ends into the cylinder walls, will help ensure the very edge of the combustion chamber is captured when the solder is compressed.

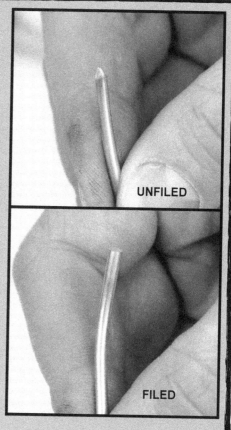
UNFILED

FILED

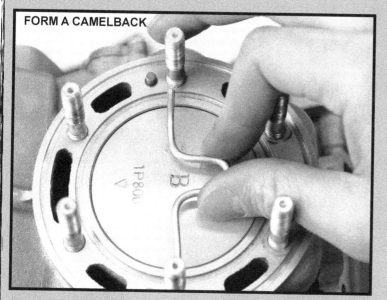
FORM A CAMELBACK

Position the crank so that the piston is BTDC and down in the bore approximately .5" (12.7mm). Center the solder strip along the axis of the wrist pin. Ensure the ends of the strip are touching the cylinder bore. Then secure the strip in place with a piece of tape. Make sure the tape does not protrude into the area being flattened.

If the cylinder head uses a gasket, install the new gasket at this time along with the head. Torque the cylinder head nuts or bolts to spec.

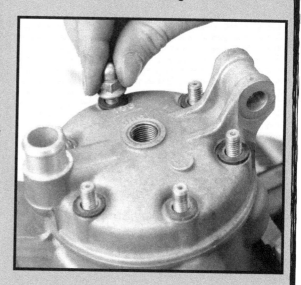

Use a wrench to rotate the engine over through TDC. You should feel a slight bump as the solder is flattened but it should not require excessive force. If the engine will not easily rotate through TDC then stop and assess the situation. It is highly likely that a strip of solder too thick for the job has been used.

Once the solder has been squashed remove the cylinder head and solder. Use a caliper to measure the thickness of the solder at each of the ends. Ideally, the thickness measured at each end will be close to equal. If it is not, the solder may have come out of position or the combustion chamber was not machined parallel to the top of the piston.

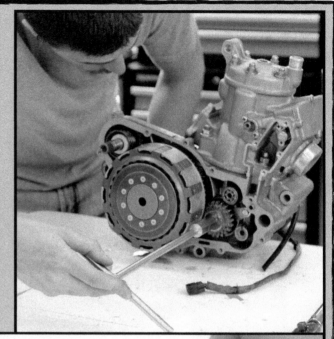

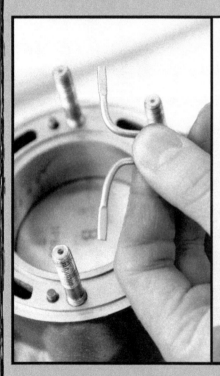

HOT TIP: Most combustion chambers feature a shallow taper in the squish band so it is important to measure as close to the tip of the squashed solder sample as possible.

It is advisable to perform a few squish clearance measurements to confirm repeatability. After this has been done the sample strips can be labeled and sent to the service performing the machining work.

RACE ENGINE TECHNIQUE

Checking Compression Ratio

For serious performance engine builds, checking and making alterations to set the compression ratio at the target value is an important step. Due to variations in manufacturing, alterations to port timing, or the desire to raise/lower the compression ratio small changes may have to be made to get the ratio exactly right.

The compression ratio will be specified one of two ways, as the geometric compression ratio or as the trapped compression ratio. The geometric compression ratio utilizes the cylinder's full swept volume in the calculation, whereas the trapped compression ratio only utilizes the swept volume above the exhaust port.

Geometric Compression Ratio = (Clearance Volume + Swept Volume) / Clearance Volume

Trapped Compression Ratio = (Clearance Volume + Swept Volume at Exhaust Port Closure) / Clearance Volume

The engine manufacturer will dictate which compression ratio is listed in the service manual. Geometric compression ratios are straightforward to calculate while trapped compression ratios require determining the exhaust port opening point and swept volume above the port prior to calculation.

Due to the fact that the squish clearance must be kept at its target value there is only one way to make adjustments to the compression ratio without changing the squish clearance. The cylinder head's combustion chamber must be machined to the correct size and shape for the desired ratio. The service enlisted to do the machining work will require the initial compression ratio measurements in order to correctly machine the combustion chamber.

Whether you choose to optimize to the compression ratio listed in the service manual or a different value will depend entirely on your build. Consulting with an engine builder experienced with your particular model and application is highly recommended when determining what modifications should be made to the compression ratio.

There are two ways to determine the compression ratio. First, with the engine together, and second, with the cylinder head off. Checking the compression ratio with the engine together is usually easier, however, the combustion chamber shape dictates what method should be used.

Toroidal combustion chamber designs where the bottom of the spark plug resides lower than the top of the combustion chamber can be difficult to measure when the cylinder head is installed on the engine. Difficulties arise because air can get trapped in the upper portion of the combustion chamber, it won't bleed out, and measurements are inaccurate.

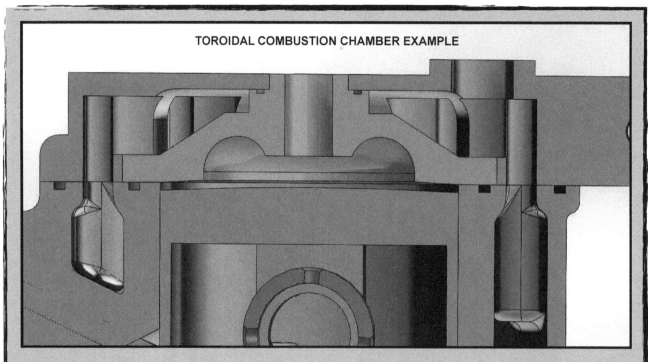

TOROIDAL COMBUSTION CHAMBER EXAMPLE

We'll start with the procedure for checking the compression ratio with the engine assembled. First, the engine should be leveled from front to back and from side to side so that the cylinder sits perfectly vertical. This way as fluid fills up the combustion chamber, air won't get trapped in the corners of the chamber and can escape out the plug hole.

Prior to installing the cylinder head, TDC must be found. This is easily done using a dial indicator and observing the point where the piston dwells and the indicator needle changes direction.

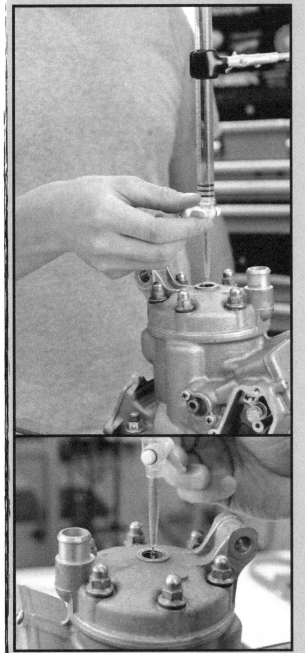

Once TDC has been found, install the cylinder head o-rings or gasket and cylinder head onto the engine. Follow the necessary tightening sequences and torque the bolts to spec so the cylinder head gasket is clamped correctly. Carefully fill a burette with transmission fluid, coolant, or your desired liquid to a specific reference mark in the burette. If you are using a fluid other than coolant or ATF, make sure it has similar surface tension properties as coolant or ATF. If the fluid is too thin/runny, it will seep past the ring ends. If the fluid is too thick, it will have difficulty dispersing in the combustion chamber.

Position the burette over the spark plug hole. You will need to have a good aim to direct the fluid into the plug hole. You may consider using a piece of tubing to bridge the gap, but this can lead to less accurate results because some fluid will always remain in the tubing. Slowly fill the combustion chamber with fluid until the fluid resides level with the bottom of the spark plug hole. A high powered flashlight is very helpful for seeing where the fluid level sits.

Once the fluid has been filled to the bottom of the hole, wait around 5 minutes so that any fluid stuck to the walls of the burette has a chance to drain down so an accurate reading can be taken. After the fluid has drained or your patience has waned, record the ending position of fluid in the burette. Be sure to take the reading at eye level, otherwise the reading will be inaccurate.

To get the fluid back out, rotate the engine over so that the piston travels approximately one quarter of the way down the cylinder bore. Turn the crankshaft one eighth of a revolution to achieve this. At this point, remove the cylinder head and use a syringe to suck up the fluid, then wipe the rest of the fluid up with a rag. If the test must be repeated, make sure to be diligent about cleaning all of the fluid off the piston, cylinder head, and cylinder so that accuracy is maintained during the second test.

The amount of fluid in the combustion chamber (clearance volume) can be determined by subtracting the ending volume of fluid in the burette from the starting volume of fluid, and then adding the volume of fluid that the spark plug can retain. Most spark plugs hold 0.1 - 0.2cc of fluid, but it is never a bad idea to do this investigation for yourself with the plug you will be using.

Clearance Volume = Starting Volume - Ending Volume + Spark Plug Volume

Once the clearance volume is known, the geometric compression ratio can be calculated.

Compression Ratio = (Swept Volume + Clearance Volume) ÷ Clearance Volume

In case you forgot, the swept volume can be found using the following formula.

Swept Volume = π (Pi) x (Bore Diameter^2 ÷ 4) x stroke

Here is an example of determining the geometric compression ratio for the Yamaha YZ250 engine.

Clearance Volume = 17.4cc

Swept Volume = 249.32cc = π x (6.64^2 ÷ 4) x 7.2

Compression Ratio = 15.33 = (249.32 + 17.4) ÷ 17.4

Unfortunately, Yamaha specifies the compression ratio as the trapped compression ratio in relation to the power valve closed and full exhaust port open points. As an example, the compression ratios listed in the service manual are 9.2 - 10.9:1. So with the power valve closed we should expect a trapped compression ratio of around 10.9:1 and with the power valve open a ratio of 9.2:1.

In order to determine the trapped compression ratio the volume above the exhaust port and/or power valve closed position will have to be found. Refer to the section on checking port timing to determine the height above the exhaust port and power valve.

Once the height above the exhaust port and power valve have been found their respective swept volumes can be calculated.

Swept Volume Above Exhaust Port = π x (Bore Diameter^2 ÷ 4) x (Exhaust Port Height - Deck Height)

Swept Volume Above Power Valve = π x (Bore Diameter^2 ÷ 4) x (Power Valve Closed Height - Deck Height)

Using the YZ250 as an example I measured 3.892cm from TDC so my swept volume is:

Swept Volume Above Exhaust Port = π x (6.64^2 ÷ 4) x 3.892 = 134.77cc

The trapped compression ratio when the power valve is open is:

Trapped Compression Ratio = (17.4 + 134.77)/17.4 = 8.75:1

A similar calculation can then be carried out to see how the compression ratio aligns with the specified value when the power valve is closed. A comparison of one or both values can be made to the specified compression ratio(s) in the service manual to determine how close the engine's actual compression ratio is to the target value.

Compression Ratio Check With Cylinder Head Off

To check the compression ratio with the cylinder head off the only thing that will be done differently is that the volume of the cylinder head and volume above the piston crown will be checked separately. To do this, a clear sheet of plastic cut to size will be required.

Keep in mind that if the cylinder head drops down into the cylinder or if the piston crown protrudes above the top of the cylinder measuring the compression ratio with the engine apart will be more difficult.

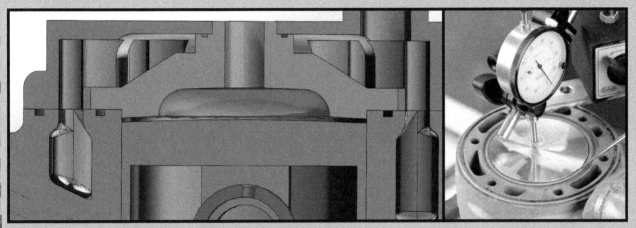

EXAMPLE OF A DROP DOWN CYLINDER HEAD

Ensure the top of the cylinder is sitting level and that the piston is at TDC. Then cut out an appropriately sized circle from the plastic so that it covers the top of the cylinder. Center the plastic cover then drill a hole in it large enough to allow the burette to pour fluid in. Next, drill a small bleed hole where you believe it will be most effective.

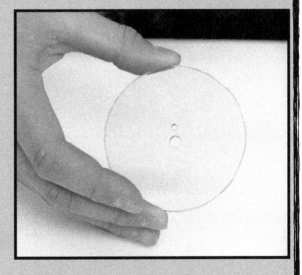

HOT TIP: If the piston protrudes above the top of the cylinder move the piston down a set distance. Then calculate the volume it displaced by using the height it had to move down in the bore and the bore diameter. Subtract this volume from the overall volume measured.

Apply grease to the top edge of the cylinder bore then center the cover and gently press it into place. Move the burette into position and slowly fill the volume above the piston crown until fluid resides at the bottom of the bleed hole. Make sure there are no air pockets in the cavity.

Install the spark plug into the head. Then repeat the measuring process to obtain the volume in the cylinder head.

Lastly, if a gasket is used the volume the gasket will add must be accounted for. This can be calculated using the formula below.

Gasket volume = π (Pi) x (Bore Diameter^2 ÷ 4) x Gasket Thickness

To determine the clearance volume use the following formula:

Clearance Volume = Volume above crown + head volume + gasket volume (if applicable)

Once the clearance volume has been determined the compression ratio can be calculated.

At this point we've collected the necessary squish clearance and compression ratio information so the head can be sent off for modification. Once the head returns all that is left to do is recheck both features to ensure that the job was done correctly.

Cylinder Head Installation

Install the cylinder head dowel pins into the cylinder, then install new cylinder head o-rings or a new gasket. Carefully lower the cylinder head down onto the cylinder. Be sure to keep the cylinder head square to the dowel pins as the head is lowered to avoid any chances of the head binding on the pins.

Once the cylinder head is in place, install the cylinder head nuts or bolts. Snug the fasteners up by hand. Adhere to any specific tightening sequences, lubrication requirements, and torque specs provided by the service manual to bring the fasteners up to their final torque spec. If the service manual only specifies a final torque value, tension the fasteners in two or three even torque steps to promote even clamping of the cylinder head gasket surfaces. Remember to use a star pattern and torque in increments at least 5Nm apart from one another.

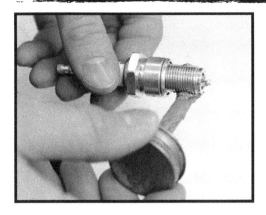

Spark Plug Installation

Carefully gap (if required) a new spark plug, apply anti-seize to the plug threads, and install the plug into the head. Be sure to use a torque wrench and follow the recommended torque specs.

Stator Cover Installation

If it makes sense to do so, the stator cover can be installed next. Before installing the stator cover be sure that both the stator plate screws have been torqued to spec and that the flywheel nut has been torqued. These items can easily be overlooked when being interrupted by the tasks of setting the ignition timing and checking the port timing.

Start by installing the dowel pins into the left crankcase. Then apply silicon grease to the stator cover gasket and install the gasket onto the crankcase. Before installing the cover, double check to confirm that the rubber plug which locates the electrical wires as they exit the stator cover is correctly positioned.

If dowel pins are utilized be sure to install them, then carefully align the stator cover with them.
Once the cover seats, install the cover bolts. Then use any specified tightening sequences or a criss-cross pattern to tighten the bolts to their final torque spec.

Power Valve Linkage Installation

Proceed to install the power valve linkage following any special instructions provided by the service manual. If a set pin is required to lock the linkage in place while tightening the bolt don't forget to insert it.

Next, install the power valve cover along with a new gasket. If a thick rubber gasket is used to seal the valve cover to the right cover ensure that the cover has seated against it correctly.

Reed Valve and Intake Manifold Installation

Prepare a new reed valve gasket for installation. Then confirm the order and orientation of the gasket, spacer (if used), reed valve, and intake manifold. Proceed to torque the bolts to spec using a criss cross pattern.

Crankcase Leak Down Check

At this point the engine should be completely back together. Before proceeding any further I highly recommend checking the integrity of the seals and gaskets by performing a crankcase leak down test on the engine. This test will provide peace of mind that the sealing abilities of the engine are sound and that there won't be any problems when it comes time to run the engine. You may wonder what the point is since you've installed all new gaskets and seals, however, on more than one occasion I can attest to finding sealing issues on new builds. For more details on performing a leak down test refer to the crankcase leak down testing section in Chapter 3.

Adding Oil

By this point the engine should be ready to go back in the chassis. I prefer to add transmission oil to the engine prior to installing it into the chassis so that if there are any leaks corrective actions can be taken without having to fight the chassis. Before adding oil, double check and confirm that the oil drain bolt has been installed and that the output shaft drive sprocket spacer has been installed. The drive sprocket spacer features a couple o-rings and seals against the output shaft seal in the crankcase. Without the spacer in place, oil can leak like a sieve when the engine is rotated while fitting it in the frame.

Reassembling the Bike

Just like the engine, the reassembly order of the bike will be roughly reverse of the disassembly sequence. There isn't much more wisdom I can pass your way and the service manual should do an adequate job of instructing you on how to get your machine back together. Below you'll find the reverse order of disassembly with the important additional steps of adding coolant and installing a new air filter.

1. Engine in
2. Swingarm pivot bolt
3. Engine mounts
4. Brake pedal
5. Clutch cable
6. Kickstart pedal
7. Engine sprocket
8. Shift pedal
9. Ignition coil
10. Throttle body or carburetor
11. Engine guards
12. Radiators
13. Add Coolant
14. Rear subframe
15. Exhaust pipe and muffler
16. Side covers
17. Fuel tank and radiator shrouds
18. New air filter
19. Seat
20. Break In!

Installing the Engine Into the Frame

A lot of time may have passed since the engine was removed from the frame, however you will want to think back to the magic you performed to remove the engine. Doing the exact reverse will be the best and easiest way to get the engine back in. Remember to keep the swingarm back and out of the way as you install the engine. Once the engine is in the frame, the swingarm can be moved forward and repositioned. Be sure the swingarm pivot bolt is clean and apply grease or anti-seize to the pivot to ensure it won't present a problem coming out in the future.

Carburetor Advice

If you have rebuilt a carbureted bike and the carburetor has sat out for an extended period of time (2+ weeks), consider cleaning the carburetor before reinstalling it. Fuel can easily evaporate, leaving a filmy residue behind that can clog the jets. Completely assembling the bike only to find that it won't start due to a clogged pilot jet can be very frustrating when you are anxious to get out and ride.

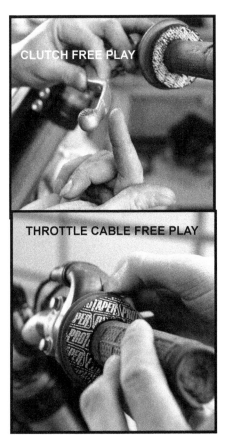

CLUTCH FREE PLAY

THROTTLE CABLE FREE PLAY

Setting Up Clutch Free Play

A sure way to wear out a perfectly good clutch is to incorrectly tension the clutch cable. Make sure when installing the clutch cable that there is free play in the cable. Normally service manuals will specify that the clutch lever has around 0.25 - 0.50" (6 - 12mm) of free play after the cable has been adjusted.

Setting Throttle Cable Free Play

To ensure the throttle cables don't prematurely wear or snap, they should have a little bit of slack in them when the throttle is closed. Refer to the service manual for specifics and adjust the cable adjusters as necessary to achieve the correct amount of free play. The twist grip should normally have around 0.125 - 0.250" (3 - 6mm) of free play when the cables are set correctly.

Adding Coolant

Once the radiators have been installed and the coolant hoses hooked up, it's not a bad idea to fill the engine with coolant at this point. If for some reason there is a problem, it will be less work to fix it now as opposed to finding a leak when the bike is completely assembled. Be sure to recheck the coolant level after the engine has been run as well.

Installing New Exhaust O-Rings or Gasket

Don't forget to install new exhaust o-rings or a gasket when installing the exhaust pipe! New o-rings are crucial in preventing exhaust leaks and can occasionally be overlooked when reassembling the bike.

Installing A New Air Filter

Don't forget to install a new air filter to keep your new engine breathing clean air. Make sure a generous amount of air filter oil is applied to the filter. During installation be wary of old dirt in the airbox, which can make its way down the intake tract into your new engine.

Final Assembly Notes

Once your bike is back together, give yourself a pat on the back for a job well done! Double check that you haven't forgotten any parts and that all the electrical connections have been made. Nothing is more frustrating than kicking over a new engine that won't start only to find a missed connection was the culprit. Proceed to add fresh fuel and begin the break in procedure!

CH 15

CHECKING DYNAMIC IGNITION TIMING

This chapter serves as a reminder and quick walk through for those who are working on engines which require the final ignition timing be checked while the engine is running. If this type of procedure is required, your service manual should explicitly state so and provide detailed information to ensure an accurate assessment. It has been my experience that most modern two-strokes utilize ignition timing procedures which can be checked and adjusted without the engine running. Dynamic timing checks are more common on older engines.

As with any timing procedure, the goal of checking the timing while the engine is running is to ensure that the ignition timing coincides with the specified timing provided by the service manual. To do this, a timing light is required, which in very simplistic terms, converts the ignition event into a visual event via a strobe light for the operator. Timing marks on the flywheel, crankcase, and/or stator plate are illuminated with the timing light and the position of the timing marks are compared to one another. Typically, at a specified engine speed if the ignition timing is set correctly, the timing marks should be in alignment with one another. This is the generic basis for how dynamically checking ignition timing works. Once again, your service manual will provide detailed specifications and instructions.

At this point, I can only provide a basic walkthrough of how to go about the procedure because the procedures differ depending on the engine. I was also unable to acquire a bike that required this type of timing check during the course of writing this book. To start with, a tachometer will need to be used so that engine RPM can be monitored. I recommend buying an hour meter with a tachometer function that permanently mounts to the bike. The hour meter is essential for logging engine run time and the tach function is great for this procedure, recording max RPM, and setting idle speed.

A timing light will need to be hooked up to the engine and, most likely, a power source as well, unless the bike is equipped with a battery. Refer to your timing light's instructions for power source details, but typically a 12 volt battery is required. The inductive pick up connects to the engine's spark plug lead and the positive and negative leads connect to the battery.

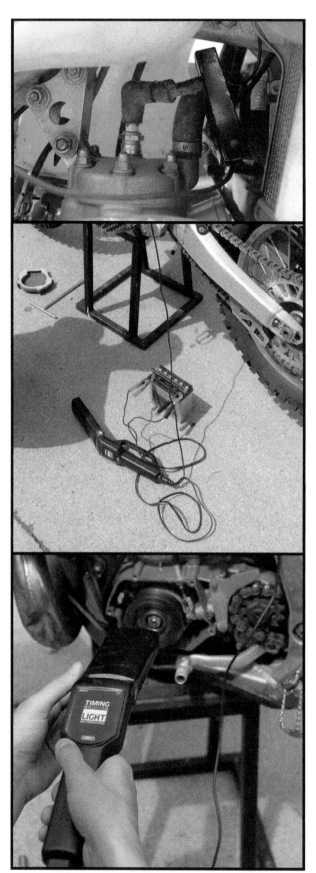

The stator cover will need to be removed so that the marks on the flywheel, crankcase, and/or stator plate can be observed. The service manual will detail the exact operating parameters that should be adhered to. Once the procedure is understood the engine can be started and warmed up. The engine can then be set at the procedure's outlined RPM and the timing light can be used to illuminate the timing marks on the flywheel. At this point the timing marks will either coincide in the correct locations or the timing will require adjustment. Specific adjustment instructions will be defined in the service manual. Usually, the position of the stator plate will be adjusted in order to achieve the desired timing. This of course, should be done with the engine off!

HOT TIP: Employing the help of a friend so that engine RPM can be monitored and controlled is a huge help as this is next to impossible to do while focusing on operating the timing light.

That's all the insight I can provide on dynamically checking ignition timing. Coupled with the instructions provided by the service manual and manufacturer of the timing light, you should have all the information you need to nail your engine's specified ignition timing. Remember to work carefully and once finished making any adjustments, ensure all hardware has been torqued to spec.

CH 16 | ENGINE BREAK-IN

If you have ever researched engine break-in procedures then I'm sure you have found that everyone under the sun has a tried and true method for breaking in their engine. The frustrating part is that many of the methods differ from one another and it is hard to determine what works the best. Over the years I have witnessed and observed a lot of different methods myself and have formulated my own opinions and methodology on what works. Within this chapter I'll share my break-in procedure and explain why I break an engine in the way that I do.

There are two parts to my break-in procedure. The first part focuses on the need for new parts which are sliding or rotating against one another to mate together. To achieve a good fit between the sliding and rotating components, the engine is started and allowed to warm up to operating temperature. This usually takes around 3 to 5 minutes. By placing your hand on the radiators, you can get a good sense of when the engine has warmed up. The engine is allowed to run at a normal idle and there is no blipping of the throttle. Once the engine has warmed up, the engine is shut off and allowed to cool completely. This warming and cooling process is often referred to as a "heat cycle".

By warming the engine up, new parts are allowed to expand and contract at normal rates. High spots on parts, such as the piston, are allowed to wear off and conform to their mating parts. On the contrary to a gradual warm up, some have suggested the engine be ridden right away. If parts are expanded too fast at different rates, parts may wear too quickly which leaves more clearance than desired when temperatures have stabilized within the engine.

After the first heat cycle, the engine is then started and brought up to operating temperature once more and shut off and allowed to cool again. By this point the engine has around 6 - 10 minutes of run time on it and new parts have started to get acquainted with their neighbors. While the engine is running, the engine should be checked over for leaks originating from fittings and gaskets. Once the engine has cooled, the radiators should be checked one final time to confirm the coolant level is set correctly.

The second part of the break-in procedure emphasizes ring sealing. Ring sealing is what determines how much power the engine will produce, which is extremely important. In order to achieve good ring sealing, the rings must be exposed to pressure that forces them against the cylinder wall. In order to achieve good ring sealing, the the bike is ridden and the engine is put under load.

Before riding, allow the engine to warm up completely. The first 10 minutes of riding are devoted to below half throttle, riding only within the first two or three gears. Engine RPM is varied and the engine is accelerated and decelerated repeatedly. Within the next 10 minutes the same procedure applies, only the throttle is opened to three quarters and higher gears can be used. Finally the last 10 minutes of break-in are dedicated to hard full throttle accelerations through all the gears. The two main things to avoid while breaking the engine in are constant throttle positions and lugging the engine. The engine should always be being loaded and unloaded, and throttle positions varied. This will seat the rings the best.

Using "special" or specific oils whether it be for the oil mixed with the fuel or in the gearbox for break-in is the last point I want to touch on. I always break my engines in using the normal oil that I will be running in the engine throughout its life. Selecting a mineral or castor oil over a synthetic may lead to faster break-in; however, I don't see any huge advantages to selecting one over the other. The important thing is to be consistent with the type and oil ratio used. Also, keep in mind there is no need to add more oil to the fuel for break-in. This can actually cause the cylinder walls to glaze over and prohibit ring sealing.

In summary, the break-in procedure I recommend goes as follows:

1. Initial startup - The engine is allowed to reach normal operating temperature (3-5 minutes), then the engine is shut off and allowed to cool to the ambient temperature.

2. Second startup - Same procedure as first. A final check for leaks is performed and the coolant level is checked one last time before riding.

3. First 10 minutes of riding - The bike is accelerated and decelerated constantly, throttle is moderated to no more than half, and the first two or three gears are used.

4. Second 10 minutes of riding - The throttle position and engine loading continue to be varied. The max throttle position is increased to three quarters and fourth gear can be used.

5. Last 10 minutes of break-in riding - The throttle can be fully opened, the engine should be accelerated and decelerated hard, and engine loading and throttle positions should continue to be varied.

7. Unrestricted fun commences! Remember to change out the gearbox oil after 2 - 3 hours runtime.

CH 17 | MAINTENANCE LOGGING

Now that your freshly rebuilt engine is up and running, it is a great idea to monitor it throughout its life. There is no better time to start keeping track of maintenance and engine hours than right after the engine is rebuilt. Keeping track of basic service tasks and other engine related maintenance from the beginning can be very beneficial later in the engine's life when components are starting to wear out and are nearing the end of their useful lives.

The compression test and/or leak down test should be relied on heavily to keep tabs on engine health from the time the engine is new to the time it must be serviced again. As I discussed in Chapter 3, leak down and compression tests are a great way to quantify how well the rings are sealing. Below are some of my thoughts on how to best utilize the aforementioned tests and inspections.

Leak Down and Compression Tests

After the first hour or two of riding, at which point the engine should be broken in, perform a leak down and compression test on the engine. By performing both of these tests when the engine is new a baseline for cylinder leakage and compression can be established. Once good leakage and compression numbers have been determined subsequent tests performed later on in the engine's life can be compared back to the initial leakage and compression values to determine if any parts have worn or performance has been lost. By referencing the baseline values you will more easily be able to determine when problems arise and know with more certainty the overall condition of the engine.

How often you may want to consider performing a leak down or compression test will be determined by the type of riding the bike is used for. Racing bikes and engines inherently need a lot of TLC and it is never a bad idea to assess the condition of the engine after every race weekend or five hours if competing at a high level. For the average trail or woods rider a 15 - 20 hour interval is more appropriate.

Hour Meters

Installing an hour meter and keeping track of the number of hours the engine runs is the most accurate way to keep track of how much time engine parts have on them. Hour meters are fantastic because they only count running engine time, not break time, or any other time which can occasionally get counted when keeping track of things using a clock. Once the run time is known it is very easy to keep tabs on maintenance tasks such as oil changes, power valve cleanings, and piston replacements.

Logging

All this engine monitoring does no good without a dedicated place to keep track of everything.

Whether you like using pen and paper or an online spreadsheet be sure to have a dedicated place where you can easily see the past maintenance history of the bike. Not only will it be easier to remember what maintenance has been done to the bike but keeping good maintenance records will also give any potential buyers confidence in your competency as an owner and help with resale. A maintenance spreadsheet can be created similar to the example below. Or if you want a spreadsheet that is free and downloadable, grab one from the DIY Moto Fix website at:

https://www.diymotofix.com/freebies

Ride	Date	Location	Engine Hours	Temp (°F)	Jetting	Suspension Settings	Maintenance Performed	Comments
0								
1								
2								
3								
4								

CH 18 — CLOSING THOUGHTS

At this time I want to thank you for reading my book. I hope you have enjoyed it, learned from it, and have become a better engine builder because of it. My sincerest hope is that if you have the ebook version, your electronic device is filthy with grease, and if you have the print book, the pages are no longer white! If this is the case, I have done my job and provided you with a good resource.

For some of you, this may be your first motor build. For others, perhaps you have a few under your belt. Whatever the case may be, there is always something fascinating about watching an engine come to life that you have assembled with your own two hands. I've put together quite a few engines now and I still get giddy for the first start, grin like an idiot when it fires up, and celebrate when it makes awesome noises. When it comes time to start your new engine, I hope you are overcome with the same emotion!

Lastly, congratulations on completing your build. I know from experience that builds can suffer many setbacks, take more time than you originally plan, and cost more money than you want to spend. In the grand scheme of things, these are small frustrations and you should be proud for persevering and completing the job to the best of your abilities. Many of your fellow motorheads would never dare take on such a task. You should take great pride in knowing that you are able to properly dismantle, service, and reassemble an entire engine.

Now enough with the shop work. Get out and ride!

CPSIA information can be obtained
at www.ICGtesting.com
Printed in the USA
LVHW07s0736050418
572371LV00002B/2/P